SET THEORY

BY

FELIX HAUSDORFF

TRANSLATED FROM THE GERMAN
BY
JOHN R. AUMANN, ET AL.

SECOND EDITION

CHELSEA PUBLISHING COMPANY
NEW YORK, N. Y.

THE PRESENT WORK IS A TRANSLATION FROM THE ORIGINAL GERMAN, INTO ENGLISH, OF THE THIRD (1937) EDITION OF MENGENLEHRE BY Felix Hausdorff

Library of Congress Catalogue Card Number 62-19176

PRINTED IN THE United States of America

EDITOR'S PREFACE

Because the present translation of Felix Hausdorff's famous *Mengenlehre* is the work of more than one hand, and because during the considerable length of time in which this translation was in preparation, other duties, both personal and professional, have arisen to prevent the translators from seeing the work of translation through to completion, it has devolved upon me to make such changes, in terminology as well as language, as consistency in style would require.

A. G.

PREFACE TO THE SECOND ENGLISH EDITION

Professor R. L. Goodstein has been kind enough to write two appendixes for the present edition: Appendix E, on the contradictions in Naive Set Theory, and Appendix F, on the Axiom of Choice. The Editor wishes to thank Professor Goodstein for pointing out that such supplementation is desirable and for his kindness in acceeding to the Editor's request that he write the Appendixes.

Thanks are also due to Professor Smbat Abian and Mr. Coley C. Mills, Jr. for the correction of a number of errata in the First Edition.

A. G.

FROM THE PREFACE TO THE SECOND EDITION

The present book has as its purpose an exposition of the most important theorems of the Theory of Sets, along with complete proofs, so that the reader should not find it necessary to go outside this book for supplementary details while, on the other hand, the book should enable him to undertake a more detailed study of the voluminous literature on the subject. The book does not presuppose any mathematical knowledge beyond the differential and integral calculus, but it does require a certain maturity in abstract reasoning; qualified college seniors and first year graduate students should have no difficulty in making the material their own. More difficult topics, at the end of individual chapters, may be skipped on a first reading. The reader who is interested only in acquiring the simplest facts of point-set theory can, after a quick perusal of the first two chapters, immediately attack the sixth. The mathematician will, I hope, find in this book some things that will be new to him, at least as regards formal presentation and, in particular, as regards the strengthening of theorems, the simplification of proofs, and the removal of unnecessary hypotheses.

The selection of material must of necessity be somewhat subjective, since the subject is so extensive and is still growing almost from day to day. Unavoidably, various expectations regarding the book, including some of the author's own, could not be realized. A textbook, after all, can not aim at the completeness of a comprehensive report. In this case, there was the additional restriction that the new edition had to be substantially curtailed in length as compared to the first edition (*Grundzüge der Mengenlehre,* Leipzig 1914 [Repr., Chelsea, 1955]); this would have necessitated a revision down to the smallest detail, and I found a complete rewriting of the book preferable. I thought it might be easiest to sacrifice, of the topics treated in the first edition, most of the theory of ordered sets, a subject that stands somewhat by itself, as well as the introduction to Lebesgue's theory of integration, which does not lack for exposition elsewhere. What is more to be regretted is the abandonment, owing to the necessity of saving space, of the *topological* point of view in point-set theory, which seems to have attracted many people to the first edition of this book; in this new edition, I have restricted myself to the simpler theory of *metric* spaces and have given only a quick survey (§ 40) of topological spaces, which is a rather inadequate substitute. Finally, I have cut down the generality in the other direction as well, by omitting the special theory of Euclidean space (e.g., the Jordan Curve Theorem for Plane Curves); that is, roughly speaking, I have omitted all of the material that is based on approximate polygons and polyhedra. Thus, the reader will find a large number of theorems concerning Euclidean space, but only such theorems as hold for Euclidean space considered as a special case of a separable or a complete or a locally connected space, or the like.

As against this omission there are some additions, such as a more complete treatment of Borel Sets and Suslin Sets (discovered in 1917) as well as of the Baire functions. Also, continuous mappings and homeomorphisms are treated in more detail than they were in the first edition. As to a discussion of the so-called paradoxes and of questions regarding the foundations of the subject, I have decided to omit this from the present edition as well.

PREFACE TO THE THIRD EDITION

Set Theory has continued its steady and active development, and this in itself might have made desirable an actual revision of this book. However, circumstances have prevented my doing this. Accordingly, the first nine chapters are an almost unchanged reprint of the second edition; but in order to do at least partial justice to the progress achieved by the subject in the meantime, I have added a new — tenth — chapter covering two subjects that seem to be especially worthy of detailed exposition, and I have also touched upon three further topics in short supplements — without proofs, however. Had it not been for lack of space, the number of additional topics could have been considerably extended.

TABLE OF CONTENTS

PRELIMINARY REMARKS

Intervals of real numbers are written with brackets or parentheses according to whether the end points are included or not. Thus if $a < b$,

$$[a, b], \qquad [a, b), \qquad (a, b], \qquad (a, b)$$

are sets of numbers x that satisfy the conditions

$$a \leqq x \leqq b \qquad a \leqq x < b \qquad a < x \leqq b \qquad a < x < b$$

respectively. $[a, b]$ is called a *closed* interval, and (a, b) an *open* interval; the other two may be called either half-closed or half-open. For intervals that are infinite in one direction (closed and open half-lines, or rays), we use the improper end points $+\infty$ and $-\infty$, which are not to be counted as belonging to the interval; thus

$$[a, +\infty) \quad (a, +\infty) \quad (-\infty, b] \quad (-\infty, b)$$

are the sets of numbers x that satisfy the respective conditions

$$x \geqq a \qquad x > a \qquad x \leqq b \qquad x < b.$$

$(-\infty, +\infty)$ is the set of all the real numbers (the entire straight line).

The largest and the smallest of a finite number of real numbers $x_1, x_2, \ldots, x_n$ are called their *maximum* and their *minimum* respectively and are denoted by

$$\max [x_1, x_2, \ldots, x_n], \quad \min [x_1, x_2, \ldots, x_n];$$

for example, $\max [2, -3] = 2$, $\min [2, -3] = -3$, $\max [2, 2] = \min [2, 2] = 2$. The same notation is also used for the largest and smallest numbers, if any, of an infinite set of numbers.

If a sequence of real numbers $x_1, x_2, \ldots$ is bounded from above – that is, if there are numbers v for which $v \geqq x_n$ for every n – then there is among these numbers v a smallest one, say v_1. It is variously called the *least upper bound* (the abbreviation l.u.b is very common), the *supremum*, and sometimes the *upper boundary* of the sequence x_n; in the German-language editions of this book the term used (following Weierstrass) is *obere grenze*; we shall write

$$v_1 = \sup [x_1, x_2, \ldots] = \sup x_n.$$

For example, sup [0, 1/2, 2/3, 3/4, . . .] = sup [(n − 1)/n] = 1. If the sequence has a maximum, this coincides with the supremum. The *greatest lower bound* (g.l.b), or *infimum,* or *lower boundary* (or *untere grenze*)

$$u_1 = \inf [x_1, x_2, \ldots] = \inf x_n$$

of a sequence bounded from below is defined in an exactly similar way. The same terms are also applied to sets of numbers that are not given in the form of a sequence; for instance,

$$\sup_{a \leqq x \leqq b} f(x).$$

For a sequence bounded from above there exist all of the suprema

$$v_n = \sup [x_n, x_{n+1}, x_{n+2}, \ldots]$$

with $v_1 \geqq v_2 \geqq \ldots$; if these v_n are bounded from below and hence have a (g.l.b) v, this is called the *upper limit,* or *limit superior,* of the sequence; in symbols,

$$v = \limsup x_n = \overline{\lim}\, x_n.$$

The *lower limit,* or *limit inferior*

$$u = \liminf x_n = \underline{\lim}\, x_n$$

is defined correspondingly.

If the assumptions concerning boundedness do not hold, the symbols $\pm \infty$ are used. For example, in the case of a sequence x_n not bounded from above, we write $\sup x_n = + \infty$ and $\overline{\lim}\, x_n = + \infty$; in the case of a sequence x_n bounded from above for which the suprema v_n are not bounded from below, we say that $\overline{\lim}\, x_n = - \infty$.

For the convergence of sequences and functions we will, as a rule, use the arrow as symbol, e.g.,

$$x_n \to x \quad \text{means} \quad \lim x_n = x;$$

likewise for proper divergence ($x_n \to + \infty$ and $x_n \to - \infty$).

A statement about the natural number n (= 1, 2, 3, . . .) holds *ultimately,* or for *almost all n* (Kowalewski), if it holds from a particular n on ($n \geqq n_0$), or for all values of n with at most a finite number of exceptions; it holds *infinitely often* if it holds for an *infinite number* of values of n (e.g., for $n = 2, 4, 6, 8, \ldots$). When we speak of almost all or of infinitely many terms of a sequence x_n we mean the terms x_n belonging to almost all or to infinitely many values of n, respectively, regardless of whether the terms themselves are different or not.

CHAPTER I

SETS AND THE COMBINING OF SETS

§ 1. Sets

A set is formed by the grouping together of single objects into a whole. A set is a plurality thought of as a unit. If these or similar statements were set down as definitions, then it could be objected with good reason that they define *idem per idem*[1] or even *obscurum per obscurius*.[2] However, we can consider them as expository, as references to a primitive concept, familiar to us all, whose resolution into more fundamental concepts would perhaps be neither competent nor necessary. We will content ourselves with this construction and will assume as an axiom that an object M inherently determines certain other objects $a, b, c, \ldots$ in some undefined way, and vice versa. We express this relation by the words: The set M consists of the objects $a, b, c, \ldots$.

A set can consist of a natural number (positive whole number) of objects, or not; it is called *finite* or *infinite* accordingly. Examples of finite sets are: the set of the inhabitants of a city, the set of hydrogen atoms in the sun, and the set of natural numbers from 1 to 1000; examples of infinite sets are: the set of all natural numbers, the set of all the points of a line, and the set of all the circles in a plane. It is to the undying credit of Georg Cantor (1845-1918) that, in the face of conflict, both internal and external against apparent paradoxes, popular prejudices, and philosophical dicta (*infinitum actu non datur*[3]) and even in the face of doubts that had been raised by the very greatest mathematicians, he dared this step into the realm of the infinite. In so doing, he became the creator of a new science, Set Theory – the consideration of finite sets being nothing more than elementary arithmetic and combinatorial analysis – which today forms the basis of all mathematics. In our opinion, it does not detract from the merit of Cantor's ideas that some antinomies that arise from allowing excessively limitless construction of sets still await complete elucidation and removal.

---

[1] Something in terms of that same something.

[2] The obscure by the still more obscure.

[3] There is no actual infinite.

Following G. Peano, we designate the fundamental relation between an object a and a set A to which it belongs in the following terms and using the following notation:

$$a \text{ is an element of } A: \qquad a \,\varepsilon\, A.$$

The negation of this statement reads:

$$a \text{ is not an element of } A: a \,\bar{\varepsilon}\, A.$$

Two sets are defined to be equal, in symbols

$$A = B,$$

if and only if each element of one is also an element of the other and vice versa (i.e., if they both contain the same elements). Hence a set is uniquely determined by its elements; we express this by writing the elements of the set, enclosed in braces, as a notation for the set, elements not listed explicitly being indicated by dots. Thus

$$A = \{a\}, \quad A = \{a, b\}, \quad A = \{a, b, c\}$$

are the sets consisting of the element a, the two elements a, b, and the three elements a, b, c, respectively;

$$A = \{a, b, c, \ldots\}$$

is a set consisting of the elements a, b, c, and (possibly) others. Naturally, it must be specified in some way what the other elements are that have been indicated by dots; some examples are

the set of all natural numbers $\{1, 2, 3, \ldots\}$,
the set of all even natural numbers $\{2, 4, 6, \ldots\}$,
the set of all squares $\{1, 4, 9, \ldots\}$,
the set of all powers of 2 $\{1, 2, 4, 8, \ldots\}$,
and the set of all prime numbers $\{2, 3, 5, 7, \ldots\}$.

A distinction must certainly be made, at least conceptually, between the object a and the set $\{a\}$ consisting of only this one element (even if the distinction is of no importance from a practical point of view), if for no other reason than that we will admit sets (or systems) whose elements are themselves sets. The set $a = \{1, 2\}$ consists of the two elements 1, 2, while the set $\{a\}$ consists of the single element a.

For reasons of expedience, we also admit the *null set,* or *empty set,* denoted by 0, which contains no elements.[1] By the definition of equality of sets, there is only one null set. $A = 0$ means that the set A has no elements, is empty, "vanishes." If we were not to admit the null set as a set, then in countless cases where we speak of a set we would have to add "if this set exists." For, the definition of the elements of a set often does not tell us in the least whether such elements exist; for instance, it is not yet known whether the set of natural numbers n for which the equation $x^{n+2} + y^{n+2} = z^{n+2}$ has a solution in natural numbers x, y, and z is empty or non-empty (that is, whether Fermat's celebrated Last Theorem is true or false). Thus, the statement $A = 0$ may, in many cases, represent real knowledge but, in other cases, only a triviality; many mathematical statements – or, if one is not repelled by artificial devices, all mathematical statements – can be put in the form $A = 0$. The introduction of the null set, like that of the number zero, is dictated on grounds of expedience; on the other hand, it sometimes forces one to state explicitly, as one of the hypotheses of a theorem, that a set does not vanish (just as it is sometimes necessary to state explicitly that a number does not vanish).

If A and B are two sets, then the question arises whether the elements of one may not perhaps also belong to the other. If a and b denote elements of A and B respectively, then we first consider the following two pairs of alternatives:

Every $a \varepsilon B$,	not every $a \varepsilon B$,
every $b \varepsilon A$,	not every $b \varepsilon A$.

By combining these we obtain four possible cases, the first three of which are denoted in symbols by the accompanying formulas:

(1) Every $a \varepsilon B$ and every $b \varepsilon A$: $A = B$;
(2) every $a \varepsilon B$ and not every $b \varepsilon A$: $A < B$;
(3) not every $a \varepsilon B$ and every $b \varepsilon A$: $A > B$;
(4) not every $a \varepsilon B$ and not every $b \varepsilon A$.

In case (1), the two sets are equal, by the earlier explanation. In case (2), A contains only elements of B, but not all of them, which characterizes A as the smaller set and B as the larger set; this is expressed in symbols by $A < B$, which is supposed to be reminiscent of the notation $\alpha < \beta$ in the case of numbers. In case (3), we have the opposite situation,

[1] Whether the symbol 0 denotes the null set or the number zero will always be apparent from the context.

so that the statement $A > B$ amounts to the same as $B < A$. In general, what we will have will be none of these three cases, but rather case (4); but there is no reason to have a special notation for this case.

The relation "smaller than" is *transitive*; that is, from $A < B$ and $B < C$ it follows that $A < C$. (This also holds, of course, for the relations "greater than" and "equal to.")

If every $a \varepsilon B$, so that either case (1) or case (2) holds, then we denote this combination[1] by

$$A \leqq B, \qquad A \text{ is a } \textit{subset} \text{ of } B$$

(also, A is a *part* of, or *contained in*, B); when we have the more restrictive $A < B$, then A is sometimes called a *proper subset* of B. *Among the subsets of B we therefore include B itself as well as the null set;* for when $A = 0$, then the relation "every $a \varepsilon B$" is satisfied, trivially to be sure, by virtue of the fact that there is no a at all.[2] Thus $0 < B$ or $B > 0$ means that B is not empty. The usefulness of this convention becomes apparent, for instance, in counting the subsets of a finite set. The subsets of $\{1, 2, 3,\}$ are:

$$0, \ \{1\}, \ \{2\}, \ \{3\}, \ \{1, 2\}, \ \{1, 3\}, \ \{2, 3\}, \ \{1, 2, 3\};$$

there are $8 = 2^3$ of them. A set of n elements contains $\binom{n}{m}$ subsets that contain m elements each, where $\binom{n}{m} = \frac{n!}{m!\,(n-m)!}$ is the binomial coefficient and where $\binom{n}{0} = \binom{n}{n} = 1$. The total number of subsets is

$$\binom{n}{0} + \binom{n}{1} + \cdots + \binom{n}{n-1} + \binom{n}{n} = 2^n.$$

This simple result speaks in favor of the concept of subset as introduced above.

If $A \leqq B$, then we let

$$B - A$$

---

[1] The equality sign is dispensed with in some texts; in place of our rounded less than sign, other variants of the symbol are in use.

[2] More explicitly: The statement "If $a \varepsilon A$, then $a \varepsilon B$ also" is true because the hypothesis $a \varepsilon A$ is never satisfied; a statement of this kind is said to be *vacuously true.* If p and q are statements, then the statement "If p is true, then q is true" (p implies q) is certainly true when p is false. A false statement implies any statement; if $2 \times 2 = 5$, then ghosts exist.

denote the set of elements of B that are not elements of A: this *difference* of the two sets is also called the *complement of A in B*. Clearly,

$$B - 0 = B,\ B - B = 0,$$
$$B - (B - A) = A.$$

Since some other authors follow a different usage, we wish to emphasize explicitly that in forming a difference we always assume that the subtrahend is a subset of the minuend. For instance, when we write $C - (B - A)$, we assume first of all that $A \leqq B$, and second that $B - A \leqq C$. *Example:* Let $A = \{5, 6, 7, \ldots\}$ be the set of all the natural numbers from five on, $B = \{1, 2, 3, \ldots\}$ the set of all the natural numbers, and $C = \{1, 2, 3, 4, 5, 6\}$ the set of the first six natural numbers. Then we have $B - A = \{1, 2, 3, 4\}$, $C - (B - A) = \{5, 6\}$.

§ 2. Functions

The concept of function is almost as fundamental and primitive as the concept of set. A functional relation is formed from *pairs of elements* just as a set is formed from *individual elements*.

We consider, instead of individual elements, a grouping together of two elements *in a definite order* – or, as we shall call it, an *ordered pair* (a, b) of elements – where a is the first element and b the second. Two such ordered pairs will be considered to be the same if and only if they have the same first element and the same second element:

$$(a^*, b^*) = (a, b) \quad \text{means} \quad a^* = a \quad \text{and} \quad b^* = b.$$

Accordingly, the pairs (a, b) and (b, a) are different if $a \neq b$; on the other hand, nothing prevents us from forming an ordered pair (a, a) of two equal elements. For instance, by combining natural numbers, we obtain the ordered pairs

$$(1, 1), (1, 2), (2, 1), (1, 3), (2, 2), (3, 1), \ldots ;$$

the double subscripts of the elements of a matrix or a determinant are ordered pairs of this kind. By combining real numbers, we obtain ordered pairs of numbers (x, y); the use of such pairs of cartesian coordinates, where the abscissa x and the ordinate y may not be interchanged, makes it possible to represent the points of the plane.

The ordered pair (a, b) is a different concept from the set $\{a, b\}$; in the latter, a and b are assumed to be distinct, and it does not matter in what order they occur.

Ordered pairs make possible the introduction of the concept of function, and they will also serve to define multiplication (§ 4) and the ordering (§ 9) of sets. Let P be a set of ordered pairs $p = (a, b)$; for every pair p that occurs in $P (p \varepsilon P)$, we call b an *image* of a and a a *pre-image* (or *inverse image*) of b. Let A be the set of all pre-images a (i.e., all the first elements of pairs $p \varepsilon P$), B the set of all images b (i.e., all the second elements of pairs $p \varepsilon P$). Each a determines its images, each b its pre-images; and this, then, is the connection that the set of pairs P establishes between the sets A and B; we say that we have a *mapping* from one set onto the other.

In the particular case in which each a has only a single image b, we denote this element b, which is determined by a and depends on a, by

$$b = f(a),$$

and we say that this is a *single-valued* (or *one-valued*) or *univalent function of a defined on the set A.* For instance, the set of pairs $(1, 2), (2, 1), (3, 2)$ defines a mapping of the set $A = \{1, 2, 3\}$ onto the set $B = \{1, 2\}$; in fact, it defines a function that is single-valued on the set A, namely the function

$$f(1) = 2, \qquad f(2) = 1, \qquad f(3) = 2.$$

If in addition to this, each b has only a single pre-image a, then this element a determined by b will be denoted by

$$a = g(b),$$

and we thus have a single-valued function of b defined in B. Each of these functions is said to be *the inverse* of the other; both are said to be *one-to-one;* we call the mapping between A and B *one-to-one* (or *one-one,* or *schlicht,* or *bi-unique*), sometimes referring to it as a *one-to-one correspondence,* and we say that two sets A and B that can have this relation to each other are *equivalent*: in symbols,

$$A \sim B, \quad B \sim A.$$

This basic concept of equivalence will be fundamental for the second chapter; let us content ourselves here with the example of the equivalence between the set A of all natural numbers and the set B of all (positive) even numbers. The set of ordered pairs

$$(1,2),\ (2,4),\ (3,6)\ ,\ \ldots$$

represents the one-to-one correspondence, since it assigns to every natural number a the image $b=2a$ and to every even number b the pre-image $a=\frac{1}{2}b$.

If the element a has several images, then the notation $b=f(a)$ can be retained with the understanding that $f(a)$ represents not one but several (perhaps infinitely many) elements b; we then have a *many-valued function* $f(a)$. The corresponding statement holds for $g(b)$. These two functions, which are in general many-valued functions, are still called inverse to each other. A case which will come up often is the one in which $f(a)$ is single-valued while the inverse $g(b)$ is many-valued. For instance, the set of ordered pairs $(a, \sin a)$, where a runs through all the real numbers, defines a mapping of the set A of all real numbers onto the set B of the numbers $-1 \leqq b \leqq 1$ which is such that although $b=\sin a$ is single-valued, $a=\arcsin b$ is, as is well known, many-valued, arc sin b denoting not only some one number a_0 for which $b=\sin a_0$, but also all the numbers $2k\pi + a_0$ and $(2k+1)\pi - a_0$ (k, an integer). However, if we restrict a to the interval $-\frac{\pi}{2} \leqq a \leqq \frac{\pi}{2}$, then the correspondence between the two sets becomes one-to-one.

The definition of the concept of function given here will appear somewhat abstract to the beginner who is still accustomed to thinking in terms of elementary functions or perhaps continuous functions; but this definition is necessary in order to allow this fundamental concept its full scope and generality. As regards a single-valued function $f(a)$, the only thing that counts is that once a is given, $f(a)$ should be uniquely determined by some definite rule (which was given above by the set of pairs P); it is immaterial whether or not this rule can be given in terms of "analytic expressions" or otherwise; it is also immaterial whether or not in any given case our knowledge and the tools at our disposal allow us to carry through even for a single a the actual determination of $f(a)$. What we have said here about the general concept of function, defined by Dirichlet, could also have been said about Cantor's concept of set. The set of rationals is well defined, even though we do not know whether or not π^π belongs to it; the function $f(a)$ which is 1 for rational a and 0 for irrational a is well defined, even though we do not know the value of $f(\pi^\pi)$.

§ 3. Sum and Intersection

If A, B, are two sets, then by their *sum*,[1] or union,

$$S = A \dotplus B$$

we mean the set of all elements that belongs to A *or* B (or both) ; by their *intersection*

$$D = AB$$

we mean the set of all elements that belong to both A *and* B. If $D = 0$, that is, if A and B have no element in common, then they are called *disjoint* (or *mutually exclusive* or *non-overlapping*) ; in this case, and in this case only, we also use the notation

$$S = A + B$$

for the sum, and we note that in this case we clearly have $S - A = B$, $S - B = A$.

Example: Let A be the interval[2] $[1, 3]$, i.e., the set of all real numbers x for which $1 \leqq x \leqq 3$, and let B be the interval $[2, 4]$. Then S is the interval $[1, 4]$; D, the interval $[2, 3]$.

If A, B, are disjoint finite sets and if A consists of m elements and B of n elements, then $A + B$ consists of $m + n$ elements.

We have

$$S - A = B - D, \qquad S - B = A - D,$$

the first of these being the set of all elements that belong to B and not to A. Thus the intersection

$$D = B - (S - A) = A - (S - B)$$

may be written in terms of the sum and the difference.

The formation of sums and intersections may be immediately extended to any number of sets, finitely many or infinitely many. As a symbol for the sum, we use the German letter $\mathfrak{S}$; in the case of disjoint summands

[1] The more common notation for the $\dotplus$ sign is $\cup$; this notation, however, fails to take into account the distinction between $\dotplus$ and $+$. On the other hand, in many places one can find the sum denoted by a simple plus sign (without the dot). The symbol $\dotplus$ was introduced by Carathéodory.

[2] For the notation for intervals, see p. 9.

we may use the Greek Σ instead; and as a symbol for the intersection we use the German $\mathfrak{D}$. Let us assume that there correspond to the natural numbers 1, 2, . . . , k, or for that matter to all of the natural numbers 1, 2, . . . , sets A_1, A_2, . . . (so that we are already making use of the concept of single-valued function given in § 2) which, moreover, need by no means all be distinct; then their sum

$$S = A_1 \dotplus A_2 \dotplus \cdots = \underset{m}{\mathfrak{S}} A_m$$

is the set of all the elements that belong to at least one of the A_m, and their intersection

$$D = A_1 A_2 \cdots = \underset{m}{\mathfrak{D}} A_m$$

is the set of all elements that belong to all the A_m simultaneously. In case the summands are *disjoint,* i.e., *pairwise non-overlapping,* or, in symbols,

$$A_m A_n = 0 \quad \text{for} \quad m \neq n,$$

and in this case only, we may write the sum also in the form

$$S = A_1 + A_2 + \cdots = \sum_m A_m.$$

Finally, we have the general case: To each element m of a set $M = \{m, n, p, \ldots\}$ let there correspond a set A_m; then the sum of these sets,

$$S = A_m \dotplus A_n \dotplus A_p \dotplus \cdots = \overset{M}{\underset{m}{\mathfrak{S}}} A_m$$

is the set of all the elements that belong to at least one A_m, and the intersection of these sets,

$$D = A_m A_n A_p \cdots = \overset{M}{\underset{m}{\mathfrak{D}}} A_m$$

is the set of all the elements that belong to all of the A_m simultaneously; in case the summands are disjoint (pairwise non-overlapping), we also write

$$S = A_m + A_n + A_p + \cdots = \sum_m^M A_m.$$

Examples: Let $M = \{0, 1, 2, \ldots\}$ be the set of integers $\geqq 0$, and let A_m be the set of natural numbers that are divisible by precisely the m-th power of 2 (i.e., that are divisible by 2^m but not by any higher power of 2), so that

$$\begin{aligned} A_0 &= \{1,\ 3,\ 5,\ 7, \ldots\} \\ A_1 &= \{2,\ 6, 10, 14, \ldots\} \\ A_2 &= \{4, 12, 20, 28, \ldots\} \\ A_3 &= \{8, 24, 40, 56, \ldots\} \\ &\cdots\cdots \end{aligned}$$

then

$$S = A_0 + A_1 + A_2 + \cdots = \sum_m^M A_m$$

is the set of all natural numbers.

Let M be the set of real numbers $m > 1$, and let $A_m = [0, m)$ be the interval $0 \leqq x < m$. Then

$$D = \mathfrak{D}_m^M A_m = [0, 1]$$

is the interval $0 \leqq x \leqq 1$.

These two operations, the forming of the sum and the forming of the intersection, are *commutative, associative,* and *distributive* with respect to each other; that is, to give only the simplest cases, we have

$$\begin{gathered} A \dot{+} B = B \dot{+} A, \qquad AB = BA, \\ (A \dot{+} B) \dot{+} C = A \dot{+} (B \dot{+} C) = A \dot{+} B \dot{+} C, \quad (AB)C = A(BC) = ABC, \\ (A \dot{+} B)\, C = AC \dot{+} BC, \\ AB \dot{+} C = (A \dot{+} C)(B \dot{+} C). \end{gathered}$$

Of the last two formulas — the distributive ones — the first is obvious and the second is also easy to see; we also note the next most general case

$$\begin{aligned} C \cdot \mathfrak{S}_m A_m &= \mathfrak{S}_m C A_m, \\ C \dot{+} \mathfrak{D}_m A_m &= \mathfrak{D}_m (C \dot{+} A_m). \end{aligned}$$

If all the A_m are subsets of an encompassing set E, and if $B_m = E - A_m$ are their respective complements, then

$$E = \mathfrak{S}_m A_m + \mathfrak{D}_m B_m = \mathfrak{D}_m A_m + \mathfrak{S}_m B_m.$$

For, every element of E belongs either to at least one A_m (and so to $\mathfrak{S} A_m$), or to none, in which case it belongs to all the B_m (and so to $\mathfrak{D} B_m$). This important formula can be expressed in concise form as follows: *The complement of a sum is the intersection of the complements, and the complement of an intersection is the sum of the complements.* Thus, if a set P is formed from the sets A_m by the repeated taking of sums and intersections, then its complement $Q = E - P$ can be obtained by replacing the A_m by their complements B_m and at the same time interchanging the operations $\mathfrak{S}$ and $\mathfrak{D}$. Thus from one of the formulas that constitute the distributive law,

$$A \cdot \mathfrak{S} A_m = \mathfrak{S} A A_m,$$

there immediately follows the other,

$$B \dot{+} \mathfrak{D} B_m = \mathfrak{D}(B \dot{+} B_m).$$

If this process, the transition to complements, is applied to an *inequality* between sets (*set-theoretic inequality*), then the $<$ and $>$ signs must also be interchanged (because $P < P^*$ implies $Q > Q^*$ for the complements).

Let $A_1, A_2, A_3, \ldots,$ be a sequence of sets, i.e., to every natural number n let there correspond a set A_n. By its *upper limit* (or *limes superior*), denoted by

$$\overline{A} = \overline{\text{Lim}}\, A_n$$

(or by Lim sup), we shall mean the set of those elements x that belong to *infinitely many* A_n ($x \varepsilon A_n$ for infinitely many n); by its *lower limit* (*limes inferior*), denoted by

$$\underline{A} = \underline{\text{Lim}}\, A_n$$

(or by Lim inf), we shall mean the set of those elements x that belong *almost all*[1] A_n ($x \varepsilon A_n$ for almost all n). Since the second requirement is more stringent than the first, we always have $\overline{A} \geqq \underline{A}$; if, in particular the equality sign holds, then the set $\overline{A} = \underline{A} = A$ is called the *limit* of the sequence A_n of sets, and the sequence is called *convergent;* we write

$$A = \text{Lim}\, A_n.$$

Examples: The sequence $M, N, M, N, \ldots$ has $M \dot{+} N$ as its upper limit and MN as its lower limit; it converges only if $M = N$. An increasing sequence $A_1 \leqq A_2 \leqq \cdots$ converges to the sum $\mathfrak{S} A_n$, a decreasing sequence $A_1 \geqq A_2 \geqq \cdots$ converges to the intersection $\mathfrak{D} A_n$, and a sequence of disjoint sets converges to the null set. Let A_1 denote the interval $[0, 1]$; A_2 and A_3, the intervals $[0, \frac{1}{2}]$ and $[\frac{1}{2}, 1]$, respectively; A_4, A_5, and A_6, the intervals $[0, \frac{1}{3}]$, $[\frac{1}{3}, \frac{2}{3}]$, and $[\frac{2}{3}, 1]$, respectively; and so on. Then the upper limit of the sequence A_n is the interval $[0, 1]$, and the lower limit is the null set.

[1] For the meaning of *almost all,* see the Introduction.

If E is once again a set containing all the A_n, and if $B_n = E - A_n$, then we have

$$E = \underline{A} + \overline{B} = \overline{A} + \underline{B}.$$

For, an $x \varepsilon E$ belongs *either* to almost all A_n, i.e., to only finitely many B_n, *or* to infinitely many B_n.

The sets $\overline{A}$ and $\underline{A}$ may be formed from the A_n by the repeated use of the sum and intersection; in fact

$$\begin{aligned} \underline{A} &= D_1 \dot{+} D_2 \dot{+} D_3 \dot{+} \cdots, \quad & D_n &= A_n A_{n+1} A_{n+2} \cdots, \\ \overline{A} &= S_1 S_2 S_3 \ldots \quad &, \quad S_n &= A_n + A_{n+1} \dot{+} A_{n+2} \dot{+} \cdots. \end{aligned}$$

The first formula follows at once from the definition, and the simplest way of proving the second is by taking complements.

The sets $\overline{A}$ and $\underline{A}$ remain unchanged if we add, remove, or change a finite number of sets of the sequence A_n. Furthermore, if A_p is a subsequence (where p runs through a sequence of natural numbers), then we clearly have

$$\underline{\text{Lim}}\, A_n \leqq \underline{\text{Lim}}\, A_p \leqq \overline{\text{Lim}}\, A_p \leqq \overline{\text{Lim}}\, A_n.$$

If the whole sequence converges to A, so does every subsequence.

Characteristic functions (C. de la Vallée Poussin). There can be associated with every subset A of a fixed set E a function $f(x)$ defined on E which takes on only the values 0 and 1, and which uniquely determines and is uniquely determined by A; namely the function

$$f(x) = 1 \text{ for } x \varepsilon A, \quad f(x) = 0 \text{ for } x \varepsilon E - A.$$

This is called the *characteristic function* of the set A; we denote it simply by $[A]$, omitting the argument x and thus emphasizing only its dependence on A. To the whole set E there corresponds the constant function $[E] = 1$; to the null set 0, the constant function $[0] = 0$.

To the combinations of sets there correspond simple combinations of the characteristic functions. Thus

$$[B - A] = [B] - [A] \qquad (A \leqq B)$$

is an equation which, like those that follow, holds for every x. In fact, for the three possible cases, we have

$$\begin{array}{rccc} x\,\varepsilon & E-B, & B-A, & A: \\ [A]= & 0\;, & 0\;, & 1 \\ [B]= & 0\;, & 1\;, & 1 \\ [B-A]= & 0\;, & 1\;, & 0. \end{array}$$

In particular, we have

$$[E-A]=1-[A].$$

Furthermore,

$$[AB]=[A][B],$$

and by forming the complements, we obtain

$$[A\dot{+}B]=1-(1-[A])(1-[B]),$$
$$[A\dot{+}B]+[AB]=[A]+[B],$$

and in particular, for disjoint summands,

$$[A+B]=[A]+[B].$$

On the other hand, we also have

$$[A+B]=\mathbf{max}\,[[A],[B]], \qquad [AB]=\mathbf{min}\,[[A],[B]]\;;$$

and more generally, for the sum $S=\mathfrak{S}A_m$ and the intersection $D=\mathfrak{D}A_m$ of an arbitrary number of sets, we have

$$[S]=\mathbf{max}\,[A_m], \qquad [D]=\mathbf{min}\,[A_m].$$

For the upper limit $\bar{A}=\overline{\text{Lim}}\,A_n$ and the lower limit $\underline{A}=\underline{\text{Lim}}\,A_n$ of a sequence of sets, we have

$$[\bar{A}]=\overline{\mathbf{lim}}\,[A_n], \qquad [\underline{A}]=\underline{\mathbf{lim}}\,[A_n];$$

for, $\overline{\text{lim}}\,[A_n]$ is $=1$ if and only if $[A_n]=1$ (i.e., $x\,\varepsilon\,A_n$) *infinitely often,* so that $x\,\varepsilon\,\bar{A}$ (otherwise $\overline{\text{lim}}\,[A_n]=0$); and $\underline{\text{lim}}\,[A_n]$ is $=1$ if and only if $x\,\varepsilon\,A_n$ *ultimately,* that is, for all n greater than some fixed N, so that $x\,\varepsilon\,\underline{A}$. In the case of the limit $A=\text{Lim}\,A_n$ of a convergent sequence of sets, we have $[A]=\lim\,[A_n]$.

§ 4. Products and Powers

It remains to define the *product* of sets. Let us form from two sets A and B the set P of *ordered pairs* (§ 2) $p=(a,b)$, where a runs through all the elements of A and b runs through all the elements of B, so that

$$p \varepsilon P \text{ means that } a \varepsilon A \text{ and } b \varepsilon B.$$

If the sets[1] are finite, A consisting of m elements and B of n elements, then P consists of mn elements, so that this set of pairs has in fact the character of a product. Note that this *complete* set of pairs, which contains *all* the pairs for which $a \varepsilon A$ and $b \varepsilon B$, has as subsets all those sets of pairs that, by § 2, define a functional relation between A and B; it itself defines the "most-valued" mapping, the mapping that is the most strongly many-valued – in the sense that every b corresponds under the mapping to each a, and every a to each b. The simple notation AB, already having been used for the intersection, is no longer available as a symbol for the product. But we can form an ordered pair (A, B) from the sets A and B themselves, and we are free to let this new symbol denote a set also: we define the *ordered pair of sets* to be the *set of ordered pairs of elements.* That is, for ordered pairs of elements and of sets we shall define the ε-relation

$$(a, b) \varepsilon (A, B) \text{ to mean } a \varepsilon A \text{ and } b \varepsilon B,$$

while objects other than pairs of elements are not to be admitted as elements of a set (A, B). Thus

$$P = (A, B)$$

is the product of the two sets.

Example: Let A and B be sets of real numbers. Let the pair of numbers (a, b) be represented by the point of the plane with cartesian coordinates a and b or, for short, by the point (a, b); through every point $(a, 0)$ $(a \varepsilon A)$ of the x-axis draw a line parallel to the y-axis, and through every point $(0, b)$ $(b \varepsilon B)$ of the y-axis draw a line parallel to the x-axis; then the intersections (a, b) of these lines form the product (A, B).

The product may be thought of as the sum of equivalent summands (§ 6).

There is no difficulty in generalizing the product to more than two factors. *Ordered triples* (a, b, c) may be defined analagously to ordered pairs (a, b); they are groupings together of three elements in a definite order, so that equality is defined thus:

[1] They do not have to be disjoint and could even be identical.

$(a^*, b^*, c^*) = (a, b, c)$ means that $a^* = a$, $b^* = b$, and $c^* = c$;

moreover, these three elements do not have to be distinct. The ordered triples (a, b, c), where a runs through all the elements of A, b runs through all the elements of B, and c runs through all the elements of C, by definition form the set (A, B, C) – the *product* of the three sets A, B, and C. We may proceed similarly for any finite number of factors.

The commutative and associative laws hold for the product – not, to be sure, in the sense of equality, but in the sense of equivalence (§ 2). Thus, although the elements (a, b) and (b, a) of the sets (A, B) and (B, A) respectively are not the same, they are nevertheless in one-to-one correspondence, so that $(A, B) \sim (B, A)$. Similarly, the elements $((a, b), c)$ of $((A, B), C)$, i.e., the ordered pairs whose first elements are ordered pairs (a, b) and whose second elements are elements c, are not identical with the triples (a, b, c) – the members of (A, B, C) – but are in one-to-one correspondence with them, and we have

$$((A, B), C) \sim (A, (B, C)) \sim (A, B, C).$$

In order to define products with an arbitrary set of factors, we first generalize the concept of ordered pair or ordered triple by assigning to each element m of a set $M = \{m, n, q, \ldots\}$ some quite arbitrary element a_m; in other words, we define a single-valued function $f(m) = a_m$ on M. Grouping these elements together yields what is called a *complex*, or *element complex*

$$p = (a_m, a_n, a_q \ldots)$$

or (following Cantor) a *covering* of the elements m by the elements a_m. Neither name implies a new construction; both are just synonyms for the function $f(m)$ defined on M. Two complexes are said to be equal if and only if there corresponds to every m the same element a_m (as its image), that is,

$(a_m^*, a_n^*, a_q^*, \ldots) = (a_m, a_n, a_q, \ldots)$ means that $a_m^* = a_m$, $a_n^* = a_n$, $a_q^* = a_q, \ldots$

or, in other words, two functions are considered to be equal if and only if they have the same "value" for every m: $f^*(m) = f(m)$; this rule replaces the requirement of a definite order in which the elements must appear in the ordered pairs, triples, etc. Moreover, the complexes depend on the basic set M, a fact that is not fully expressed in the above notation;

a complex of three elements that assigns to the elements 1, 2, 3 the elements a, b, c as images is not the same as one that assigns to the elements 4, 5, 6 the same elements a, b, c, and therefore it is also not the same as an ordered triple (a, b, c), which assigns the elements a, b, c to three definite places in a written or printed array. However – and, after all, this is what counts – the triples (a, b, c) can certainly be brought into one-to-one correspondence with the complexes that assign to the members of an arbitrary set of three elements the three elements a, b, c as images.

If we now assign a set A_m to every $m \varepsilon M$, then we obtain a *set complex*

$$P = (A_m, A_n, A_q, \ldots)$$

and, at the same time, we define this to be a set of complexes, namely, the *set of element complexes* $p = (a_m, a_n, a_q, \ldots)$, in which a_m runs through all the elements of A_m, a_n runs through all the elements of A_n, etc. P is defined to be the *product* of the sets $A_m, A_n, A_q, \ldots$. Using the Greek Π as an abbreviation for the product, we also write

$$P = \prod_m^M A_m.$$

The correspondence between the m and the A_m amounts to a definition of a single-valued function $F(m) = A_m$ on M, a function whose "values" are not elements, but sets. And the product P is the set of all single-valued functions $f(m)$ for which

$$f(m) \varepsilon F(m) \text{ for every } m \varepsilon M.$$

Finally, if we let all the A_m coincide – $A_m = A$ for all m – then we define the *power*

$$P = A^M$$

(with base A and exponent M) as a product of factors that are all equal. This, therefore, is the set of all element complexes $p = (a_m, a_n, \ldots)$ whose elements belong to A ($a_m \varepsilon A$, $a_n \varepsilon A, \ldots$) or the set of all single-valued functions $a = f(m)$ that assign an image $a \varepsilon A$ to every $m \varepsilon M$.

An important example: Let $A = \{a, b\}$ consist of two elements; A^M is the set of functions $f(m)$ for which

$$f(m) = a \text{ or } b.$$

Each such function[1] $f(m)$ determines the set M_a of those m for which

[1] For $a = 1$, $b = 0$, $f(m)$ is the *characteristic function* (§ 3) of M_a.

$f(m) = a$, and the set M_b of those m for which $f(m) = b$, where

$$M = M_a + M_b$$

is a decomposition of M into two complementary subsets. Conversely, if M_a is an arbitrary subset of M, and $M_b = M - M_a$ is its complement in M, and if we define

$$f(m) = a \quad \text{for} \quad m \,\varepsilon\, M_a, \qquad f(m) = b \quad \text{for} \quad m \,\varepsilon\, M_b,$$

then we have one of our functions $f(m)$. The functions $f(m)$ and the sets $M_a \leqq M$ are thus in one-to-one correspondence, that is, *A^M is equivalent to the set of all subsets of M.*

It can be seen similarly that, for a set $A = \{a, b, c\}$ with three elements, A^M is equivalent to the set of all partitions

$$M = M_a + M_b + M_c$$

into three disjoint summands, where the order of the summands counts; that is, the partition $M = M_a^* + M_b^* + M_c^*$ is to be considered the same as the above if and only if $M_a^* = M_a$, $M_b^* = M_b$, $M_c^* = M_c$.

What has been said in this chapter about the basic concepts so far introduced should only be regarded as preliminary orientation. In particular, the construction of sets by means of sum and intersection will have to be dealt with more thoroughly later on (Chapter V). In the next three chapters, the intersection will play a minor role as compared with the other combinatorial operations on sets; in the later chapters, on the other hand, the product will play the minor role.

CHAPTER II

CARDINAL NUMBERS

§ 5. Comparison of Sets

We called two sets equivalent (§ 2), in symbols

$$A \sim B,$$

if there exists a one-to-one correspondence between their elements such that to each a there corresponds a unique $b = f(a)$ and to each b a unique $a = g(b)$. Clearly, we have

$$A \sim A;$$
$$\text{if } A \sim B, \text{ then } B \sim A;$$
$$\text{if } A \sim B, \quad B \sim C, \text{ then } A \sim C;$$

we say that the relation of equivalence is *reflexive, symmetric,* and *transitive.*

Finite sets[1] are obviously equivalent if and only if they have the same number of elements. We shall therefore say in general that equivalent sets have the same *cardinal number* or *cardinality* (or *power*). That is, we assign to each set A an object $\mathfrak{a}$ in such a way that equivalent sets, and equivalent sets only, have the same object corresponding to them:

$$\mathfrak{a} = \mathfrak{b} \text{ means that } A \sim B.$$

We call these new objects cardinal numbers or powers and say: A has the cardinality $\mathfrak{a}$, $\mathfrak{a}$ is the cardinality of A, A has cardinal number $\mathfrak{a}$, $\mathfrak{a}$ is the cardinal number of A, and also (using $\mathfrak{a}$ linguistically as a number) A has $\mathfrak{a}$ elements.

This formal explanation says what the cardinal numbers are supposed to do, not what they are. More precise definitions have been attempted, but they are unsatisfactory and unnecessary. Relations between cardinal

[1] A complete theory of sets should also formulate precisely the theory of finite sets and of the natural numbers; we shall assume here that these preliminaries have been taken care of.

numbers are merely a more convenient way of expressing relations between sets; we must leave the determination of the "essence" of the cardinal number to philosophy.

A finite set consisting of n elements ($n = 1, 2, 3, \ldots$) will be assigned the number n as its cardinality; the null set, the number 0.

The cardinality of the set $\{1, 2, 3, \ldots\}$ of natural numbers is called $\aleph_0$ (read: aleph-null).[1] Sets of this cardinality, which can be written in the form of a *sequence,*

$$\{a_1, a_2, a_3, \ldots\} \qquad (a_m \neq a_n \text{ for } m \neq n)$$

are all *countable*[2] (or *enumerable* or *denumerable*).

We assign to the set of all real numbers and to the equivalent set of all the points of a straight line the cardinality $\aleph$ (Alef); it is called the *cardinality of the continuum.*

The cardinality of countable sets is often denoted by $\mathfrak{a}$; that of the continuum, by $\mathfrak{c}$.

When we first introduced the concept of equivalence, we mentioned that the set of all natural numbers is equivalent with the set of all even numbers. As is shown by the following diagram, in which the numbers in the same column correspond, the sets of all natural numbers, of all even numbers, of all odd numbers, of all squares, of all powers of 10, are all equivalent to each other, and therefore all have the same cardinality

1	2	3	$\ldots\ n$	$\ldots$	
2	4	6	$\ldots\ 2n$	$\ldots$	
1	3	5	$\ldots\ 2n-1$	$\ldots$	
1	4	9	$\ldots\ n^2$	$\ldots$	
10	100	1000	$\ldots\ 10^n$	$\ldots$	
2	3	5	$\ldots\ p_n$	$\ldots$	(p_n is the n-th prime).

One can extend the list and form sequences of numbers that have ever faster rates of growth (consider, for example, 10, 10^{10}, $10^{10^{10}}$, $\ldots$), which nevertheless, no matter how sparsely they are sown in the set of all natural numbers, have a cardinality no smaller than that of the whole set. This violation of the axiom *"totum parte majus"* (the whole is

---

[1] $\aleph$ (aleph) is the first letter of the Hebrew alphabet.

[2] Its elements can be "counted" (enumerated) by means of all the natural numbers. Sets that are finite (including the null set) or countable will be called *at most countable*; infinite sets that are not countable are called *uncountable* (or *nonenumerable* or *nondenumerable*).

greater than any of its parts) is one of those so-called paradoxes of the infinite which one must get used to; there are, of course, differences between the laws that pertain to finite sets and those that pertain to infinite sets; these differences do not, of course, in the least justify any objections to infinite sets.

The sets of points (or of numbers) constituting the intervals $0 \leqq x \leqq 1$ and $0 \leqq y \leqq 1000$ have the same cardinality even though the second is a thousand times as long as the first; the one-to-one correspondence is given by $y = 1000x$ or by any other projection. The interval $-\pi/2 < x < \pi/2$ and the set of all real numbers have the same cardinality by virtue of the correspondence $y = \tan x$.

We shall see in a moment that this relation — the equivalence between a set and a proper subset thereof — is characteristic of infinite sets.

I. *Every infinite set contains a countable subset.*

Let a_1 be an element of the infinite set A, a_2 an element of the (still) infinite set $A - \{a_1\}$, a_3 an element of the (still) infinite set $A - \{a_1, a_2\}$, etc. The pairwise distinct elements $a_1, a_2, a_3, \ldots$ constitute a countable subset of A.

II. *Every infinite set is equivalent to a proper subset.*

By removing from the infinite set A a countable subset and denoting its complement in A by B, obtain

$$A = \{a_1, a_2, \ldots , a_n, \ldots\} + B;$$

this is equivalent with, say,

$$\{a_2, a_3, \ldots, a_{n+1}, \ldots\} + B$$

(let a_n in the first set correspond to a_{n+1} in the second set, and let each $b \varepsilon B$ correspond to b itself).

Conversely, no set that is equivalent to one of its proper subsets can be finite. This property therefore characterizes infinite sets (and was used by Dedekind as the definition of infinite sets).

III. Equivalence Theorem of F. Bernstein: *If each of two given sets is equivalent to a subset of the other, then the two given sets are themselves equivalent.*

Let $A \sim B_1$, $B \sim A_1$, where A_1 is a subset of A, and moreover a proper subset, as otherwise there is nothing to prove; thus $A_1 < A$, $B_1 < B$. By the one-to-one mapping of B onto A_1, B_1 is also mapped onto a proper subset A_2 of A_1, so that

$$A > A_1 > A_2, \quad A \sim B_1 \sim A_2.$$

Thus the theorem is reduced to the following:

$$\text{If } A > A_1 > A_2, \quad A \sim A_2 \text{ , then } A \sim A_1,$$

i.e., *if a set lies between two equivalent sets, it is equivalent to them.*

Under the one-to-one mapping from A onto A_2, let A_1 be mapped onto A_3, A_2 onto A_4, A_3 onto A_5, etc., so that

$$A > A_1 > A_2 > A_3 > A_4 > A_5 > \cdots .$$

If

$$D = AA_1A_2 \ldots$$

is the intersection of the sets A_n, then

$$\begin{aligned} A &= D + (A - A_1) + (A_1 - A_2) + (A_2 - A_3) + (A_3 - A_4) + \cdots \\ A_1 &= D \qquad\qquad\quad\; + (A_1 - A_2) + (A_2 - A_3) + (A_3 - A_4) + \cdots . \end{aligned}$$

For to prove, say, the first formula, we note that an element $a \varepsilon A$ either belongs to all the A_n, and thus to D, or there exists a first A_n to which it does not belong while it still belongs to A_{n-1}, so that $a \varepsilon A_{n-1} - A_n$ (where we have set $A_0 = A$). From

$$A - A_1 \sim A_2 - A_3 \sim A_4 - A_5 \sim \cdots,$$

it follows that

$$(A - A_1) + (A_2 - A_3) + \cdots \sim (A_2 - A_3) + (A_4 - A_5) + \cdots,$$

the set on the left-hand side being mapped onto the set on the right. By mapping the remaining elements of A onto themselves, we obtain a one-to-one mapping of A onto A_1, so that $A \sim A_1$.

Until now we have only discussed equivalence, that is, the equality of two cardinal numbers. The next question would be: If two sets are not equivalent, so that their cardinal numbers are unequal, then can one of these cardinal numbers be defined in a natural way as being the larger and the other as the smaller? In short, do cardinal numbers have the character of magnitude? Can they be compared with one another?

It seems at first that the answer would have to be in the negative. If A and B denote sets, and A_1 and B_1 any subsets of A and B respectively, then there are four possibilities:

(1) There is an $A_1 \sim B$, and a $B_1 \sim A$.
(2) There is no $A_1 \sim B$, but there is a $B_1 \sim A$.
(3) There is an $A_1 \sim B$, but no $B_1 \sim A$.
(4) There is no $A_1 \sim B$, and no $B_1 \sim A$.

In case (1) we have, by the Equivalence Theorem, $\mathfrak{a} = \mathfrak{b}$; in case (2) it is natural to define $\mathfrak{a} < \mathfrak{b}$, and in case (3) to define $\mathfrak{a} > \mathfrak{b}$. In case (4), because of its symmetry with respect to the two sets, it is obviously impossible to define either $\mathfrak{a} < \mathfrak{b}$ or $\mathfrak{a} > \mathfrak{b}$, for both would have to hold; equally inadmissible is $\mathfrak{a} = \mathfrak{b}$, which would contradict the natural definition of equality that we have been using so far. We thus have a fourth relation, which we write as $\mathfrak{a} \parallel \mathfrak{b}$ and call *incomparability* between $\mathfrak{a}$ and $\mathfrak{b}$, while in the first three cases $\mathfrak{a}$ and $\mathfrak{b}$ will be called comparable. Thus:

$$\left.\begin{array}{l}(1)\ \mathfrak{a} = \mathfrak{b}\\ (2)\ \mathfrak{a} < \mathfrak{b}\\ (3)\ \mathfrak{a} > \mathfrak{b}\end{array}\right\} \mathfrak{a}, \mathfrak{b} \quad \text{comparable}$$
$$(4)\ \mathfrak{a} \parallel \mathfrak{b} \quad \mathfrak{a}, \mathfrak{b} \quad \text{incomparable.}$$

Comparability could therefore only be saved if we could show that the fourth case can never actually occur. With two finite sets this is indeed the case; for if, numbering the elements, we set $A = \{a_1, a_2, \ldots, a_m\}$, $B = \{b_1, b_2, \ldots, b_n\}$ and if, by means of a one-to-one correspondence, we form the pairs (a_1, b_1), (a_2, b_2), etc., then the process ends as soon as one of the sets is used up. (A finite set and an infinite set are also always comparable, the former being the smaller.) In a similar way, the precise basis for which will be given later (using the well-ordering of sets, § 13), we shall show that (4) can never occur, so that two cardinal numbers are always comparable.

If A is equivalent to a subset of B (case (1) or (2)), then $\mathfrak{a} = \mathfrak{b}$ or $\mathfrak{a} < \mathfrak{b}$, which we write as the single expression $\mathfrak{a} \leqq \mathfrak{b}$. The Equivalence Theorem can then be written in the suggestive form: If $\mathfrak{a} \leqq \mathfrak{b}$ and $\mathfrak{a} \geqq \mathfrak{b}$, then $\mathfrak{a} = \mathfrak{b}$.

If

$$\mathfrak{a} = \mathfrak{b}, \quad \mathfrak{a} < \mathfrak{b}, \quad \mathfrak{a} > \mathfrak{b}, \quad \mathfrak{a} \parallel \mathfrak{b},$$

then

$$\mathfrak{b} = \mathfrak{a}, \quad \mathfrak{b} > \mathfrak{a}, \quad \mathfrak{b} < \mathfrak{a}, \quad \mathfrak{b} \parallel \mathfrak{a}.$$

If $\mathfrak{a} = \mathfrak{b}$ and $\mathfrak{b}\ \mathrm{R}\ \mathfrak{c}$, then $\mathfrak{a}\ \mathrm{R}\ \mathfrak{c}$, where R denotes any one of the four relations.

If $\mathfrak{a} < \mathfrak{b}$ and $\mathfrak{b} < \mathfrak{c}$, then $\mathfrak{a} < \mathfrak{c}$; the relation $<$ is transitive.

Every infinite cardinal number is $\geqq \aleph_0$ (Theorem 1); $\aleph_0$ is the smallest infinite cardinal number.

Every infinite subset of a countable set (the set of all primes, for example) is countable, since its cardinality is $\leqq \aleph_0$ and at the same time is $\geqq \aleph_0$, so that by the Equivalence Theorem it is $= \aleph_0$.

§ 6. Sum, Product, and Power

Let A and B be disjoint. If both are finite, and A consists of m elements and B of n elements, then $A + B$ consists of $m + n$ elements. Furthermore, if $A \sim A_1$, $B \sim B_1$, and A_1 and B_1 are also disjoint, then $A + B \sim A_1 + B_1$. These remarks justify the following definition:

The *sum* $\mathfrak{a} + \mathfrak{b}$ of two cardinal numbers is the cardinality of the set-theoretic sum $A + B$, where A and B are any two disjoint sets having the cardinalities $\mathfrak{a}$ and $\mathfrak{b}$ respectively.

More generally, if the cardinalities $\mathfrak{a}_m$ correspond to the elements m of a set

$$M = \{m, n, p, \ldots\},$$

then

$$\sum_m^M \mathfrak{a}_m = \mathfrak{a}_m + \mathfrak{a}_n + \mathfrak{a}_p + \cdots$$

is the cardinality of the set-theoretic sum

$$\sum_m^M A_m = A_m + A_n + A_p + \cdots,$$

where the A_m are disjoint (pairwise non-overlapping) sets of cardinality $\mathfrak{a}_m$.

Examples: The set of all natural numbers may be decomposed into $\{1, 2, \ldots, n\} + \{n + 1, n + 2, \ldots\}$, where the second summand is countable. This yields

$$n + \aleph_0 = \aleph_0 + n = \aleph_0.$$

The set of all natural numbers may be decomposed into the set of odd numbers and the set of even numbers, both of which are countable, so that

$$\aleph_0 + \aleph_0 = \aleph_0;$$

or it may be decomposed into those three sets of numbers that, when divided by 3, yield the remainders 0, 1, and 2 respectively, so that

$$\aleph_0 + \aleph_0 + \aleph_0 = \aleph_0;$$

this follows from the associative law as well,

$$\aleph_0 + \aleph_0 + \aleph_0 = \aleph_0 + (\aleph_0 + \aleph_0) = \aleph_0 + \aleph_0 = \aleph_0.$$

Similarly, for every finite number of summands, we have

$$\aleph_0 + \aleph_0 + \cdots + \aleph_0 = \aleph_0.$$

The set of all natural numbers can moreover be split into countably many countable sets, as the following arrays, among others, show:

$$\begin{array}{llll} 1 & 3 & 5 & 7\ldots \\ 2 & 6 & 10 & 14\ldots \\ 4 & 12 & 20 & 28\ldots \\ 8 & 24 & 40 & 56\ldots \\ \multicolumn{4}{l}{\ldots\ldots\ldots\ldots} \end{array} \qquad \begin{array}{llll} 1 & 2 & 4 & 7\ldots \\ 3 & 5 & 8 & \ldots \\ 6 & 9 & \ldots & \\ 10 & \ldots & & \\ \multicolumn{4}{l}{\ldots\ldots\ldots\ldots} \end{array}$$

(dyadic array) (diagonal array)

In the first, the n-th row consists of those numbers that are divisible by 2^{n-1} and by no higher power of 2; in the second, the numbers are arranged diagonally (from upper right to lower left). We thus obtain the equation

$$\aleph_0 + \aleph_0 + \aleph_0 + \cdots = \aleph_0$$

or, more precisely,

$$\mathfrak{a}_1 + \mathfrak{a}_2 + \mathfrak{a}_3 + \cdots = \aleph_0 \quad \text{for } \mathfrak{a}_1 = \mathfrak{a}_2 = \mathfrak{a}_3 = \cdots = \aleph_0 .$$

But

$$1 + 1 + 1 + \cdots = \aleph_0,$$

also, as can be seen from the decomposition of a countable set into its individual elements, and therefore, by the Equivalence Theorem,

$$\mathfrak{a}_1 + \mathfrak{a}_2 + \mathfrak{a}_3 + \cdots = \aleph_0 \quad \text{for } 1 \leqq \mathfrak{a}_n \leqq \aleph_0,$$

e.g.

$$2 + 2 + 2 + \cdots = \aleph_0,$$
$$1 + 2 + 3 + \cdots = \aleph_0.$$

The interval $(-\pi/2, \pi/2)$ is equivalent with the set of all real numbers (p. 29), and by linear transformation this can be extended to any interval (α, β). Hence every set of numbers that contains an interval has, by the Equivalence Theorem, the cardinality $\aleph$ of the continuum. Placing two intervals together, for instance $[0, 1) + [1, 2) = [0, 2)$, yields

$$\aleph + \aleph = \aleph;$$

and hence (n being a finite number)

$$\aleph \leqq n + \aleph \leqq \aleph_0 + \aleph \leqq \aleph + \aleph = \aleph,$$

so that

$$n + \aleph = \aleph_0 + \aleph = \aleph + \aleph = \aleph.$$

The union of the countably many intervals $[n-1, n)$ $(n = 1, 2, \ldots)$ to form the half line yields

$$\aleph + \aleph + \aleph + \cdots = \aleph.$$

more precisely, $\mathfrak{a}_1 + \mathfrak{a}_2 + \mathfrak{a}_3 + \cdots = \aleph$ for $\mathfrak{a}_1 = \mathfrak{a}_2 = \mathfrak{a}_3 = \cdots = \aleph$.

For every infinite cardinal number $\mathfrak{a}$, we have $\mathfrak{a} + \aleph_0 = \mathfrak{a}$. For by § 5, I, we may write $\mathfrak{a} = \mathfrak{b} + \aleph_0$, so that

$$\mathfrak{a} + \aleph_0 = (\mathfrak{b} + \aleph_0) + \aleph_0 = \mathfrak{b} + (\aleph_0 + \aleph_0) = \mathfrak{b} + \aleph_0 = \mathfrak{a}.$$

The cardinality of an infinite set is not reduced by the elimination of a finite number of elements; that is, if $\mathfrak{a} = \mathfrak{b} + n$, where $\mathfrak{a}$ is infinite and n finite, then $\mathfrak{a} = \mathfrak{b}$. In fact,

$$\mathfrak{a} = \mathfrak{a} + \aleph_0 = \mathfrak{b} + (n + \aleph_0) = \mathfrak{b} + \aleph_0 = \mathfrak{b},$$

since $\mathfrak{b}$ is also infinite.

If A consists of m and B of n elements, then the product (A, B) has mn elements (§ 4). Furthermore, we have in general: If $A_1 \sim A$ and $B_1 \sim B$, then $(A_1, B_1) \sim (A, B)$. This justifies the following definition:

The *product* $\mathfrak{a}\mathfrak{b}$ of two cardinal numbers is the cardinality of the set-theoretic product (A, B), where A and B are any two sets with the cardinalities $\mathfrak{a}$ and $\mathfrak{b}$ respectively.

(In this case A and B do not have to be disjoint.)

And in general: If the elements m of a set

$$M = \{m, n, p, \ldots\}$$

have the cardinalities $\mathfrak{a}_m$, then

$$\prod_m^M \mathfrak{a}_m = \mathfrak{a}_m \mathfrak{a}_n \mathfrak{a}_p \ldots$$

is the cardinality of the set-theoretic product

$$\prod_m^M A_m = (A_m, A_n, A_p, \ldots),$$

where the A_m are any sets that have cardinality $\mathfrak{a}_m$.

Finally, we make the following definition:

If $\mathfrak{a}$ and $\mathfrak{m}$ are two cardinal numbers, then the *power* $\mathfrak{a}^{\mathfrak{m}}$ is the cardinality of the power A^M, where A and M are any two sets with the cardinalities $\mathfrak{a}$ and $\mathfrak{m}$ respectively.

If there corresponds to every $m \varepsilon M$ the same cardinal number $\mathfrak{a}_m = \mathfrak{a}$, then

$$\sum_m^M \mathfrak{a}_m = \mathfrak{a}\mathfrak{m}, \quad \prod_m^M \mathfrak{a}_m = \mathfrak{a}^{\mathfrak{m}},$$

where $\mathfrak{m}$ denotes the cardinality of M; thus in the realm of the infinite also, the addition of equal summands leads to multiplication, and the multiplication of equal factors leads to the forming of powers. To prove the first formula, let us consider those members of the set (A, M) of pairs (a, m) with $a \varepsilon A$ and $m \varepsilon M$ whose second members are all equal to some given m; these form a set A_m equivalent to A, and the equation between cardinal numbers then follows from the set-theoretic equation

$$(A, M) = \sum_m^M A_m.$$

To prove the second formula, we can simply set $A_m = A$ in $\prod_m^M A_m$ and obtain A^M.

The commutative, associative, and distributive laws hold for the processes just defined, but we will not plague the reader with a complete exposition of them; we will content ourselves with quickly sketching the proof of the *rules for the taking of powers.*

If $M = M_1 + M_2$, then any function $f(m)$ defined on M may be obtained by combining into a pair of functions the function $f(m_1)$ defined on M_1, and the function $f(m_2)$ defined on M_2. This yields the equivalence

$$A^{M_1+M_2} \sim (A^{M_1}, A^{M_2})$$

and in general, for an arbitrary sum $\sum_n M_n$ of disjoint summands,

$$A^{M_1+M_2+\cdots} \sim (A^{M_1}, A^{M_2}, \ldots).$$

If we allow the index n of M_n to run through a set N and then take all the M_n to be equivalent to one and the same set M, then we obtain

$$A^{(M,N)} \sim (A^M)^N.$$

On the other hand, let $A = (A_1, A_2)$: define the pair (a_1, a_2) as a function of m by combining two functions $a_1 = f_1(m)$, $a_2 = f_2(m)$ to form a pair; it follows from this that

$$(A_1, A_2)^M \sim (A_1^M, A_2^M)$$

and for an arbitrary product

$$(A_1, A_2, \ldots)^M \sim (A_1^M, A_2^M, \ldots);$$

if once again the index n of A_n runs through a set N and all the A_n are taken equal to a set A, we obtain

$$(A^N)^M \sim (A^M)^N.$$

For cardinal numbers we therefore have the following rules for the taking of powers:[1]

$$\begin{aligned} \mathfrak{a}^{\mathfrak{m}_1+\mathfrak{m}_2+\cdots} &= \mathfrak{a}^{\mathfrak{m}_1}\mathfrak{a}^{\mathfrak{m}_2}\ldots \\ (\mathfrak{a}_1\,\mathfrak{a}_2\ldots)^{\mathfrak{m}} &= \mathfrak{a}_1^{\mathfrak{m}}\,\mathfrak{a}_2^{\mathfrak{m}}\ldots \\ (\mathfrak{a}^{\mathfrak{m}})^{\mathfrak{n}} &= \mathfrak{a}^{\mathfrak{m}\mathfrak{n}}. \end{aligned}$$

Examples of product and power:

$$\begin{aligned} 2\aleph_0 &= \aleph_0 + \aleph_0 = \aleph_0 \\ n\aleph_0 &= \aleph_0 + \cdots + \aleph_0 = \aleph_0 \end{aligned}$$

and from the sum of countably many summands each of which is $\aleph_0$ we obtain

$$\begin{aligned} \aleph_0\aleph_0 &= \aleph_0 + \aleph_0 + \cdots = \aleph_0, \\ \aleph_0^2 &= \aleph_0\aleph_0 = \aleph_0, \\ \aleph_0^n &= \aleph_0\aleph_0\ldots\aleph_0 = \aleph_0. \end{aligned}$$

$\mathfrak{a}^{\aleph_0}$ is the cardinality of the set of all functions $a = f(n)$ (n a natural number, $a \varepsilon A$), or, alternatively, of all *sequences*

$$(a_1, a_2, \ldots) \qquad (a_n \varepsilon A),$$

where A denotes a set of cardinality $\mathfrak{a}$; for instance, $2^{\aleph_0}$ is the cardinality of the set of all *dyadic* sequences, i.e., of those sequences formed from the digits 0 and 1; while $10^{\aleph_0}$ is the cardinality of the set of all *decimal* sequences, i.e., of those sequences formed from 0, 1, ..., 9.

The set of all subsets of a set M of cardinality $\mathfrak{m}$ *has the cardinal number* $2^{\mathfrak{m}}$.

For as we have seen (§ 4), this set is equivalent to A^M, where A consists of two elements.

§ 7. The Scale of Cardinal Numbers

At this point we do not yet know whether there are distinct infinite cardinal numbers, or whether perhaps the popular prejudice is justified that sees in the infinite merely and simply the flat negation of the finite.

I. *We always have* $2^{\mathfrak{m}} > \mathfrak{m}$; *that is, the set of subsets of M has greater cardinality than has M itself.*

[1] We set $\mathfrak{a}^0 = 1$, $1^{\mathfrak{m}} = 1$, $0^{\mathfrak{m}} = 0$; a product vanishes if one of its factors does. It would serve no purpose to define 0^0.

First of all, there exists a system of subsets equivalent to M, namely the subsets consisting of the single elements $\{m\}$, $m \varepsilon M$. Hence $2^{\mathfrak{m}} \geqq \mathfrak{m}$.

On the other hand, let us suppose that there exists an arbitrary system of subsets equivalent to M; that is, we allow a subset $M_m \leqq M$ to correspond one-to-one to each $m \varepsilon M$; we wish to show that there then exists still another $N \leqq M$, different from all the M_m, so that equation $2^{\mathfrak{m}} = \mathfrak{m}$ is then impossible. The element m may either belong to the set M_m corresponding to it, or not:

$$\text{either} \quad m \varepsilon M_m \quad \text{or} \quad m \bar{\varepsilon} M_m;$$

the set N consisting of those elements of the second kind is then certainly different from all the M_m. For since

$$m \varepsilon N \quad \text{means} \quad m \bar{\varepsilon} M_m$$

if we were to have $N = M_m$ for some m, we would come out with the contradiction $m \varepsilon N$ and $m \bar{\varepsilon} N$. Expressed differently: If m belongs to M_m, then it does not belong to N; if m does not belong to M_m, then it belongs to N; M_m and N therefore always differ, since m belongs to one set but not to the other.

I. ensures the existence of distinct infinite cardinal numbers, and in fact of an infinite number of distinct ones; starting with one infinite $\mathfrak{m}$ (for instance $\aleph_0$ or $\aleph$), we can form

$$\begin{aligned} \mathfrak{m}_1 &= 2^{\mathfrak{m}} > \mathfrak{m}, \\ \mathfrak{m}_2 &= 2^{\mathfrak{m}_1} > \mathfrak{m}_1, \\ \mathfrak{m}_3 &= 2^{\mathfrak{m}_2} > \mathfrak{m}_2, \\ &\dots \end{aligned}$$

(I. also holds, by the way, for finite $\mathfrak{m}$: $1 = 2^0 > 0$, $2 = 2^1 > 1, \dots$).

Furthermore $\mathfrak{m} + \mathfrak{m}_1 + \mathfrak{m}_2 + \cdots$ is then an even greater cardinal number, and one can continue the process by this means; in general, we have:

II. *If a cardinal number* $\mathfrak{a}_m$ *corresponds to every* $m \varepsilon M$, *and if there is no greatest among them, then the sum*

$$\mathfrak{a} = \sum_m^M \mathfrak{a}_m$$

exceeds every $\mathfrak{a}_m$.

For, first of all, we certainly have $\mathfrak{a} \geqq \mathfrak{a}_m$ for each m; but equality is impossible, for then $\mathfrak{a}$ would be the largest of the given cardinal numbers.

For example, if there existed incomparable cardinals $\mathfrak{a}$ and $\mathfrak{b}$, then $\mathfrak{a} + \mathfrak{b}$ would exceed both.

I and II make possible an unboundedly ascending series of cardinal numbers. Admittedly they also present an opportunity for an antinomy (p. 11): Since to every set of cardinal numbers there corresponds a still larger one, no such set can encompass *all* cardinal numbers, and the "set of all cardinal numbers" is therefore unconceivable. We are thus confronted with the fact that the condition that "all" things of a certain kind be made into a collection may not always be capable of fulfillment; when we think we have them all, they are not *all* in the collection after all. The unsettling thing about this antimony is not that we obtain a contradiction, but that we were not prepared for one: the set of all cardinal numbers seems a priori to be as innocuous as the set of all natural numbers. This creates an uncertainty as to whether other infinite sets — perhaps even all of them — may not be such sham sets, pseudo-sets, sets that are not really sets, and creates the problem of removing this uncertainty. Set Theory must be built on a new basis — an axiomatic basis — in such a way that antinomies are impossible. In this book, we cannot go into the investigations, begun by Zermelo, whose purpose is to do this, investigations that give every promise of success; and we must adhere to our "naive" concept of set.[1]

III. (König's Theorem) *If to every $m \varepsilon M$ there correspond two cardinal numbers $\mathfrak{a}_m$ and $\mathfrak{b}_m$, and if we always have $\mathfrak{a}_m < \mathfrak{b}_m$, then*

$$\sum_m^M \mathfrak{a}_m < \prod_m^M \mathfrak{b}_m .$$

This is a generalization of Theorem I, which may be obtained from it by setting $\mathfrak{a}_m = 1$ and $\mathfrak{b}_m = 2$.

Proof. For the sake of convenience, we denote some of the elements of M by 1, 2, 3, ... Let the A_m be disjoint sets of cardinality $\mathfrak{a}_m$; the B_m, disjoint sets of cardinality $\mathfrak{b}_m$. Since the B_m can be replaced by equivalent sets, A_m may be assumed to be a subset of B_m, so that

$$A_m < B_m, \quad B_m = A_m + C_m, \quad C_m > 0 .$$

If we set $A = \sum_m^M A_m = A_1 + A_2 + A_3 + \cdots + A_m + \cdots$

$$B = \prod_m^M B_m = (B_1, B_2, B_3, \ldots, B_m, \ldots),$$

then we must prove that $\mathfrak{a} < \mathfrak{b}$. B is the set of complexes

$$p = (b_1, b_2, b_3, \ldots, b_m, \ldots) \qquad (b_m \varepsilon B_m).$$

[1] Compare Appendix E.

First of all, $\mathfrak{a} \leqq \mathfrak{b}$. For if c_m is a fixed element of $C_m = B_m - A_m$, then the complexes

$$\begin{array}{ll} (a_1, c_2, c_3, \ldots, c_m, \ldots) & (a_1 \varepsilon A_1) \\ (c_1, a_2, c_3, \ldots, c_m, \ldots) & (a_2 \varepsilon A_2) \\ \ldots\ldots\ldots\ldots\ldots\ldots & \\ (c_1, c_2, c_3, \ldots, a_m, \ldots) & (a_m \varepsilon A_m), \\ \ldots\ldots\ldots\ldots\ldots\ldots & \end{array}$$

each of which contains only one of the elements a_m (which runs through the set A_m) and otherwise contains only c's, are subsets of B that are pairwise non-overlapping and equivalent to $A_1, A_2, \ldots, A_m, \ldots$, respectively; A is thus equivalent to a subset of B.

On the other hand, let

$$P = \sum_m^M P_m = P_1 + P_2 + P_3 + \cdots + P_m + \cdots$$

be a subset of B equivalent to A $(P_m \sim A_m)$. We will show that it cannot be equivalent to the whole set B; this makes the equation $\mathfrak{a} = \mathfrak{b}$ impossible, leaving only $\mathfrak{a} < \mathfrak{b}$.

Let us consider the complexes

$$p_m = (b_{m1}, b_{m2}, \ldots, b_{mm}, \ldots)$$

belonging to P_m, and in particular, the elements b_{mm} belonging to them; they form a subset D_m of B_m of cardinality $\leqq \mathfrak{a}_m$. For, there are only $\mathfrak{a}_m$ complexes p_m, and since the b_{mm} that correspond to distinct p_m do not even have to be distinct, it follows that there at most $\mathfrak{a}_m$ distinct b_{mm}. Hence we have $D_m < B_m$ or, in other words, $B_m = D_m + E_m$, $E_m > 0$. If we now choose an arbitrary element e_m of E_m for every $m \varepsilon M$, then the complex

$$p = (e_1, e_2, e_3, \ldots, e_m, \ldots)$$

differs from all the p_m (since $e_m \neq b_{mm}$), and in fact it differs from all the p_m for every m. Hence it does not belong to P, and $P = B$ was not possible. This proves König's Theorem.

If, in particular $0 < \mathfrak{a}_1 < \mathfrak{a}_2 < \cdots$ is a sequence of increasing cardinal numbers, then

$$\mathfrak{a}_1 + \mathfrak{a}_2 + \mathfrak{a}_3 + \cdots < \mathfrak{a}_2 \mathfrak{a}_3 \mathfrak{a}_4 \ldots;$$

if we set $\mathfrak{a} = \mathfrak{a}_1 + \mathfrak{a}_2 + \mathfrak{a}_3 + \cdots$ and $\mathfrak{b} = \mathfrak{a}_1 \mathfrak{a}_2 \mathfrak{a}_3 \ldots$, then

$$\begin{aligned} \mathfrak{a} = \mathfrak{a}_1 + \mathfrak{a}_2 + \mathfrak{a}_3 + \cdots &< 1 \cdot \mathfrak{a}_2 \mathfrak{a}_3 \cdots \leqq \mathfrak{a}_1 \mathfrak{a}_2 \mathfrak{a}_3 \cdots \\ &= \mathfrak{b} \leqq \mathfrak{a}\mathfrak{a}\mathfrak{a} \cdots = \mathfrak{a}^{\aleph_0}, \quad \mathfrak{a} < \mathfrak{b} \leqq \mathfrak{a}^{\aleph_0}. \end{aligned}$$

Thus there exist cardinal numbers $\mathfrak{a}$ for which $\mathfrak{a} < \mathfrak{a}^{\aleph_0}$, and in fact there are an infinite number of such cardinal numbers, since one can start with an arbitrarily large $\mathfrak{a}_1$. However, in the same way there exist cardinal numbers $\mathfrak{c}$ for which $\mathfrak{c} = \mathfrak{c}^{\aleph_0}$; these are the cardinal numbers of the form $\mathfrak{d}^{\aleph_0}$, inasmuch as $(\mathfrak{d}^{\aleph_0})^{\aleph_0} = \mathfrak{d}^{\aleph_0 \aleph_0} = \mathfrak{d}^{\aleph_0}$.

Under the conditions of III we of course also have

$$\sum_m^M \mathfrak{a}_m \leqq \sum_m^M \mathfrak{b}_m, \quad \prod_m^M \mathfrak{a}_m \leqq \prod_m^M \mathfrak{b}_m;$$

however, we might have equality in this case. Thus, for instance,

$$1 + 2 + 3 + \cdots = 2 + 3 + 4 + \cdots = \aleph_0,$$
$$1 \cdot 2 \cdot 3 \cdots = 2 \cdot 3 \cdot 4 \cdots = 2^{\aleph_0};$$

for, the product is $\geqq 2 \cdot 2 \cdot 2 \cdots = 2^{\aleph_0}$ and

$$\leqq \aleph_0 \aleph_0 \aleph_0 \cdots = \aleph_0^{\aleph_0} \leqq (2^{\aleph_0})^{\aleph_0} = 2^{\aleph_0}.$$

§ 8. The Elementary Cardinal Numbers

We shall call the following three cardinal numbers elementary:

The cardinality $\aleph_0$ of countable sets;
The cardinality $\aleph$ of the continuum, which we note is identical with $2^{\aleph_0}$;
The cardinal number $2^{\aleph}$.

The cardinal number $\aleph_0$ (the smallest infinite cardinal number): We already know that the sum of a finite or countably infinite number of summands $\aleph_0$ or the product of a finite number of factors $\aleph_0$ is itself equal to $\aleph_0$. Let us list a few countable sets in addition to the ones we have already given.

(1) *The set of all integers* $\gtreqless 0$.

The negative integers, the number 0, and the positive integers together form a set of cardinality $\aleph_0 + 1 + \aleph_0 = \aleph_0$. The integers can be put into the form of a simple sequence $\{a_1, a_2, \ldots\}$ by ordering them as follows:

$$0,\ 1,\ -1,\ 2,\ -2,\ 3,\ -3,\ \ldots.$$

(2) *The set of all pairs of natural numbers.*

Its cardinality is $\aleph_0 \aleph_0 = \aleph_0$. One can construct a one-to-one correspondence between the pairs of natural numbers and the natural numbers themselves, or convert a double sequence into a simple one, by combining the pairs of numbers in a matrix (where (p, q) appears in the p-th row and q-th column)

$$\begin{matrix} (1,1) & (1,2) & (1,3) & \dots \\ (2,1) & (2,2) & (2,3) & \dots \\ (3,1) & (3,2) & (3,3). & \dots \\ . & . & . & \dots \\ . & . & . & \dots, \end{matrix}$$

at the same time arranging all the natural numbers in a similar matrix (two examples may be found on p. 34) and letting the elements having the same position correspond to each other. The diagonal array yields the correspondence

$$\begin{matrix} n: & 1 & 2 & 3 & 4 & 5 & 6 & \dots \\ (p,q): & (1,1) & (1,2) & (2,1) & (1,3) & (2,2) & (3,1) & \dots, \end{matrix}$$

where the pairs of numbers are arranged according to increasing value of the sum $p + q$ and, if the sum is the same, according to increasing p. The dyadic array yields the correspondence

$$n = 2^{p-1}(2q-1),$$

which is uniquely solvable for p and q.

(3) *The set of all finite complexes, or n-tuples, of natural numbers* (p_1), (p_1, p_2), (p_1, p_2, p_3), $\dots$, $(p_1, p_2, \dots, p_k)$, $\dots$, *where* k *and* p_k *run through all natural numbers.*

Its cardinality is

$$\aleph_0 + \aleph_0^2 + \aleph_0^3 + \cdots = \sum_k \aleph_0^k = \sum_k \aleph_0 = \aleph_0 \aleph_0 = \aleph_0.$$

The correspondence between these n-tuples and the natural numbers n can be given, for instance, by developing the numbers n dyadically as follows:

$$n = 2^{p_1 - 1} + 2^{p_1 + p_2 - 1} + \cdots + 2^{p_1 + p_2 + \cdots + p_k - 1};$$

for example, there corresponds to the number $27 = 1 + 2 + 2^3 + 2^4$ the n-tuple $(1, 1, 2, 1)$.

(4) *The set of the rational numbers.*

If we allow the positive rational number p/q, where p and q are relatively prime natural numbers, to correspond to the pair of numbers (p, q) (Example (2)), then the set of numbers p/q becomes equivalent to a part of the set of the (p, q), and therefore it has a cardinality $\leqq \aleph_0$; however, since it is infinite, the cardinality must be $\aleph_0$. The diagonal array yields an arrangement of the p/q according to increasing $p + q$; and if the sum $p + q$ is the same for two fractions, they are arranged with numerators in ascending order,

$$\tfrac{1}{1}, \tfrac{1}{2}, \tfrac{2}{1}, \tfrac{1}{3}, \tfrac{3}{1}, \tfrac{1}{4}, \tfrac{2}{3}, \tfrac{3}{2}, \tfrac{4}{1}, \tfrac{1}{5}, \tfrac{5}{1}, \ldots,$$

the reducible fractions being thus omitted.

The set of all rational numbers also is countable, and so is the set of all the rational numbers in an interval. The rational numbers in the interval (0, 1) may be put in the form of a simple sequence by arranging them, say, with denominators in ascending order and, in case the denominators are equal, with numerators in ascending order,

$$\tfrac{1}{2}, \tfrac{1}{3}, \tfrac{2}{3}, \tfrac{1}{4}, \tfrac{3}{4}, \tfrac{1}{5}, \tfrac{2}{5}, \tfrac{3}{5}, \tfrac{4}{5}, \ldots.$$

That the set of all rational numbers — which, after all, is everywhere dense on the straight line (geometrically speaking) — does not have a larger cardinality than the set of integers, is just another of the many facts of set theory that appear surprising and even paradoxical.

(5) *The set of (real) algebraic numbers.*

This set also, itself much finer and more dense than that of the rational numbers, is only countable. We prove this for real and for complex algebraic numbers simultaneously. An algebraic number of the k-th degree is a root of an irreducible equation

$$x^k + r_1 x^{k-1} + \cdots + r_{k-1} x + r_k = 0$$

with rational coefficients (which is uniquely determined by it). There are infinitely many such equations, but surely no more than there are n-tuples $(r_1, r_2, \ldots, r_k)$ of rational numbers (since not all n-tuples yield irreducible equations); so there are at most $\aleph_0^k = \aleph_0$ such equations. Thus there are $\aleph_0$ irreducible equations of the k-th degree, each one of which has k roots; so there are $k\aleph_0 = \aleph_0$ algebraic numbers of the k-th degree and $\sum_k \aleph_0 = \aleph_0 \aleph_0 = \aleph_0$ algebraic numbers altogether.

The set of all pairs, triples, etc., of algebraic or rational numbers is, of course, also countable. The set of all elements each of which can be represented by a finite number of symbols of a finite or countable system of symbols is countable if, in the case of a finite system of symbols, we admit n-tuples with arbitrarily large n. For we have

$$\begin{aligned} \aleph_0 + \aleph_0^2 + \cdots + \aleph_0^k &= \aleph_0, \\ \aleph_0 + \aleph_0^2 + \cdots &= \aleph_0, \\ n + n^2 + \cdots &= \aleph_0. \end{aligned}$$

For instance, the set of all arbitrarily long "words" (i.e., n-tuples of letters, which may or may not make sense) constructible from a finite alphabet is countable, as is the set of all possible books, symphonies, and the like.

The cardinality $\aleph$ *of the continuum.*

We have already found (p. 34) that the sum of finitely or countably many summands $\aleph$ is equal to $\aleph$:

$$n\aleph = \aleph_0 \aleph = \aleph.$$

By means of the decimal representation $0.a_1 a_2 a_3 \ldots$, every number of the interval $[0, 1]$ is represented at least once and at most twice. Hence

$$\aleph \leqq 10^{\aleph_0} \leqq 2\aleph = \aleph,$$

so that $\aleph = 10^{\aleph_0}$. The same of course holds if, instead of the decimal representation, we make use of any other representation to a base > 1, so that

$$\aleph = 2^{\aleph_0} = 3^{\aleph_0} = \cdots$$

(but $1^{\aleph_0} = 1$). It then follows that

$$\aleph^{\aleph_0} = (2^{\aleph_0})^{\aleph_0} = 2^{\aleph_0 \aleph_0} = 2^{\aleph_0} = \aleph,$$

that is, $\aleph$ belongs to that category of cardinal numbers, already considered, that equal their $\aleph_0$-th power, and is certainly not the sum of an increasing sequence of cardinal numbers. By the Equivalence Theorem we then certainly have

$$\aleph = \aleph^2 = \aleph^3 = \cdots = \aleph^{\aleph_0}$$

(or directly: $\aleph^2 = \aleph\aleph = 2^{\aleph_0} \cdot 2^{\aleph_0} = 2^{\aleph_0 + \aleph_0} = 2^{\aleph_0} = \aleph$)

as well as $\aleph = 2^{\aleph_0} = 3^{\aleph_0} = \cdots = \aleph_0^{\aleph_0} = \aleph^{\aleph_0}$.

In these formulas there is again a surprise in store for us: for $\aleph^2 = \aleph\aleph$ is, after all, the cardinality of the set of all pairs (x, y) of real numbers, or of all points of the plane: $\aleph^3$ is the cardinality of three-dimensional space, or of the set of all number triples (x, y, z), etc., until we get to $\aleph^{\aleph_0}$, which is the cardinality of $\aleph_0$-dimensional space, that is, of the set of all sequences $(x_1, x_2, x_3, \ldots)$ of real numbers. So we have: *All spaces that have a finite or a countable number of dimensions have the same cardinality* $\aleph$. This, too, sounds paradoxical enough, and it seems to overthrow the concept of dimension, which will later be reinstated only by means of quite a different order of ideas (namely, the requirement of not only a one-to-one but a bi-continuous mapping); and yet the fact that the line and the plane have, in a manner of speaking, the same number of points is no more puzzling than the fact that the natural numbers may be divided into odd and even ones; that is, $\aleph\aleph = \aleph$ is basically nothing but $\aleph_0 + \aleph_0 = \aleph_0$. For, by splitting the decimal representation of a number, we can make two; and from two representations we can make one, by interweaving the two; that is the entire secret. To make the equivalence between line and surface perfectly clear, we represent every real number of the interval $J = (0, 1]$ (i.e., $0 < x \leqq 1$) by a dyadic fraction with infinitely many ones (with a modification of the usual expansion to avoid its two-valuedness), that is we can put it in the form

$$x = (\tfrac{1}{2})^{x_1} + (\tfrac{1}{2})^{x_1+x_2} + (\tfrac{1}{2})^{x_1+x_2+x_3} + \cdots ,$$

where the x_n are natural numbers; this can always be done and can be done in only one way, and it incidentally illustrates the equation $\aleph = \aleph_0^{\aleph_0}$. Let us write this representation for short as

$$x = [x_1, x_2, x_3, \ldots].$$

From two such numbers x and $y = [y_1, y_2, y_3, \ldots]$ we then obtain a single one

$$t = [x_1, y_1, x_2, y_2, \ldots] ,$$

and conversely from

$$t = [t_1, t_2, t_3, t_4, \ldots]$$

we again obtain

$$x = [t_1, t_3, t_5, \ldots] , \; y = [t_2, t_4, t_6, \ldots] ,$$

so that the ordered pairs (x, y) of numbers and the numbers t are brought into one-to-one correspondence; that is, the square $0 < {x \atop y} \leqq 1$ is mapped biuniquely onto the line-segment $0 < t \leqq 1$, and the product of intervals (J, J) is mapped biuniquely onto the interval J. We deal similarly with number triples (x, y, z) and with finite n-tuples; for sequences of numbers $(x, y, z, \ldots)$ we represent the mapping by means of the diagonal array:

$$t = [x_1, x_2, y_1, x_3, y_2, z_1, \ldots]$$

and conversely,

$$\begin{aligned} x &= [t_1, t_2, t_4, \ldots] \\ y &= [t_3, t_5, t_8, \ldots] \\ z &= [t_6, t_9, t_{13}, \ldots] \\ &\ldots\ldots\ldots\ldots . \end{aligned}$$

From $\aleph = 2^{\aleph_0}$ it follows that $\aleph > \aleph_0$; *the continuum is not countable.* A conjecture that was made at the beginning of Cantor's investigations, and that remains unproved to this day, is that $\aleph$ is the cardinal number *next larger than* $\aleph_0$; this conjecture is known as the *continuum hypothesis,* and the question as to whether it is true or not is known as the *problem of the continuum.* The uncountability of the continuum may also be seen as follows: No *countable* set of real numbers (of the interval J)

$$\begin{aligned} a &= [a_1, a_2, a_3, \ldots] \\ b &= [b_1, b_2, b_3, \ldots] \\ c &= [c_1, c_2, c_3, \ldots] \\ &\ldots \end{aligned}$$

can include *all* these numbers, as there are others

$$x = [x_1, x_2, x_3, \ldots] \qquad (x_1 \neq a_1, x_2 \neq b_2, x_3 \neq c_3, \ldots).$$

This "diagonal process" is the simplest model for the proof of Theorem I, § 7.

As there are only $\aleph_0$ rational and algebraic numbers, there certainly must exist irrational and transcendental numbers, and in fact as many ($\aleph$) of them as of real numbers. For, the cardinality of a *non-denumerable* (i.e., infinite and not countable) set is not diminished by the removal of a countable number of elements. (The proof is like that of the corresponding remark on p. 35.) The real numbers $0 < x \leqq 1$ can be mapped onto the irrational numbers $0 < y < 1$ by means of, say,

$$\begin{aligned} x &= [x_1, x_2, x_3, \ldots] \\ y &= \frac{1|}{|x_1} + \frac{1|}{|x_2} + \frac{1|}{|x_3} + \cdots, \end{aligned}$$

where x is given by the above dyadic representation and y by the continued fraction formed from the sequence of natural numbers $x_1, x_2, \ldots$.

The cardinal number $2^{\aleph}$.

This cardinal number, which is in turn $> \aleph$, belongs to the set of all subsets of the continuum (that is, to the set of all sets of real numbers) or to the set of all linear, planar, or spatial point sets; it is also the cardinality of the set all single-valued functions $f(x)$ of a real variable where $f(x)$ can take on two values; however, from

$$\aleph^{\aleph} = (2^{\aleph_0})^{\aleph} = 2^{\aleph_0 \aleph} = 2^{\aleph}$$

it follows at once that the set of all the functions $f(x)$ that can run through all the real numbers is also only of the cardinality $2^{\aleph}$. The cardinality of special classes of functions may of course be smaller; the set of all *continuous* functions $f(x)$, for instance, only has the cardinality

$\aleph$. For, $f(x)$ is then determined by its values $f(r)$ at the rational points r; the set of all $f(r)$ has the cardinality $\aleph^{\aleph_0} = \aleph$, and the set of all continuous $f(x)$ has a cardinality which is $\leqq \aleph$ (since not every $f(r)$ gives rise to a continuous $f(x)$), and also $\geqq \aleph$ (the functions $f(x) =$ constant already form a set of cardinality $\aleph$, and hence the cardinality of this set is exactly equal to $\aleph$.

We close with a collection of formulas for $\mathfrak{a} + \mathfrak{b}$, $\mathfrak{a}\mathfrak{b}$, and $\mathfrak{a}^{\mathfrak{b}}$, where the cardinal numbers involved are $\aleph$, $\aleph_0$ and the natural numbers n; to the extent that they are not proved above, they follow from the Equivalence Theorem.

$$(\alpha) \qquad 1^{\aleph_0} = 1^{\aleph} = 1$$

$$(\beta) \qquad n + \aleph_0 = n\aleph_0 = \aleph_0^n = \aleph_0 + \aleph_0 = \aleph_0\aleph_0 = \aleph_0$$

$$(\gamma) \qquad (n+1)^{\aleph_0} = \aleph_0^{\aleph_0} = n + \aleph = n\aleph = \aleph^n = \\ = \aleph_0 + \aleph = \aleph_0\aleph = \aleph^{\aleph_0} = \aleph + \aleph = \aleph\aleph = \aleph$$

$$(\delta) \qquad (n+1)^{\aleph} = \aleph_0^{\aleph} = \aleph^{\aleph} = 2^{\aleph}.$$

CHAPTER III

ORDER TYPES

§ 9. Order

Many sets present themselves at the outset in a natural *order,* in which for each two distinct elements, one precedes and one follows. We express such an ordering by the usual way in which a set is written, the element that precedes being to the left of the one that follows. Thus letters appear in alphabetical order and the natural numbers in their order of magnitude, as follows:

$$1, 2, 3, \ldots;$$

similarly for the real numbers. However, we can also prescribe such orderings as we please: for instance, we can order the natural numbers in decreasing order of magnitude

$$\ldots, 3, 2, 1,$$

or we can put the odd numbers before the even numbers, ordering each class according to increasing or decreasing order of magnitude:

$$1, 3, 5, \ldots, 2, 4, 6, \ldots$$
$$1, 3, 5, \ldots, \ldots, 6, 4, 2$$
$$\ldots, 5, 3, 1, 2, 4, 6, \ldots$$
$$\ldots, 5, 3, 1, \ldots, 6, 4, 2.$$

We can order a set of people according to their weight, their height, their age, the alphabetical order of their names, or the numbers on the stubs of their theatre tickets.

Thus, a set is ordered by assigning an order of precedence to any two distinct elements a and b, that is, by a rule that states of two distinct elements a and b that one precedes and the other follows. If a is to come before b, and b after a, then we write[1]

[1] It seems to us unnecessary to use other forms of the symbols $<$ and $>$.

$$a < b, \quad b > a.$$

The relation $<$ is to be transitive, that is,

$$\text{if} \quad a < b \quad \text{and} \quad b < c, \quad \text{then} \quad a < c.$$

Of course, the space-like or time-like characteristics which seem to attach to this explanation because of the use of the prepositions "before" and "after" are of no consequence, and we will convince ourselves by the use of other definitions that what we have here is nothing but an application of the concept of function.

Let us form the set of ordered pairs $p = (a, b)$ from *distinct* elements of the set A (which must of course contain at least two elements); the pairs p and $p^* = (b, a)$ are distinct and will be called *inverse* to each other. We then split the set of all ordered pairs into two complementary subsets $P + P^*$ by means of the following rule:

(a) Of two inverse pairs, one belongs to P, the other to P^*;

(b) If $p = (a, b)$ and $q = (b, c)$ belong to P, then so does $r = (a, c)$.

If we then write

$$a < b \quad \text{or} \quad b > a$$

for $(a, b) = p \,\varepsilon\, P$, then an ordering in the above sense is defined. (And conversely: Every ordering yields a partition $P + P^*$, which we define by considering those pairs $p = (a, b)$ as elements of P for which $a < b$). Here it is clear that the idea of "preceding" and "following" introduces nothing new or mysterious, but that it is only a question of distinguishing one pair of two inverse pairs, or one element of two distinct elements. We call P the *ordering set.*

Even simpler is the following explanation: With every element a of A we associate a unique set $M(a)$ such that the a are in one-to-one correspondence with the $M(a)$ and such that the $M(a)$ are comparable (in the sense of p. 13); by virtue of the one-to-one correspondence, it follows that

$$M(a) \lesseqgtr M(b) \qquad \text{for} \quad a \neq b.$$

If we then write $a < b$ instead of $M(a) \subset M(b)$, an ordering of the set A is defined; conversely, from any ordering we can form a system of sets $M(a)$ of the kind indicated.

For instance: For each a, let

$$M(a) = \text{the set of all elements of } A \text{ that are } < a.$$

The actual existence of orderings of A or of sets of pairs P or of systems of sets $M(a)$ of the kind indicated does not as yet follow from the above considerations; later on (§ 12) we shall see that every set can not only be ordered, but can also even be ordered in a special way (well-ordered). An upper bound on the number of distinct orderings, that is, on the cardinality of the set of distinct orderings of a set A is $2^{\mathfrak{a}\mathfrak{a}}$, where $\mathfrak{a}$ is the cardinality of A. For, (A, A), which has the cardinality $\mathfrak{a}\mathfrak{a} = \mathfrak{a}^2$, is the set of all pairs (a, b) of (equal or distinct) elements of A; and the ordering set P is a subset of (A, A). There are $2^{\mathfrak{a}\mathfrak{a}}$ subsets of (A, A), and hence at most $2^{\mathfrak{a}\mathfrak{a}}$ ordering sets, or distinct orderings, of P. For instance, for a finite set of n elements, the number of distinct orderings is

$$n! = 1 \cdot 2 \cdot \cdots n < 2^{nn}.$$

Until further notice, capital italic letters shall denote ordered sets, and the equation $A = B$ shall mean that A and B have not only the same elements but also the same ordering when individual elements are given, the order in which they are written from left to right will denote their order in the set as well; thus

$$A = \{\ldots, a, \ldots, b, \ldots, c, \ldots\}$$

is a set in which $a < b < c$, where the dots indicate the presence of other elements before a, between a and b, between b and c, and after c. Accordingly,

$$A = \{a, \ldots, b, \ldots\}$$

denotes a set in which there is no element before a, so that a is the *first* element;

$$A = \{\ldots, b, \ldots, c\}$$

denotes a set in which there is no element after c, so that c is the *last* element; and

$$A = \{\ldots, a, b, \ldots\}$$

denotes a set in which there is no element between a and b, so that a and b are neighboring elements.

If we interchange the symbols $<$ and $>$ throughout A, then we obtain the *inverse* ordered set

$$A^* = \{\ldots, c, \ldots, b, \ldots, a, \ldots\},$$

whose ordering set is P^*.

Two ordered sets are called *similar,* written

$$A \cong B,$$

if there exists a one-to-one correspondence $b = f(a)$, $a = g(b)$ between them that preserves the order; that is, $a < a_1$ when and only when $b < b_1$.

For instance, the set $\{1, 2, 3, 4, \ldots\}$ is similar to $\{2, 3, 4, \ldots\}$, but not to $\{2, 3, 4, \ldots, 1\}$.

Like equivalence, similarity is reflexive, symmetric, and transitive. Two similar sets are said to have the same *order type*; that is, with every ordered set A we associate a symbol α, called its *order type* (type, for short), in such a way that similar sets, and only similar sets, have the same order type:

$$\alpha = \beta \quad \text{means} \quad A \cong B.$$

The type of the set A^* inverse to A is called α^*.

Similarity implies equivalence, but the converse is in general false: $A \cong B$ implies $A \sim B$, and $\alpha = \beta$ implies $\mathfrak{a} = \mathfrak{b}$. Hence we may say that a type α has a definite cardinal number $\mathfrak{a}$.

A finite set of n elements can be ordered (permuted) in $n!$ ways, but the resulting ordered sets are always similar to the set $\{1, 2, \ldots, n\}$; again we call this type n, since any confusion between this and the cardinal number n is quite innocuous. A set having one element shall have type 1, the null set type 0.

The set $\{1, 2, 3, \ldots\}$ of the natural numbers in their natural order shall have type ω; thus the inversely ordered set $\ldots, 3, 2, 1$ has the type ω^*.

§ 10. Sum and Product

Let A and B be disjoint ordered sets. Then

$$S = A + B$$

shall denote the sum of the two sets in the following order: The order of the elements a among themselves, and that of the elements b among themselves is retained, and every a precedes every b $(a < b)$. This sum is therefore to be distinguished from $B + A$, which, though it contains the same elements, does not contain them in the same order: *The addition of ordered sets is not commutative.*

Example:

$$A = \{1, 3, 5, \ldots\}, \quad B = \{2, 4, 6, \ldots\}.$$
$$A + B = \{1, 3, 5, \ldots, \quad 2, 4, 6, \ldots\}$$
$$B + A = \{2, 4, 6, \ldots, \quad 1, 3, 5, \ldots\}.$$

It can also be said that in $S = A + B$ we have $A < B$; the entire set A precedes the entire set B. In general, if A and B are subsets of an ordered set, then $A < B$ shall mean

$$a < b \quad \text{for all} \quad a \varepsilon A \quad \text{and} \quad b \varepsilon B;$$

the relations $a < B$ and $A < b$ shall have analogous meanings.

If A_1 and B_1 are also disjoint ordered sets and if $A_1 \cong A$, $B_1 \cong B$, then $A_1 + B_1 \cong A + B$. This justifies the following definition:

The *sum* (or type-sum) $\alpha + \beta$ is the type of $A + B$, where A and B are arbitrary disjoint sets whose types are α and β respectively.

In general, let us associate with every element m of an ordered set

$$M = \{\ldots, m, \ldots, n, \ldots, p, \ldots\}$$

an ordered set A_m, and let these sets be disjoint (pairwise non-overlapping). Then the sum

$$S = \sum_m^M A_m = \cdots + A_m + \cdots + A_n + \cdots + A_p + \cdots$$

is defined to be the set formed from all the elements of all the A_m in the following order: for each m the order of the elements $a_m \varepsilon A_m$ among themselves remains unchanged, while for $m < n$, the entire set A_m precedes the entire set A_n: $A_m < A_n$.

If we replace the summands by *similar* ones (once more, of course, these have to be disjoint), then the sum is also transformed into a similar one, and this justifies the following definition: if to the elements $m \varepsilon M$ there correspond the types α_m, then by the sum

$$\sigma = \sum_m^M \alpha_m = \cdots + \alpha_m + \cdots + \alpha_n + \cdots + \alpha_p + \cdots$$

we shall mean the type of the above set S.

A general associative law holds, of which we will adduce only the simplest case

$$(\alpha + \beta) + \gamma = \alpha + (\beta + \gamma) = \alpha + \beta + \gamma;$$

on the other hand, there is no commutative law: if the order of M is changed, then S, and in general the type σ, is changed as well.

Examples: The partition of the sequence of natural numbers (of type ω) into

$$\{1, 2, \ldots, n\} + \{n + 1, n + 2, \ldots\},$$

where the second summand is of type ω, yields

$$n + \omega = \omega.$$

On the other hand $\omega + n$ is the type of

$$\{n + 1, n + 2, \ldots, 1, 2, \ldots, n\},$$

and this set is certainly not of type ω, as it has a last element; hence

$$\omega + n \neq n + \omega;$$

and the types ω, $\omega + 1$, $\omega + 2, \ldots$ are clearly pairwise distinct. The four orderings (p. 48) of the natural numbers obtained by placing the odd numbers before the even ones have the types

$$\omega + \omega, \quad \omega + \omega^*, \quad \omega^* + \omega, \quad \omega^* + \omega^*,$$

respectively, which, as can easily be seen, are distinct from one another and from the types $\omega + n$ and their inverses $n + \omega^*$. $\omega^* + \omega$ is also the type of the set of all integers

$$\{\ldots, -2, -1, 0, 1, 2, \ldots\}$$

in their natural order.

If with every natural number m we associate a natural number a_m, then the partition of the sequence of natural numbers into groups of a_m members each yields the equation (type-equation)

$$\sum_m a_m = a_1 + a_2 + a_3 + \cdots = \omega;$$

for instance,[1]

$$1 + 1 + 1 + \ldots = \omega$$
$$1 + 2 + 3 + \ldots = \omega.$$

---

[1] Since we have also written $1 + 1 + 1 + \ldots = \aleph_0$, the undistinguishing use of the finite numbers as cardinal numbers and as order-types might arouse misgivings; on the other hand, it can be seen at once from any equation containing infinite symbols whether it is a number equation or a type equation.

On the other hand, if we divide the natural numbers into countably many sequences, for instance as follows (diagonal array),

$$\{1, 2, 4, \ldots\} + \{3, 5, 8, \ldots\} + \{6, 9, 13, \ldots\} + \cdots,$$

then we once again obtain a new type

$$\sum_m \omega = \omega + \omega + \omega + \cdots.$$

When inverting a sum, one must invert each summand and the order of the summands; that is,

$$\text{if } S = \sum_m^M A_m \text{ then } S^* = \sum_m^{M^*} A_m^* ,$$

and the corresponding result holds for types. For instance

$$(\alpha + \beta)^* = \beta^* + \alpha^*.$$

Products of finitely many factors. The ordered pairs (a, b), $a \varepsilon A$, $b \varepsilon B$, where A and B are ordered (not necessarily disjoint) sets, can be arranged in an order that is called, quite appropriately, the *lexicographic* order, or order *by first difference.* To be specific, we define

$$(a, b) < (a_1, b_1) \text{ if } \begin{cases} \text{either } a < a_1 \\ \text{or } a = a_1, b < b_1. \end{cases}$$

The set ordered in this way will again be called (A, B); it is the ordered product of the ordered pairs, and is to be distinguished from (B, A), to which it is equivalent but not, in general, similar. If $A_1 \cong A$, $B_1 \cong B$, then $(A_1, B_1) \cong (A, B)$, and this once again justifies defining the product of α and β as the type of (A, B). Unfortunately, we cannot escape an inconvenience of historical origin: *The type of (A, B) is called $\beta\alpha$, not $\alpha\beta$.*[1]

Example:

$$A = \{1, 2\}, \quad B = \{1, 2, 3, \ldots\}, \quad \alpha = 2, \quad \beta = \omega.$$

[1] Cantor originally wrote $\alpha\beta$, then changed this to $\beta\alpha$, and the latter notation became the overwhelmingly predominant one; one further change would make the confusion permanent. One could do away with the lack of agreement by ordering anti-lexicographically, i.e., by last differences; but this again would be uncomfortable.

(A, B) is the lexicographically ordered set of pairs (a, b), which therefore has the order

$$(1,1),\ (1,2),\ (1,3),\ \ldots,\ (2,1),\ (2,2),\ (2,3),\ \ldots;$$

it is of type $\beta\alpha = \omega 2 = \omega + \omega$. (B, A) is the set of all pairs (b, a) in the order

$$(1,1),\ (1,2),\ (2,1),\ (2,2),\ (3,1),\ (3,2),\ \ldots;$$

it is of type $\alpha\beta = 2\omega = \omega$.

The addition of equal summands here again leads to multiplication; that is, if all the $\alpha_m = \alpha$ and if μ denotes the type of M, then

$$\sum_m^M \alpha = \alpha\mu.$$

In fact, $\alpha\mu$ is the type of (M, A), that is, of the set of lexicographically ordered pairs (m, a). If the set of these pairs for a given m is A_m, then

$$(M, A) = \sum_m^M A_m,$$

from which, because $A_m \cong A$, the type equation follows. $\alpha\mu$ is obtained by "the insertion of α in μ," that is, by the insertion of a set of type α for every element of a set of type μ.

Examples $\omega + \omega + \omega = \omega 3$, $3 + 3 + 3 + \cdots = 3\omega = \omega$. In general, $n\omega = n + n + n + \cdots = \omega$, $\omega n = \omega + \omega + \cdots + \omega$, the latter having n summands.

The distributive law holds only with respect to the second factor; that is, we have

$$\beta \cdot \sum_m^M \alpha_m = \sum_m^M \beta\alpha_m,$$

whereas if the factor β is placed at the right, the equation need not hold.

In fact, if $A = \sum_m^M A_m$, then for every set B we have

$$(A, B) = \sum_m^M (A_m, B),$$

as can be seen at once from the lexicographical ordering of the pairs (a, b), and the type equation follows from this; it can also be deduced easily from the "insertion" of β in $\alpha = \sum_m^M \alpha_m$. In particular,

$$\gamma(\alpha + \beta) = \gamma\alpha + \gamma\beta,$$

but $(\alpha + \beta)\gamma = \alpha\gamma + \beta\gamma$ does not necessarily hold.

Example. $2(\omega + 1) = 2\omega + 2 = \omega + 2$, since (by actual insertion)

$$2(\omega + 1) = 2 + 2 + 2 + \cdots + 2 = \omega + 2.$$

On the other hand,

$$(\omega + 1)2 = (\omega + 1) + (\omega + 1) = \omega 2 + 1 \neq \omega 2 + 2 = \omega 2 + 1 \cdot 2.$$

Inversion of (A, B) yields the lexicographic ordering of the pairs (a, b) of (A^*, B^*), so that

$$(A, B)^* = (A^*, B^*) \quad \text{and} \quad (\beta\alpha)^* = \beta^*\alpha^*;$$

in the inversion of a product, the factors are to be inverted but not their order (unlike the case of addition).

The extension of multiplication to three or more factors is obvious. Thus, let (A, B, C) be the lexicographically ordered set of triples (a, b, c), in which we then have $(a, b, c) < (a_1, b_1, c_1)$ if

$$\begin{array}{ll} \text{either} & a < a_1 \\ \text{or} & a = a_1, \quad b < b_1 \\ \text{or} & a = a_1, \quad b = b_1, \quad c < c_1; \end{array}$$

its type is called $\gamma\beta\alpha$. Obviously the associative law holds:

$$\gamma(\beta\alpha) = (\gamma\beta)\alpha = \gamma\beta\alpha.$$

We can deal in a similar way with any finite number of factors, and even more: If $M = \{1, 2, 3, \ldots\}$ is the set of all the natural numbers, then the complexes (sequences)

$$p = (a_1, a_2, a_3, \ldots) \quad (a_m \varepsilon A_m)$$

can also be ordered lexicographically, for two distinct complexes p and $q = (b_1, b_2, b_3, \ldots)$ have *a first place m at which they differ*; that is,

$$a_1 = b_1, \quad \ldots, \quad a_{m-1} = b_{m-1}, \quad a_m \neq b_m;$$

and we then define $p < q$ if $a_m < b_m$. The product ordered in this way will be called $(A_1, A_2, A_3, \ldots)$, and its type will be called $\ldots \alpha_3\alpha_2\alpha_1$.

Example: If every A_m is the set of all natural numbers, then we obtain $\ldots \omega\omega\omega$ as the type of the lexicographically ordered set of *sequences* $p = (a_1, a_2, a_3, \ldots)$ *of natural numbers.* If we let the real number

$$x = \left(\frac{1}{2}\right)^{a_1} + \left(\frac{1}{2}\right)^{a_1+a_2} + \left(\frac{1}{2}\right)^{a_1+a_2+a_3} + \cdots$$

correspond to each p (biuniquely), then we see that to the lexicographic ordering of the p there corresponds the *inverse* order by magnitude of the x; that is, $p < q$ means $x > y$. Since x runs through the interval $(0, 1]$, it follows that $\ldots \omega\omega\omega$ is the type of the numbers $1 - x$ in their natural order, that is, the type of the interval $[0, 1)$.

Obviously we would be able to extend the lexicographic ordering to any product $\prod_m^M A_m$ if we could only be certain that any two of its complexes have a first piace at which they differ, or in general, *if every subset of M has a first element* (that is, if M is well-ordered (Chap. IV)).

Later (§ 16), we shall go into these and further extensions of the concept of product. A generalized concept of powers can also only be explained there: in the meantime we shall, of course, write $\alpha\alpha = \alpha^2$, $\alpha\alpha\alpha = \alpha^3, \ldots$. (The previously mentioned product $\ldots \omega\,\omega\,\omega$ would be written ω^{ω^*}.) Thus

$$\omega^2 = \omega\omega = \omega + \omega + \omega + \cdots$$

is the type of a sequence of sequences or of a double sequence, w^3 that of a sequence of double sequences, or of a triple sequence; etc. We have

$$\omega + \omega^2 = \omega(1 + \omega) = \omega\omega = \omega^2 ;$$
$$\omega^2 + \omega = \omega(\omega + 1)$$

is a type differing from the first; and

$$(\omega + \omega)\,\omega = (\omega 2)\,\omega = \omega(2\omega) = \omega\omega = \omega^2$$

is different from

$$\omega(\omega + \omega) = \omega(\omega 2) = \omega^2 2 = \omega^2 + \omega^2 .$$

The types that are obtained from ω and finite types by finitely many additions and multiplications may be called entire rational functions, or polynomials, in ω; they can be put, and (as we shall also see) put uniquely, in the form

$$\omega^n a + \omega^{n_1} a_1 + \cdots + \omega^{n_k} a_k$$
$$(n > n_1 > \cdots > n_k \geqq 0, \quad a, a_1, \ldots, a_k \text{ natural numbers}).$$

§ 11. The Types $\aleph_0$ and $\aleph$

Every type α has a definite cardinal number $\mathfrak{a}$. The various types of cardinality $\mathfrak{a}$ form a *class of types* $T(\mathfrak{a})$; to obtain this class one need only order a fixed set A of cardinality $\mathfrak{a}$ in all the ways possible, where different orderings of course do not necessarily yield distinct types.

The classes of types of finite cardinality $T(n)$ $(n = 0, 1, 2, \ldots)$ always contain only one type n. But of the types belonging to $T(\aleph_0)$ we already know infinitely many: ω, $\omega + 1$, $\omega + 2, \ldots, \omega + \omega$, and ω^*, among others.

I. *The set of countable types has the cardinality of the continuum.*

That is, $T(\aleph_0)$ has the cardinality $\aleph$. Half of this theorem we already know: There are (p. 50) at most $2^{\aleph_0 \aleph_0} = 2^{\aleph_0} = \aleph$ distinct countable types.

On the other hand, let $\zeta = \omega^* + \omega$ be the type of the set $\{\ldots, -2, -1, 0, 1, 2, \ldots\}$ of the integers in their natural order, let

$$a = (a_1, a_2, a_3, \ldots)$$

be a sequence of natural numbers, and let

$$\alpha = a_1 + \zeta + a_2 + \zeta + a_3 + \zeta + \cdots$$

be a type, obviously countable, determined by a. If we can show that α in turn determines the sequence a, that is, that there exists a one-to-one correspondence between the a and the α, then we have proved that there are also at least $\aleph_0^{\aleph_0} = \aleph$ distinct countable types and, by the Equivalence Theorem, that there are precisely $\aleph$ of them.

Thus, we have to prove that if $\beta = b_1 + \zeta + b_2 + \zeta + \cdots$ and $\alpha = \beta$, then $a_1 = b_1$, $a_2 = b_2$, ... This follows from the following statements:

(a) If $A_1 + A_2 \cong B_1 + B_2$, and if A_1 and B_1 are finite and A_2 and B_2 have no first element, then $A_1 \cong B_1$ and $A_2 \cong B_2$.

For, in the similarity mapping, an element $b_1 \varepsilon B_1$ cannot be the image of an element $a_2 \varepsilon A_2$, because b_1 has only finitely many elements preceding it (and possibly none), while infinitely many elements precede a_2. Similarly no b_2 can correspond to an a_1. Thus, the a_1 must correspond to the b_1, and the a_2 to the b_2.

(b) If $A_1 + A_2 \cong B_1 + B_2$, and A_1 and B_1 are of type ζ, then $A_2 \cong B_2$.

Here again, no b_1 can correspond to a a_2, since the set of elements preceding a_2 contains a subset (A_1) without a last element, while the set of elements preceding b_1 is of type w^* and has no subset without a last element (except, of course, for the null set). Again, therefore, A_1 must be mapped onto B_1 and A_2 onto B_2.

By (a), therefore, it follows from $a_1 + \zeta + \cdots = b_1 + \zeta + \cdots$ that

$$a_1 = b_1, \; \zeta + a_2 + \zeta + \cdots = \zeta + b_2 + \zeta + \cdots,$$

and then, by (b), that $a_2 + \zeta + \cdots = b_2 + \zeta + \cdots$, then again that $a_2 = b_2$, and so on.

We will call an (infinite) set without a first and a last element *unbounded,* and an (infinite) set without neighboring elements *dense*; we will extend these adjectives to the types of these sets as well. We therefore require that there exist elements of the set preceding any given element and following any given element, and in the second case, between any two elements. The set of all the rational numbers and the set of all the real numbers in their natural order are sets of this kind; their types will be called η and λ (λ is the type of the continuum).

II. *If A is countable and B is unbounded and dense, then A is similar to a subset of B.*

III. *Any two unbounded dense countable sets are similar.*

Proof of II. Let $A = \{a_1, a_2, \ldots\}$;[1] we maintain that A can be mapped onto a subset of B in an order-preserving way. The proof is by induction. First, we associate with a_1 an arbitrary element of B. Next, let us suppose that we already have images of the elements of $A_n = \{a_1, a_2, \ldots, a_n\}$ of the required kind; we wish to find such an image for a_{n+1}. Either a_{n+1} lies between two elements of A_n or $a_{n+1} < A_n$ or, finally, $a_{n+1} > A_n$. Thus, we need only find an element of B between two elements of B, or before such an element (the image of the first element of A_n), or after such an element, and this is possible because B is unbounded and dense. There is therefore a suitable image of a_{n+1}, and thus, one by one, we can associate images with each of the a_n with preservation of order.

Proof of III. Let $A = \{a_1, a_2, \ldots\}$ and $B = \{b_1, b_2, \ldots\}$ be unbounded and dense; by II we can map A onto a subset of B and B onto a subset of A,[2] and by setting up the individual correspondences alternately in one direction and the other, we can also map A onto B. In fact, let us associate a_1 with b_1 and write $a^1 = a_1$, $b^1 = b_1$. We now proceed by induction: let us assume that the pairs $(a^1, b^1), \ldots, (a^n, b^n)$ have already been formed in an order-preserving way, that is, that the sets

$$A^n = \{a^1, \ldots, a^n\} \quad \text{and} \quad B^n = \{b^1, \ldots, b^n\}$$

are, as subsets of A and B respectively, similar as they stand; we wish to add the pair (a^{n+1}, b^{n+1}) to them. For even n let a^{n+1} be the a_k with lowest index k that does not belong to A^n, and b^{n+1} the b_k with lowest index k that has the same position with respect to B^n that a^{n+1} has with respect to A^n. For odd n, the other way around: let b^{n+1} be the lowest b_k as yet unmapped and a^{n+1} the lowest a_k consistent with the order

[1] The order from left to right of the elements in $\{a_1, a_2, \ldots\}$ does not in this case indicate the order of A.

[2] The similarity analogue of the Equivalence Theorem (namely, that if each of two sets has a subset similar to the other then the two sets are similar) is *false*. *Example*: Two intervals, one with and one without its endpoints.

relationships. The existence of suitable images is guaranteed by the unboundedness and density of the two sets, while at the same time no element can be left out in the mapping; thus $A \cong B$.

From II (in which one can choose A as well as B to be the set of all rational numbers, of type η) and III we therefore obtain:

IV. *Every unbounded dense set contains a subset of type η. A set of type η contains countable subsets of every type. Every unbounded dense countable set is of type η.*

Examples. If M (of type μ) is finite or countable, then $\sum_m^M \eta = \eta\mu$ is always an unbounded dense countable type, so that $\eta\mu = \eta$; for example

$$\eta + \eta = \eta 2 = \eta n = \eta\omega = \eta^2 = \eta.$$

Dense countable types can only be distinguished from each other by the existence or non-existence of first or last elements; there are therefore precisely four such sets:

$$\eta, \ 1 + \eta, \ \eta + 1, \text{ and } \ 1 + \eta + 1.$$

$\sum_m^M (1 + \eta) = (1 + \eta)\mu$ (M finite or countable) is either $= 1 + \eta$ or $= \eta$, according as M does or does not have a first element; for example,

$$(1 + \eta)\, 2 = (1 + \eta)\, n = (1 + \eta)\omega = 1 + \eta,$$
$$(1 + \eta)\omega^* = (1 + \eta)\,\eta = \eta.$$

The set of all rational numbers $> a$ is of type η. Thus there exists, for instance, a function $s = f(r)$ that preserves order, i.e., increases monotonically with r, which assigns a rational number $s > a$ to every rational number $r > 0$, and vice versa. Clearly this can be extended to a continuous monotonically increasing function $y = f(x)$ that maps the half-line $x > 0$ onto the half-line $y > a$ and assigns to every rational x a rational y, and to every irrational x an irrational y. For rational a this is trivial, of course, as $y = x + a$ induces such a correspondence.

The set of all rational numbers in the interval $(0, 1)$ and that of the dyadic rationals (fractions whose denominator is a power of 2) in the same interval are similar, both having type η. The correspondence (which we will extend at once to a correspondence

$$y = f(x), \quad (0 < x \leqq 1, \quad 0 < y \leqq 1)$$

applying to the whole interval) which assigns to a dyadic rational x a rational y and vice versa, may be constructed as follows. We divide the interval $0 < x \leqq 1$ at $1/2$, $1/4$, $1/8$, ... and the interval $0 < y \leqq 1$ at $1/2$, $1/3$, $1/4$, $1/5$, ..., into the respective subintervals

$$\left(\frac{1}{2}\right)^{n_1} < x \leqq \left(\frac{1}{2}\right)^{n_1 - 1}$$
$$\frac{1}{n_1 + 1} < y \leqq \frac{1}{n_1},$$

where n_1 is a natural number. We can write

$$x = \left(\frac{1}{2}\right)^{n_1} (1 + x_1) \qquad (0 < x_1 \leqq 1)$$
$$y = \frac{1}{n_1 + 1 - y_1} \qquad (0 < y_1 \leqq 1)$$

for this.

By repeating this process for x_1 and y_1 and continuing in this way indefinitely, we obtain for x the dyadic expansion

$$x = \left(\frac{1}{2}\right)^{n_1} + \left(\frac{1}{2}\right)^{n_1+n_2} + \left(\frac{1}{2}\right)^{n_1+n_2+n_3} + \cdots$$

and for y the continued fraction

$$y = \frac{1\,|}{|\,n_1 + 1} - \frac{1\,|}{|\,n_2 + 1} - \frac{1\,|}{|\,n_3 + 1} - \cdots,$$

where $n = (n_1, n_2, n_3, \ldots)$ is a sequence of natural numbers. The correspondence between x and y defined by equal n has the desired property, namely that of associating a rational y with a dyadic rational x and vice versa; furthermore it associates a rational (but not a dyadic rational) x with a quadratic irrational y, and vice versa (Minkowski). A more detailed investigation must be left to the reader versed in the elements of the theory of continued fractions.

The type λ of the set of all real numbers is also that of an interval without end points or that of a half-line without end point ($x > a$, $x < a$).

The four intervals

	(a, b)	$[a, b)$	$(a, b]$	$[a, b]$
have the types	λ	$1 + \lambda$	$\lambda + 1$	$1 + \lambda + 1$.

From $(a, b) + [b, c) = (a, c)$ $(a < b < c)$ we obtain $\lambda + 1 + \lambda = \lambda$, whereas $\lambda + \lambda \neq \lambda$; similarly, stringing together suitable intervals yields

$$1 + \lambda = (1 + \lambda)\,2 = (1 + \lambda)\,n = (1 + \lambda)\,\omega, \quad \lambda = (\lambda + 1)\,\omega$$

among others.

To characterize λ more precisely we employ the following considerations. A partitioning

$$A = P + Q \quad (P < Q)$$

of the ordered set A into a "lower section" P and an "upper section" Q can present the following four cases

P has a last element and Q has a first element:	*Jump*
P has a last element and Q has no first element:	*Cut*
P has no last element and Q has a first element:	*Cut*
P has no last element and Q has no first element:	*Gap* .

A set without jumps is dense — the set of all rational numbers, for example, which however has gaps. A set without jumps or gaps is called *continuous* in the sense of Dedekind — the set of all real numbers, for example (hence the expression "continuum" and "cardinality of the continuum"). We form the continuum from the set of all rational numbers by filling in the gaps (by means of the irrational numbers); the well-known way in which this was done by Dedekind may be carried over to an arbitrary dense set, which we will assume in addition to be unbounded. Let us consider the partitions

$$A = P + Q$$

where P has no last element; Q may have a first element or not. These lower sections themselves form an ordered set P, where we define $P < P_1$ by $P \subset P_1$, and we assert that P *is continuous*. For, in the first place, P is dense, that is, between P_1 and $P_2 > P_1$ there always lies another P; in fact, since $P_2 - P_1$ has no last element and therefore has infinitely many elements, if we choose an element a of $P_2 - P_1$ which is not the first element of $P_2 - P_1$ and allow P to be the set of all elements of A that are $< a$, then $P_1 < P < P_2$. In the second place, P also has no gaps. For let $\mathrm{P} = \mathrm{P}_1 + \mathrm{P}_2$ be a partition of P into a lower class and an upper class, that is, into two classes of lower sections P_1 and P_2, where we always have $P_1 < P_2$. Let us form the sum $P = \mathfrak{S} P_1$ of the P_1 and the intersection $Q = \mathfrak{D} Q_1$ of their complements $(A = P_1 + Q_1)$; P and Q again form a partition $A = P + Q$, where P is thus a lower section and clearly has no last element. From $P_1 < P_2$ it then follows that $P \leqq P_2$; that is, we always have $P_1 \leqq P \leqq P_2$, and thus P is either the last element of P_1 or the first of P_2; thus $\mathrm{P}_1 + \mathrm{P}_2$ is neither a jump nor a gap, but a cut. P is thus continuous.

Let us use the following terminology:

$B \leqq A$ is said to be *dense in* A if between any two elements of A there always lies an element of B. (If B is dense in A, then it of course follows that both A and B are themselves dense.)

We can now characterize the type λ of the continuum by means of the following theorem:

V. *Every continuous set has a subset of type* λ. *Every unbounded continuous set for which there exists a countable set that is dense in it is of type* λ.

Proof. Let A be continuous; we may assume that it is unbounded. It contains (by IV) a subset B of type η. If $B = P + Q$ is a gap of B, then we must have at least one element of A lying between P and Q; otherwise, as is easy to see, A also has a gap. So A has a subset C obtainable from B by filling in its gaps, that is, a subset of type λ. On the other hand, if B is also dense in A (every set dense in A is itself unbounded and dense, and hence, if countable, is of type η), then only a single element of A can lie between P and Q, so that $A = C$. This completes the proof of the theorem.

There exist infinitely many distinct order types that have the cardinality of the continuum. If $\vartheta = 1 + \lambda + 1$ is the type of the closed interval $J = [0, 1]$, then the powers ϑ, ϑ^2 ϑ^3, ... are continuous and distinct from each other. For, let $J_2 = (J, J)$, $J_3 = (J, J, J)$, ..., J_m be the lexicographically ordered set of the complexes $x = (x_1, x_2)$, ..., $x = (x_1, x_2, \ldots, x_m)$ where each x_k runs through the interval J. That J_m is dense is obvious; that J_m has no gaps may be reduced to the corresponding property of J_{m-1} in the following way. Let $H_m(a)$ be the set of complexes $(a, x_2, \ldots, x_m)$, similar to J_{m-1}, obtained from J_m by letting x_1 have the fixed value $x_1 = a$; we have

$$J_m = \sum_a^J H_m(a).$$

In a partition $J_m = P_m + Q_m$ there are two possibilities: either (i) one of the summands $H_m(a)$ is also partitioned, so that this case is reduced to a partition $J_{m-1} = P_{m-1} + Q_{m-1}$ or (ii) the partition is of the form

$$P_m = \sum_a^P H_m(a), \quad Q_m = \sum_b^Q H_m(b), \quad J = P + Q,$$

and, if a_1 is the largest a, then P_m has the last element $(a_1, 1, \ldots, 1)$ and, if b_1 is the smallest b, then Q_m has the first element $(b_1, 0, \ldots, 0)$.

To prove that the ϑ^m are distinct, we show that *if* $m > 1$ *and* J_m *is similar to a subset of* J_n, *then* $n > 1$ *and* J_{m-1} *is similar to a subset of* J_{n-1}. Let us assume that the set J_m of complexes $x = (x_1, \ldots, x_m)$ is mapped by a similarity mapping onto a subset of J_n, the set of complexes $y = (y_1, \ldots, y_n)$. Let us assume that the images of the two complexes $(x_1, 0, \ldots, 0)$ and $(x_1, 1, \ldots, 1)$ are $y = (y_1, y_2, \ldots, y_n)$ and $\eta = (\eta_1, \eta_2, \ldots, \eta_n)$ respectively; it follows that $y < \eta$, and so $y_1 \leqq \eta_1$. It is then impossible that $y_1 < \eta_1$ throughout – that is, for every x_1 – for, the open intervals (y_1, η_1) would then be disjoint and the set of all these open intervals would, like the set of the x_1, have the cardinality $\aleph$, whereas since each of these intervals must contain a rational number, there are in fact at most countably many of them. Hence for some x_1, we have $y_1 = \eta_1$, so that, as one consequence, $n > 1$.

Let a be a value of x_1 for which the images of the complexes $(a, 0, \ldots, 0)$ and $(a, 1, \ldots, 1)$ are $(b, y_2, \ldots, y_n)$ and $(b, \eta_2, \ldots, \eta_n)$ respectively, with the same $y_1 = \eta_1 = b$; the previously introduced set $H_m(a)$ is then similar to a subset of $H_n(b)$, and hence J_{m-1} is similar to a subset of J_{n-1}. This proves the above statement.

From this it follows, finally, that when $m > n$, J_m cannot be similar to a subset of J_n (and, in particular, not to J_n itself). For J_{m-1} would then be similar to a subset of J_{n-1} and, continuing in this way, we would obtain that J_{m-n+1} would be similar to a subset of J_1, in contradiction to the above.

CHAPTER IV

ORDINAL NUMBERS

§ 12. The Well-Ordering Theorem

We define: *An ordered set is said to be well ordered if every* (non-empty) *subset has a first element.* The order type of a well-ordered set is called an *ordinal number.*

In a well-ordered set there is no subset of type ω^*, and every decreasing sequence of elements $a > b > c \ldots$ has only finitely many members. This property could also serve as definition.

After every element, unless it is the last one, there always follows a next one; for every partition $A = P + Q$, the upper section Q has a first element, whether the lower section P has a last element or not. Conversely, if for every partition (including the trivial one $0 + A$) the upper section Q has a first element, then A is well ordered; for if $B > 0$ is an arbitrary subset of A, and P the set of all elements $< B$, and if $A = P + Q$, then the first element of Q is also the first element of B.

The finite sets $\{1, 2, \ldots, n\}$, the set $\{1, 2, 3, \ldots\}$ of all natural numbers, and the set $\{1, 3, 5, \ldots, 2, 4, 6, \ldots\}$ are well ordered, and their types, n, ω, and $\omega + \omega$ are ordinal numbers. The order types ω^*, η, and λ are not ordinal numbers.

An infinite well-ordered set A has a first element a_0, then a second a_1, a third a_2, etc.; if, in addition to this sequence, it contains other elements, then there is among these a first a_ω and then a next one $a_{\omega+1}$, etc. We therefore have

$$(1) \qquad A = \{a_0, a_1, a_2, \ldots, a_\omega, a_{\omega+1}, \ldots\}.$$

The notation indicated here, which we will use in the sequel, is that the index of every element is the type of the set of elements preceding it. In order that this should hold true for finite indices as well, we have started with 0; the index of a_n is the type n of the set $\{a_0, \ldots, a_{n-1}\}$ that of a_0 the type 0 of the null set.

After this preliminary orientation we prove

Zermelo's Well-Ordering Theorem: *Every set can be well ordered.*

If we wish to arrive at a well ordering of the form (1), then we must, say, assign to every set $P_n = \{a_0, a_1, \ldots, a_{n-1}\}$ a definite element a_n as a next, or immediately following, element; that is, we must think of a definite element a_n as having been chosen from the set $Q_n = A - P_n$ of the as yet unordered elements. If we proceed in this way, then the very acts of chosing appear in a certain order: a_n may, and must, be chosen only when its predecessors $a_0, \ldots, a_{n-1}$ have been chosen. The Well-Ordering Theorem can also be proved by means of these *successive* acts of choosing, but only later on, after a more thorough investigation of ordinal numbers. In order to prove the theorem at once, we use a system of *simultaneous,* mutually independent, acts of choosing.[1] We assign *to every subset P of A other than A itself an element* $a = f(P) \varepsilon A - P$ *not belonging to it* or, we choose *from every subset Q of A other than* 0, *an element* $a = \varphi(Q) \varepsilon Q$ *belonging to it.* Both these statements mean the same thing: we have $f(P) = \varphi(A - P)$, or $\varphi(Q) = f(A - Q)$. We prefer the first form, and we shall call $a = f(P)$ the *differential element* of P, and the set formed from P by the addition of the differential element we shall call the *successor* to P. This process involves more acts of choosing than are absolutely necessary, since in the well ordering (1) the set $P = \{a_0, a_2\}$, for instance, and its differential element would not be used at all. On the other hand, as we have mentioned, this process makes it possible for the acts of choosing to be mutually independent or, expressed differently, the function $a = f(P)$ has a domain of definition which is fixed from the very beginning, namely the set of all $P < A$.

The method by which a well ordering of A necessarily results from the correspondence $a = f(P)$ is basically very simple, although it places something of a burden on the abstract thinking of the reader. We consider a system of sets $\leqq A$ that

(a) contains the null set,

(b) contains the sum of arbitrarily many sets if it contains each of them, and

(c) contains the successor P_+ to any set $P < A$ if it contains P.

Such a system is called a *chain.* There exist chains; for instance, the largest one: the system of all sets $\leqq A$. The intersection of arbitrarily many chains is clearly also a chain; therefore there exists a *smallest chain* κ, which is the intersection of *all* chains. We shall now investigate this chain, and we shall stipulate that all the sets occurring in the sequel, such as P and X, will always belong to κ.

The fundamental problem is to show that all the sets of κ are com-

[1] Compare Appendix F.

parable (in the sense of p. 13), that is, that for two sets P and X we always have one of the three relations $X \lesseqqgtr P$. Calling a set P ***normal*** if it is comparable with every set X, we must prove that all sets are normal. The first step consists in proving the following theorem:

I. *If $P < A$ is normal, then all sets are either $\leqq P$ or $\geqq P_+$.*

We show that these X ($\leqq P$ or $\geqq P_+$) form a chain; this chain must be identical with κ, since κ is the smallest chain. We must therefore establish that these sets satisfy the chain properties:

(a) The empty set is an X.

Obvious, since $0 \leqq P$.

(b) The sum of arbitrarily many X is an X.

Let $S = \mathfrak{S} X_m$; either every $X_m \leqq P$ and so $S \leqq P$, or at least one $X_m \geqq P_+$ and so $S \geqq P_+$.

(c) The successor to every $X < A$ is an X.

For $X \geqq P_+$ we have $X_+ > P_+$; for $X = P$ we have $X_+ = P_+$. For $X < P$ we must have $X_+ \leqq P$; for, in any case, X_+ is comparable with P, which is normal; but if $X_+ > P$, then $X_+ - X = (X_+ - P) + (P - X)$ would have to contain at least two elements, whereas we know that this set contains only the one element $f(X)$. We can now conclude that:

II. *All sets are normal.*

Again, we show that the normal sets form a chain, which must therefore be identical with κ.

(a) The empty set is normal.

(b) The sum of arbitrarily many normal sets is normal.

Let $P = \mathfrak{S} P_m$ be a sum of normal sets and X an arbitrary set, so that $P_m \lesseqqgtr X$. Either every $P_m \leqq X$ and therefore $P \leqq X$, or at least one $P_m > X$ and therefore $P > X$. Thus P is comparable with every X.

(c) The successor P_+ to any normal set $P < A$ is normal.

This is proved by Theorem I.

Because of the comparability of all sets, κ can now be ordered by putting the smaller of two distinct sets before the larger ($P_1 < P_2$ shall mean $P_1 < P_2$). *This ordering is a well ordering.* Since κ itself has a first element (the null set), it need only be shown that, in a partition $\kappa = \kappa_1 + \kappa_2$ into a lower section and an upper section, the latter has a first element. Let $P_1 \,\varepsilon\, \kappa_1$, $P_2 \,\varepsilon\, \kappa_2$, $P_1 < P_2$, and let P be the sum of all the P_1. Then $P_1 \leqq P \leqq P_2$, so that P is either the first P_2 or the last P_1. But in the second case, by the dichotomy of Theorem I, P_+ must be the first P_2. In either case there is a first P_2.

Finally the sets $P < A$ can be put into a one-to-one correspondence with the elements $a \varepsilon A$, and thus A will also be *well ordered*. This is accomplished by means of the relation $a = f(P)$, which determines the differential element of P. Distinct sets $P_1 < P_2$ have distinct differential elements a_1 and a_2; for, P_2 contains the successor to P_1, so that $a_1 \varepsilon P_2$, $a_2 \bar{\varepsilon} P_2$. On the other hand, every a is the differential element of one, and thus only one, set P. For let $P = F(a)$ be the sum of all the sets P_1 that do not contain a (the null set, for example, is one such set). Then we must have $a = f(P)$, for otherwise $P_+ > P$ would also not contain a. The elements $a \varepsilon A$ and the sets $P < A$ (i.e., all the sets of κ except for the last, A) can be put into one-to-one correspondence by means of

$$a = f(P), \quad P = F(a);$$

the ordering of the a induced by that of the P ($a_1 < a$ means $P_1 < P$) thus well-orders A. Since $P_1 < P$ means the same as $a_1 \varepsilon P$, it follows that $P = F(a)$ is the set of all the elements $a_1 < a$ and, conversely, $a = f(P)$ is the next element after P in the well ordering (but this only holds for those sets $P < A$ that appear in the chain κ).

An example of this process of well ordering is the following: From every set Q of natural numbers, that number $a = \varphi(Q)$ is chosen which has the least number of prime factors; if there is more than one number in Q with a minimal number of prime factors, the smallest is chosen. This induces the following well ordering of the natural numbers: First comes the number 1, then the prime numbers in order of magnitude, then the numbers containing exactly two prime factors, again in order of magnitude, and so on; this well ordering is of the type

$$\omega + \omega + \omega + \cdots = \omega^2.$$

§ 13. The Comparability of Ordinal Numbers

Every element a of the well-ordered set A determines

the *segment* $P =$ the set of all elements $< a$ and
the *remainder* $Q =$ the set of all elements $\geqq a$,

and hence determines the partition $A = P + Q$ ($P < A$, $Q > 0$).

Conversely, every partition of A into a lower section P and an upper section Q is of this form, as Q has a first element a. If a is the first element of A, then we set $P = 0$, $Q = A$.

We now have:

I. *If $b=f(a)$ is a similarity mapping of the well-ordered set A onto a subset B, then we always have $f(a) \geqq a$.*

That is, in such a transformation the image of an element can never be an earlier element. In fact, if there were elements a for which $f(a) < a$, then there would be a first among these; let this be a and let $b=f(a)$ be its image, so that $b < a$ and, because of similarity, $f(b) < f(a)$, that is, $f(b) < b$; then b would after all be an earlier element having this property.

In particular:

II. *A well-ordered set is never similar to one of its segments.*

For, if A were similar to the segment B determined by a, then we would have $f(a) \varepsilon B$ and hence $f(a) < a$.

The relation between two well-ordered sets A and B characterized by the statement that A is similar to a segment of B remains unchanged when these sets are replaced by similar ones. This justifies the following definition:

If α and β are two ordinal numbers and if A and B are well-ordered sets of these types, then

$$\alpha < \beta \quad \text{or} \quad \beta > \alpha$$

(α smaller than β, β larger than α) shall mean that A is similar to a segment of B.

Clearly the transitive law holds:

$$\text{if } \alpha < \beta \quad \text{and} \quad \beta < \gamma, \quad \text{then} \quad \alpha < \gamma$$

(A is similar to a segment of a segment of C, that is, to a segment of C).

By II, $\alpha < \alpha$ can never hold; that is, the relations $\alpha < \beta$ and $\alpha = \beta$ are mutually contradictory, as is the case with $\alpha > \beta$ and $\alpha = \beta$. But the same also holds for $\alpha < \beta$ and $\alpha > \beta$, since it would follow from them by the transitive law that $\alpha < \alpha$. Thus at most one of the relations $\alpha \lesseqgtr \beta$ can hold; we show that there is always one that does hold, i.e., that two ordinal numbers are always comparable.

We will always use the following notation: Each ordinal number α determines the set

$$W(\alpha) = \text{the set of ordinal numbers} < \alpha,$$

which will be called a *segment*. *The numbers of $W(\alpha)$ are comparable, and $W(\alpha)$, ordered by size, is of type α.* For if

$$A = \{\ldots, a, \ldots, b, \ldots\}$$

is a well-ordered set of type α, then by definition the numbers $< \alpha$ are in one-to-one correspondence with the segments of A, and this correspondence is a similarity mapping: Every a determines its segment P_a of type π_a, and if $a < b$, then P_a is a segment of P_b and $\pi_a < \pi_b$. Thus

$$W(\alpha) = \{\ldots, \pi_a, \ldots, \pi_b, \ldots\},$$

which proves the above statement. Conversely, this enables us to carry out in general the notation indicated in § 12, (1), i.e., to index the elements of a well-ordered set of type α by means of the correspondence with the numbers of

$$W(\alpha) = \{0, 1, \ldots, \xi, \ldots\} \qquad (\xi < \alpha)$$

in such a way so that in

$$A = \{a_0, a_1, \ldots, a_\xi, \ldots\} \qquad (\xi < \alpha)$$

the index of every element is the type of the segment belonging to it. We need only be careful to include the ordinal number 0 as the type of the null set, which is the segment of the first element. Thus, for example.

$$W(1) = \{0\}, \quad W(2) = \{0, 1\}, \quad W(n) = \{0, 1, \ldots, n-1\}$$

for finite $n > 0$, while $W(0) = 0$ is the null set.

Now let α and β be two ordinal numbers, $A = W(\alpha)$, $B = W(\beta)$, and $D = AB$ their intersection, that is, the set of those ordinal numbers that are at the same time $< \alpha$ and $< \beta$. D is well ordered and its type δ is an ordinal number; we claim that $\delta \leqq \alpha$. For $D = A$ we have $\delta = \alpha$; but for $D < A$ we see from

$$A = D + (A - D)$$

that D is a *lower section* and $A - D$ an upper section of A. For, if $\xi \,\varepsilon\, D$ and $\eta \,\varepsilon\, A - D$, then ξ and η, as elements of A, are comparable, so that $\xi \lesseqgtr \eta$; now $\eta < \xi < \alpha, \beta$ is impossible, as otherwise η would belong to D, so that $\xi < \eta$. But then D is a *segment* of A and $\delta < \alpha$; furthermore δ is then clearly the first element of $A - D$, and $D = W(\delta)$. We thus have

$$\delta \leqq \alpha, \quad \delta \leqq \beta.$$

The combination $\delta < \alpha$, $\delta < \beta$ is also impossible, as otherwise we would have $\delta \,\varepsilon\, D$, and thus the only remaining cases are:

$$\delta = \alpha,\quad \delta = \beta \;:\; \alpha = \beta.$$
$$\delta = \alpha,\quad \delta < \beta \;:\; \alpha < \beta.$$
$$\delta < \alpha,\quad \delta = \beta \;:\; \alpha > \beta.$$

We have thus proved:

III. (Comparability Theorem). *Two ordinal numbers* α *and* β *are always comparable; that is, one and only one of the three relations*

$$\alpha < \beta,\quad \alpha = \beta,\quad \alpha > \beta$$

holds.

If in particular $A \subseteqq B$, then $\alpha \leqq \beta$. For if $\alpha > \beta$, then B would be similar to a segment P of A (determined by $a \,\varepsilon\, A$), and in the mapping from B onto P, the image of a would be in P and thus would be $< a$, contradicting Theorem I. Nevertheless, even when $A < B$ we may have $\alpha = \beta$, but of course only if A is not a segment of B; for example, all the infinite subsets of the sequence of natural numbers are of type ω.

With the Well-Ordering Theorem and the Comparability Theorem proved, the gap in the theory of cardinal numbers is now filled in: *Two cardinal numbers are always comparable.* For, $\mathfrak{a}$ and $\mathfrak{b}$ can be considered to be the cardinalities of the *well-ordered* sets A and B of type α and β respectively, and then

$$\begin{array}{lll} \text{either} & \alpha = \beta, & \mathfrak{a} = \mathfrak{b} \\ \text{or} & \alpha < \beta, & \mathfrak{a} \leqq \mathfrak{b} \\ \text{or} & \alpha > \beta, & \mathfrak{a} \geqq \mathfrak{b}; \end{array}$$

for, $\alpha < \beta$ means that A is similar to a segment of B, so that A is equivalent to a subset of B. Reversing the implication, we obtain

$$\begin{array}{lll} \text{either} & \mathfrak{a} = \mathfrak{b}, & \alpha \lesseqqgtr \beta \\ \text{or} & \mathfrak{a} < \mathfrak{b}, & \alpha < \beta \\ \text{or} & \mathfrak{a} > \mathfrak{b}, & \alpha > \beta, \end{array}$$

where the first equation says that, in the case of equal cardinalities, various well orderings are still possible (for instance, when $\mathfrak{a} = \aleph_0$ we may have $\alpha = \omega, \omega + 1, \ldots$).

IV. *In every* (non-empty) *set of ordinal numbers there is a smallest; that is, every set of ordinal numbers ordered by magnitude is well ordered.*

For, if W is such a set and α is a number of W, but not the smallest, then the intersection $WW(\alpha)$ is well ordered because it is a subset of $W(\alpha)$, and its smallest number is also the smallest number of W.

If the set W is of type β, it can therefore be written in the form

$$W = \{\alpha_0, \alpha_1, \ldots, \alpha_\eta, \ldots\} \qquad (\eta < \beta)$$

where $\alpha_\xi < \alpha_\eta$ for $\xi < \eta$.

V. *For every set of ordinal numbers there are larger ordinal numbers; in particular, there is a next larger ordinal number.*

For we can choose (p. 38) a cardinal number $\mathfrak{a}$ larger than the cardinalities of all the ordinal numbers in W; if α is an ordinal number of cardinality $\mathfrak{a}$, then α is larger than all the ordinal numbers in W; in short, $\alpha > W$. The smallest number $> W$ is then either α itself or a certain number of $W(\alpha)$.

According to V, the concept of the "set of all ordinal numbers" is inconceivable (cf. p. 39).

The numbers $> \alpha$ are the numbers $\alpha + \beta$ $(\beta > 0)$, and conversely (A is similar to a segment of $A + B$); the smallest number $> \alpha$ is $\alpha + 1$.

A number $\lambda > 0$ that has no immediate predecessor, that is, for which $W(\lambda)$ has no last element, is called a *limit number*; the smallest limit numbers are ω, $\omega + \omega = \omega 2$, $\omega 3, \ldots$. A number that is not a limit number is called *isolated*; aside from 0, isolated numbers are numbers of the form $\alpha + 1$. If the set

$$W = \{\alpha_0, \ldots, \alpha_\eta, \ldots\} \qquad (\eta < \beta)$$

of ordinal numbers has no last element, that is, if β is a limit number, then the *next larger* number $\lambda > W$, which is clearly a limit number, is called the limit of W and is denoted by

$$\lambda = \lim W$$

or by

$$\lambda = \lim \alpha_\eta .$$

For instance, ω is the limit of $\{0, 1, 2, \ldots\}$ and of every increasing sequence $\{\alpha_0, \alpha_1, \alpha_2, \ldots\}$ of finite numbers α_ν, $\omega = \lim \nu = \lim \alpha_\nu$.

Transfinite Induction. Induction from n to $n + 1$ in the domain of finite numbers is now replaced by the following:

A statement $f(\alpha)$ concerning an ordinal number α is true for every α if $f(0)$ is true and if the truth of $f(\alpha)$ follows from the truth of $f(\xi)$ for all $\xi < \alpha$.

For if $f(\beta)$ were false and α $(\leq \beta)$ were the smallest number for which $f(\alpha)$ is false, then we reach a contradiction both for $\alpha = 0$ and for $\alpha > 0$.

Transfinite induction can be used for definitions as well as for proofs:

A function $f(\alpha)$ of the ordinal number α is defined for every α if $f(0)$ is defined and if $f(\alpha)$ is defined whenever $f(\xi)$ is defined for all $\xi < \alpha$.

If we here replace $f(0)$ by any $f(\alpha_0)$, then it is necessary to change the language slightly in order to show that $f(\alpha)$ is defined or is true, as the case may be, for $\alpha \geqq \alpha_0$.

§ 14. The Combining of Ordinal Numbers

We have already defined the sum and the product for order types. It is easily seen that a sum of ordered sets

$$S = \sum_m^M A_m$$

is well ordered if M and the summands A_m are well ordered.

We thus have: *A well-ordered sum of ordinal numbers, and a product of finitely many ordinal numbers, is itself an ordinal number.*

For instance, ω^2, ω^3, $\omega + \omega^2 + \omega^3 + \cdots$ are ordinal numbers.

In this situation we can to a certain extent also assign a meaning to subtraction and division. We first take note of the following inequalities:

From $\alpha < \beta$ it follows that

$$(1) \qquad \begin{cases} \mu + \alpha < \mu + \beta, & \alpha + \mu \leqq \beta + \mu \\ \mu\alpha < \mu\beta \ (\mu > 0), & \alpha\mu \leqq \beta\mu. \end{cases}$$

For, $\alpha < \beta$ means (we may assume that A is a segment of B) that $\beta = \alpha + \gamma$ ($\gamma > 0$), and vice versa. Hence

$$\mu + \beta = \mu + (\alpha + \gamma) = (\mu + \alpha) + \gamma > \mu + \alpha,$$
$$\mu\beta = \mu(\alpha + \gamma) = \mu\alpha + \mu\gamma > \mu\alpha \quad \text{for} \quad \mu > 0.$$

If the summand or factor μ comes after the α and the β, then equality can occur. For instance,

$$\omega + 1 < \omega + 2, \qquad 1 + \omega = 2 + \omega = \omega,$$
$$\omega 1 < \omega 2, \qquad 1\omega = 2\omega = \omega.$$

The converse of (1) yields the following

$$(2) \qquad \begin{cases} \text{From } \mu + \alpha < \mu + \beta & \text{or} \quad \alpha + \mu < \beta + \mu & \alpha < \beta & \text{follows} \\ \text{From } \mu + \alpha = \mu + \beta & & \alpha = \beta & \text{follows} \\ \text{From } \mu\alpha < \mu\beta & \text{or} \quad \alpha\mu < \beta\mu & \alpha < \beta & \text{follows} \\ \text{From } \mu\alpha = \mu\beta & \text{and} \quad \mu > 0 & \alpha = \beta & \text{follows.} \end{cases}$$

It does not follow from $\alpha + \mu = \beta + \mu$ or from $\alpha\mu = \beta\mu$ that $\alpha = \beta$.

Subtraction As we have just seen, α and $\beta > \alpha$ always uniquely define a number ξ satisfying the equation

$$\alpha + \xi = \beta,$$

and we denote it by

$$\xi = -\alpha + \beta,$$

so that $\alpha + (-\alpha + \beta) = \beta$. ξ is the type of $W(\beta) - W(\alpha)$, that is, of a *remainder* (p. 68) of $W(\beta)$ or, for short, a *remainder type* of β. What is more, for fixed β and $\alpha < \alpha_1 < \beta$ we clearly have $\xi \geqq \xi_1$; the distinct remainder types therefore form an *inversely* well-ordered set, which however is also well ordered, since the remainder types are ordinal numbers; it follows that *there are only finitely many distinct remainder types for a given ordinal number.*

For instance, the only remainder type of ω is ω; $\omega + 3$ has the remainder types $\omega + 3$, 3, 2, and 1, respectively, corresponding to the partitions (ν finite)

$$\omega + 3 = \nu + (\omega + 3) = \omega + 3 = (\omega + 1) + 2 = (\omega + 2) + 1.$$

On the other hand, when $\beta > \alpha$ the equation

$$\eta + \alpha = \beta$$

is not always solvable for η (in order that the equation be meaningful, α must be a remainder type of β); for instance, $\eta + \omega = \omega + 1$ is not solvable, since the left-hand side is the type of a set without a last element, while the right-hand side is that of a set with a last element. If the equation is solvable, then for $\alpha \geqq \omega$ it always has infinitely many solutions $\eta = \eta_0, \eta_0 + 1, \eta_0 + 2, \ldots$, whereas for finite α it has only a single one; for it then says that $\eta + (\alpha - 1)$ is the unique predecessor of β, $\eta + (\alpha - 2)$ the predecessor of $\eta + (\alpha - 1)$, and so forth, so that η is uniquely determined after finitely many steps. Only in this case do we denote the solution by

$$\eta = \beta - \alpha,$$

so that $(\beta - \alpha) + \alpha = \beta$; this equation therefore means that α is a natural number and that η is formed from β by leaving out the last α elements. For instance, $\beta - 1$ is the predecessor of β (where β is assumed to be an isolated number > 0).

Division. Every number $\zeta < \alpha\beta$ can be represented in the form

$$\zeta = \alpha\eta + \xi \quad (\xi < \alpha,\ \eta < \beta), \tag{3}$$

where ξ and η are uniquely determined by α, β, and ζ.

For, if A and B are well ordered and of type α and β respectively, then $\alpha\beta$ is the type of the product (B, A), that is, of the lexicographically ordered set of pairs (b, a). ζ is the type of a segment of (B, A), which we suppose to be determined by (b, a); this segment consists of the pairs (y, x) for which $y < b$ and $x \varepsilon A$, and of the pairs (b, x) for which $x < a$. Thus if ξ and η are the types of the segments of A and B determined by a and b, then the above formula follows; at the same time, it can be seen that (b, a) and ξ, η are determined by ζ, α, and β. Letting β be arbitrary, we can say:

If $\alpha > 0$, then every number can be represented in the form

$$\zeta = \alpha\eta + \xi \quad (\xi < \alpha), \tag{4}$$

where ξ and η are uniquely determined by α and ζ.

For, one can choose β so large (for instance $\beta = \zeta + 1$) that $\zeta < \alpha\beta$, and one can then apply (3); what is more, the representations (4) corresponding two distinct β cannot differ, as then there would be two distinct representations (3) for the larger of these two β.

Thus we have here a (one-sided) analogue of the situation in the finite case: η is in a manner of speaking the quotient, and ξ the remainder, of the division of ζ by α; when $\xi = 0$, ζ is divisible by α as a left-hand factor.

The Euclidean Algorithm can also be carried over:

$$\alpha = \alpha_1\eta_1 + \alpha_2 \quad (\alpha_1 > \alpha_2)$$
$$\alpha_1 = \alpha_2\eta_2 + \alpha_3 \quad (\alpha_2 > \alpha_3)$$
$$\dots\dots\dots\dots\dots\dots$$

with decreasing, and therefore finitely many, remainders among which zero must ultimately occur. This leads to the development of *ordered pairs* of ordinal numbers into continued fractions, so that they can be ordered analogously to rational numbers; we will not go into this.

Extension of Multiplication. We have already, on p. 56, discussed products with infinitely many factors, say $\dots \alpha_3\, \alpha_2\, \alpha_1$; but even if the factors are ordinal numbers, the products themselves do not have to be. For instance, $\dots \omega\omega\omega = 1 + \lambda$ is the type of the interval $[0, 1)$. We will now explain products in which the order of factors is well-ordered, like $\alpha_1\, \alpha_2\, \alpha_3 \dots$. Superficially, the present definition has nothing to do with the previous one, and only a consideration in the sequel (§ 16) will show that the two are in fact special cases of a general concept of product.

The present explanation depends on transfinite induction (p. 72); for the sake of symmetry we will define addition once again, by transfinite induction, that is, reduce it to the addition of two summands, although we have already defined it more simply before, and in greater generality, namely for order *types*.

Let an ordinal number μ_α be associated with every ordinal number α. We define the sum

$$f(\alpha) = \sum_{\xi}^{W(\alpha)} \mu_\xi = \mu_0 + \mu_1 + \cdots + \mu_\xi + \cdots$$

-which is to be regarded as a function of α only when the summands are fixed – as an ordinal number by means of the following inductive rule:

$$(5)\begin{cases} f(0) = 0; \\ \text{for } \alpha > 0,\ f(\alpha) \text{ is the smallest number} \geqq f(\xi) + \mu_\xi \ (\text{for all } \xi < \alpha). \end{cases}$$

If for the sake of simplicity we take all $\mu_\alpha > 0$ (summands $= 0$ are to be left out), then for $\alpha > \xi$ we have

$$f(\alpha) + \mu_\alpha > f(\alpha) \geqq f(\xi) + \mu_\xi > f(\xi),$$

the numbers $f(\alpha)$ as well as the numbers $f(\alpha) + \mu_\alpha$ having the same order as their arguments α. In particular, therefore,

$$(6) \qquad f(\alpha + 1) = f(\alpha) + \mu_a.$$

If furthermore α is a limit number, then

$$(7) \qquad f(\alpha) = \lim f(\xi) \quad (\xi < \alpha);$$

for in that case $\xi < \alpha$ implies $\xi + 1 < \alpha$ and the first number $\geqq f(\xi + 1)$ is identical with the first number $> f(\xi)$, so that $f(\alpha)$ is identical with $\lim f(\xi)$ (compare (5) and 6)).

It is easy to see that this present definition of sum is identical with the earlier one, that is, that the earlier concept of sum has the property (5) or the properties (6) and (7). By (7) the sum is the limit of partial sums, as in the convergent series of Analysis; for instance

$$f(\omega) = \lim f(\nu), \qquad \mu_0 + \mu_1 + \mu_2 + \cdots = \lim (\mu_0 + \mu_1 + \cdots + \mu_{\nu-1}).$$

We proceed similarly in the case of the product, which we reduce to that of the product of two factors. Let us suppose that there is associated with every ordinal number α an ordinal number $\mu_\alpha > 0$ (products containing zero as a factor shall themselves equal zero). We define the product

$$f(\alpha) = \prod_{\xi}^{W(\alpha)} = \mu_0 \mu_1 \cdots \mu_\xi \cdots$$

as an ordinal number, which is to be regarded as a function of α, by the rule

$$(8)\begin{cases} f(0) = 1; \\ \text{for } \alpha > 0,\ f(\alpha) \text{ is the smallest number} \geqq f(\xi)\mu_\xi \ (\text{for all } \xi < \alpha). \end{cases}$$

If for the sake of simplicity we take all the factors to be > 1 (ones are to be omitted), then first of all it is clear that $f(\alpha) > 0$, and that

$$f(\alpha)\,\mu_\alpha > f(\alpha) \geqq f(\xi)\,\mu_\xi > f(\xi),$$

and we obtain as before

(9) $$f(\alpha + 1) = f(\alpha)\,\mu_\alpha$$

and for a limit number α

(10) $$f(\alpha) = \lim f(\xi) \qquad (\xi < \alpha).$$

Products with finite α agree with our earlier products,

$$f(1) = \mu_0, \quad f(2) = \mu_0\mu_1, \ \ldots,$$

and hence $f(\omega) = \lim f(\nu), \quad \mu_0\mu_1\mu_2 \ldots = \lim \mu_0\mu_1 \ldots \mu_{\nu-1};$
for instance[1] $2.\,3.\,4.\ldots = \lim \{2, 6, 24, \ldots\} = \omega$.

In particular, if all the factors $\mu_\alpha = \mu > 1$, we define the product to be the *power* $f(\alpha) = \mu^\alpha$. Thus

(11) $$\mu^{\alpha+1} = \mu^\alpha \cdot \mu,$$

and for a limit number α,

(12) $$\mu^\alpha = \lim \mu^\xi \qquad (\xi < \alpha);$$

for instance $\quad 2^\omega = \lim 2^\nu = \lim \{2, 4, 8, \ldots\} = \omega,$
and in general $\quad 2^\omega = 3^\omega = 4^\omega = \cdots = \omega,$
whereas $\quad \omega^\omega = \lim \omega^\nu = \lim \{\omega, \omega^2, \omega^3, \ldots\},$
for which, inasmuch as $1 + \omega = \omega,\ \ 1 + \omega + \omega^2 = \omega(1 + \omega) = \omega^2$, etc., we can also write

$$\omega^\omega = 1 + \omega + \omega^2 + \cdots = \sum_\nu \omega^\nu.$$

We have the following rules of exponentiation

(13) $$\mu^\alpha \mu^\beta = \mu^{\alpha+\beta}, \quad (\mu^\alpha)^\beta = \mu^{\alpha\beta},$$

which are most readily proved by induction (they are true for β if they are true for $\eta < \beta$). Of course, a commutative law cannot hold; $(\mu\nu)^2 = \mu\nu\ \mu\nu$ is in general distinct from $\mu^2\nu^2 = \mu\mu\ \nu\nu$.

We emphasize again that products and powers as defined here do not at first seem to have any connection at all with the earlier ones; they

[1] In the case of cardinal numbers, 2. 3. 4. ... = $2^{\aleph_0}$; the use of finite numbers for both meanings might appear to be particularly questionable, and yet it is not.

are in general not the types of set products. Hence α^β, for instance, does not necessarily have cardinality $\mathfrak{a}^\mathfrak{b}$ (while $\alpha + \beta$ and $\alpha\beta$ have the cardinalities $\mathfrak{a} + \mathfrak{b}$ and $\mathfrak{a}\mathfrak{b}$ respectively); $2^\omega = \omega$ has only the cardinality $\aleph_0$, not $2^{\aleph_0}$.

Just as a natural number can be expressed by means of the powers of 10, so every ordinal number can be expressed by means of the powers of an arbitrary *basis* $\beta > 1$. Let $\zeta > 0$ be an ordinal number and β^γ the smallest power of β that is $> \zeta$ (that there are such powers can be easily seen from the inequality, easily proved by induction, $\beta^\gamma \geqq \gamma$, from which it follows that $\beta^{\zeta+1} > \zeta$). γ is not a limit number, because otherwise for every $\xi < \gamma$ we would also have $\xi + 1 < \gamma$, so that

$$\beta^{\xi+1} \leqq \zeta, \quad \beta^\xi < \zeta, \quad \beta^\gamma = \lim \beta^\xi \leqq \zeta.$$

Therefore γ (> 0) must have an immediate predecessor α, and we have

$$\beta^\alpha \leqq \zeta < \beta^{\alpha+1},$$

from which (for a fixed basis) α is uniquely determined by ζ. The number $\zeta < \beta^\alpha \cdot \beta$ can, by (3), be represented in the form

$$\zeta = \beta^\alpha \eta + \zeta_1 \qquad (\eta < \beta, \ \zeta_1 < \beta^\alpha),$$

η and ζ_1 being determined by ζ. Now if ζ_1 is > 0, then we obtain further

$$\zeta_1 = \beta^{\alpha_1} \eta_1 + \zeta_2 \qquad (\eta_1 < \beta, \ \zeta_2 < \beta^{\alpha_1}),$$

etc. But since $\zeta \geqq \beta^\alpha > \zeta_1 \geqq \beta^{\alpha_1} > \zeta_2 \geqq \cdots$, so that $\zeta > \zeta_1 > \zeta_2 > \cdots$, $\alpha > \alpha_1 > \alpha_2 > \ldots$, the process must ultimately end with remainder 0,

$$\zeta_n = \beta^{\alpha_n} \eta_n,$$

and we have the representation

$$\zeta = \beta^\alpha \eta + \beta^{\alpha_1} \eta_1 + \cdots + \beta^{\alpha_n} \eta_n \qquad \begin{pmatrix} \alpha > \alpha_1 > \cdots > \alpha_n \geqq 0 \\ 0 < \eta, \eta_1, \ldots, \eta_n < \beta \end{pmatrix}, \tag{14}$$

where everything is uniquely determined by ζ: the number of terms $n + 1$ (for $n = 0$, $\zeta = \beta^\alpha \eta$), the exponents α, and the coefficients η. And what is more, not only is the representation just constructed uniquely determined, but so is every representation of the form (14), no matter how obtained. For the expression (14) is $< \beta^{\alpha+1}$, as can be inferred from the induction from n to $n + 1$: in fact, we have $\zeta < \beta^\alpha \eta + \beta^{\alpha_1+1} \leqq \beta^\alpha (\eta + 1) \leqq \beta^{\alpha+1}$. Thus we must have $\beta^\alpha \leqq \zeta < \beta^{\alpha+1}$, and the exponents and coefficients are determined exactly as above.

Examples. $\beta = 2$: $\zeta = 2^{\alpha} + 2^{\alpha_1} + \cdots + 2^{\alpha_n}$.

$\beta = \omega$: (15) $\zeta = \omega^{\alpha}\nu + \omega^{\alpha_1}\nu_1 + \cdots + \omega^{\alpha_n}\nu_n$
($\nu, \ldots, \nu_n$ natural numbers).

In particular, every number $\zeta < \beta^{\omega}$ can be represented as a *polynomial* in β (with finite exponents), and in fact it has a unique representation of the form (14).

In the representation (14) it can happen, moreover, that ζ is not expressed at all by means of smaller numbers, but that the equation

$$\zeta = \beta^{\zeta} \tag{16}$$

holds (which is impossible for finite numbers when $\beta > 1$); thus, as we have found, $\omega = 2^{\omega}$. If the numbers ζ_ν are defined for $\nu = 0, 1, 2, 3, \ldots$ by $\zeta_0 = 1$, $\zeta_{\nu+1} = \beta^{\zeta_\nu}$, then ($\beta > 1$)

$$\begin{aligned} &\zeta_0 < \zeta_1, \text{ so that } \beta^{\zeta_0} < \beta^{\zeta_1}, \\ &\zeta_1 < \zeta_2, \text{ so that } \beta^{\zeta_1} < \beta^{\zeta_2}, \\ &\zeta_2 < \zeta_3, \quad \text{etc.} \end{aligned}$$

When $\zeta = \lim \zeta_\nu$,

$$\zeta = \lim \zeta_{\nu+1} = \lim \beta^{\zeta_\nu} = \beta^{\zeta},$$

so that ζ is a number with the property (16); it is the limit of

$$1, \beta, \beta^{\beta}, \beta^{\beta^{\beta}}, \ldots .$$

(Numbers for which $\zeta = \omega^{\zeta}$ are called ε-numbers by Cantor.)

The powers ω^{α} of ω are characterized by the property that they themselves are their only remainder types (p. 74). In fact, it follows from (15) that if ζ has no remainder type $< \zeta$, then the number of terms in the expansion must be 1, as otherwise we would have $\omega^{\alpha_n} < \zeta$ and hence $\zeta = \omega^{\alpha}\nu$; moreover $\nu = 1$, as otherwise $\omega^{\alpha} < \zeta$ would be a remainder type; and hence $\zeta = \omega^{\alpha}$. Conversely, the only remainder type of ω^{α} is ω^{α} itself; that is, we have

$$\eta + \omega^{\alpha} = \omega^{\alpha} \qquad (\eta < \omega^{\alpha}).$$

For if $\eta = \omega^{\beta}\nu + \eta_1$ ($\eta > 0$, ν a natural number, $\eta_1 < \omega^{\beta}$) is the beginning of the expansion of η, where $\beta < \alpha$, and if we set $\omega^{\alpha} = \omega^{\beta+1} + \varrho$ (for $\beta + 1 = \alpha$, $\varrho = 0$), then

$$\begin{aligned} \omega^{\alpha} &\leqq \eta + \omega^{\alpha} \leqq \omega^{\beta}(\nu + 1) + \omega^{\alpha} \\ &= \omega^{\beta}(\nu + 1 + \omega) + \varrho = \omega^{\beta+1} + \varrho = \omega^{\alpha}, \end{aligned}$$

so that $\eta + \omega^\alpha = \omega^\alpha$.

Since a remainder type of a remainder type of ζ is itself a remainder type of ζ, it follows that the smallest remainder type of a number ζ is always a power of ω (one possibility being $\omega^0 = 1$); in the expansion (15) ω^{α_n} is the smallest remainder type of ζ.

Natural Sums and Products. The expansion (15) exhibits an ordinal number as a kind of polynomial in ω, in general with infinite exponents. If we compute with these polynomials as with ordinary polynomials, then we obtain, following Hessenberg, *natural sums* $\sigma(\xi, \eta)$ and *natural products* $\pi(\xi, \eta)$ of ordinal numbers, constructs that are considerably closer to the corresponding ones for finite numbers than $\xi + \eta$ and $\xi\eta$ are.

Let us write the expansion in powers of ω in the simple form

$$\xi = \sum_\alpha \omega^\alpha x_\alpha = \cdots + \omega^\omega x_\omega + \cdots + \omega^2 x_2 + \omega x_1 + x_0,$$

where the exponents α run through *all* the ordinal numbers less than a sufficiently large bound and where the coefficients x_α are assumed to be finite integers $\geqq 0$; actually, only finitely many of the coefficients differ from 0. (When $\xi = 0$, all $x_\alpha = 0$.) The representation is uniquely determined. Then for two ordinal numbers

$$\xi = \sum_\alpha \omega^\alpha x_\alpha \text{ and } \eta = \sum_\alpha \omega^\alpha y_\alpha ,$$

we define

$$\sigma(\xi, \eta) = \sum_\alpha \omega^\alpha (x_\alpha + y_\alpha) = \sigma(\eta, \xi).$$

This may agree neither with $\xi + \eta$ nor with $\eta + \xi$; for example $\sigma(\omega, \omega^2 + 1) = \omega^2 + \omega + 1$ differs from $\omega + (\omega^2 + 1) = \omega^2 + 1$ and from $(\omega^2 + 1) + \omega = \omega^2 + \omega$.

For a given ζ the equation $\sigma(\xi, \eta) = \zeta$ has only finitely many solutions ξ, η. For, we must have $x_\alpha + y_\alpha = z_\alpha$, and the only possible values for x_α are $0, 1, \ldots, z_\alpha$. The number of solutions is the product of all factors of the form $1 + z_\alpha$, of which only finitely many can be > 1.

The inequality $\xi < \eta$ means that the *first* non-vanishing difference $y_\alpha - x_\alpha$ is positive (the first, that is, in the ordering of the sum by decreasing exponents; the one belonging to the highest exponent). That is, there exists an ordinal number $\beta \geqq 0$ for which $x_\beta < y_\beta$ and $x_\gamma = y_\gamma$ for $\gamma > \beta$. Hence it follows that $\sigma(\xi, \eta)$ increases with each of its summands: if $\xi_0 < \xi$ then $\sigma(\xi_0, \eta) < \sigma(\xi, \eta)$. Hence if $\sigma(\xi_0, \eta_0) = \sigma(\xi, \eta)$ and $\xi_0 < \xi$, then we must have at the same time $\eta_0 > \eta$.

If $\zeta_0 < \zeta = \sigma(\xi, \eta)$, then the equation $\sigma(\xi_0, \eta_0) = \zeta_0$ has a solution for which $\xi_0 \leqq \xi$, $\eta_0 \leqq \eta$ (at least one equality sign being excluded). In fact, let us write

$$\xi = \sum_\gamma \omega^\gamma x_\gamma + \omega^\beta x_\beta + \sum_\alpha \omega^\alpha x_\alpha$$
$$\eta = \sum_\gamma \omega^\gamma y_\gamma + \omega^\beta y_\beta + \sum_\alpha \omega^\alpha y_\alpha$$
$$\zeta_0 = \sum_\gamma \omega^\gamma c_\gamma + \omega^\beta c_\beta + \sum_\alpha \omega^\alpha c_\alpha ,$$

where the first term β in which ζ_0 and ζ differ has been set off, $\gamma > \beta > \alpha$, $x_\gamma + y_\gamma = c_\gamma$ and $x_\beta + y_\beta > c_\beta$. We then determine two integers a_β, b_β for which $0 \leqq a_\beta \leqq x_\beta$, $0 \leqq b_\beta \leqq y_\beta$, and $a_\beta + b_\beta = c_\beta$; for instance, $a_\beta = \min [x_\beta, c_\beta]$ and $b_\beta = c_\beta - a_\beta$ satisfy these conditions.

Then at least one of the inequalities $a_\beta < x_\beta$ and $b_\beta < y_\beta$ is satisfied; for instance, if the first, then we set

$$\xi_0 = \sum_\gamma \omega^\gamma x_\gamma + \omega^\beta a_\beta + \sum_\alpha \omega_\alpha c_\alpha,$$
$$\eta_0 = \sum_\gamma \omega^\gamma y_\gamma + \omega^\beta b_\beta,$$

and conclude that $\sigma(\xi_0, \eta_0) = \zeta_0$, $\xi_0 < \xi$ and $\eta_0 \leqq \eta$.

Natural sums, then, behave completely like finite sums; in the sequel, we shall often make use of this fact.

We obtain the natural product by multiplying

$$\xi = \sum_\alpha \omega^\alpha x_\alpha, \qquad \eta = \sum_\beta \omega^\beta y_\beta$$

like polynomials, adding the exponents naturally, so that

$$\pi(\xi, \eta) = \sum_{\alpha\beta} \omega^{\sigma(\alpha, \beta)} x_\alpha y_\beta = \pi(\eta, \xi)$$

or

$$\pi(\xi, \eta) = \sum_\gamma \omega^\gamma z_\gamma, \qquad z_\gamma = \sum^\gamma x_\alpha y_\beta,$$

where $\sum^\gamma$ is extended over the finitely many pairs for which $\sigma(\alpha, \beta) = \gamma$. We do no more than mention this, and leave it to the reader to establish the analogy with finite products that holds here also.

§ 15. The Alefs

All cardinal numbers can be looked upon as being the cardinalities of well-ordered sets (by the Well-Ordering Theorem) and therefore are comparable. By a *number class* $Z(\mathfrak{a})$ we shall mean the set of all ordinal numbers α that have cardinal number $\mathfrak{a}$; it is a subset of the corresponding *type class* $T(\mathfrak{a})$ (p. 57). For finite $n = 0, 1, 2, \ldots, Z(n)$ consists only of the single ordinal number n; we are already acquainted with infinitely many representatives of $Z(\aleph_0)$, namely

$$\omega,\ \omega+1,\ \omega+2,\ldots,\ \omega\,2,\ldots,\ \omega\,3,\ldots,\ \omega^2,\ldots,\ \omega^3,\ldots,\ \omega^\omega,\ldots$$

If $\mathfrak{a} < \mathfrak{b}$ and if α and β are any two ordinal numbers of the number classes $Z(\mathfrak{a})$ and $Z(\mathfrak{b})$ respectively, then $\alpha < \beta$.

I. *Every set of cardinal numbers when ordered according to size is well ordered.*

For, if we associate with every cardinal number an ordinal number from the corresponding number class, then the set of cardinal numbers is similar to a set of ordinal numbers and is therefore well ordered (§ 13, Chap. IV).

II. *For every set of cardinal numbers there exist larger ones, and in particular, there exists a unique next larger one.*

The first statement follows from § 7 and the second follows from I; for, if there exists any cardinal number $\mathfrak{a} > \kappa$ (where κ is a set of cardinal numbers), then either $\mathfrak{a}$ is the smallest such number or there exists a smallest in the well-ordered set of cardinal numbers that are $> \kappa$ and $< \mathfrak{a}$. (We do not say that there is a smallest element in the set of all cardinal numbers $> \kappa$, because this set is just as inconceivable as the set of all cardinal numbers).

The cardinal number $\mathfrak{b}$ next larger than the cardinal number $\mathfrak{a}$ is obtained by looking for the ordinal number β next larger than $Z(\mathfrak{a})$; its cardinal number is $\mathfrak{b}$. Whether the cardinal number $2^{\mathfrak{a}} > \mathfrak{a}$ is the *next larger* than $\mathfrak{a}$ is not yet known for any infinite $\mathfrak{a}$; for $\mathfrak{a} = \aleph_0$ this question is the problem of the continuum (p. 45).

The infinite cardinal numbers ($\geqq \aleph_0$) are called *alefs*. The first of these is $\aleph_0$, the cardinality of the set of all natural numbers; the next larger is called $\aleph_1$, the succeeding one $\aleph_2$, and so on; the smallest one that exceeds all the $\aleph_\nu$ with finite index is denoted by $\aleph_\omega$, the next larger one by $\aleph_{\omega+1}$, and so on. That is, *every Alef $\aleph_\alpha$ has as its subscript the type of the set of all the preceding alefs.*

For instance, the cardinality $\aleph$ of the continuum is $> \aleph_0$, so that $\aleph \geqq \aleph_1$; the question as to whether the equality sign holds or not is the problem of the continuum.

The smallest ordinal number ω_α belonging to the class of numbers $Z(\aleph_\alpha)$ is called the *beginning number* of this class. The smallest beginning number is $\omega_0 = \omega$, after which follow $\omega_1, \omega_2, \ldots, \omega_\omega, \omega_{\omega+1}, \ldots$; the index of every beginning number ω_α is the type of the set of all the preceding beginning numbers. Hence

$$Z(\aleph_\alpha) = \text{the set of all numbers } \omega_\alpha \leqq \mu < \omega_{\alpha+1}$$
$$= W(\omega_{\alpha+1}) - W(\omega_\alpha)$$

or, in the sense of the addition of ordered sets,

(1) $$W(\omega_{\alpha+1}) = W(\omega_\alpha) + Z(\aleph_\alpha),$$

(2) $$W(\omega_\alpha) \quad = W(\omega_0) + \sum_{\xi<\alpha} Z(\aleph_\xi),$$

where for $\alpha = 0$ we set the last sum $= 0$, and $W(\alpha)$ denotes, as before, the set of all ordinal numbers $< \alpha$. $W(\omega_0) = W(\omega)$ represents the union of the finite classes $Z(0)$, $Z(1)$, ... ; moreover (following Cantor), $W(\omega)$ is often called the first class, $Z(\aleph_0)$ the second class, $Z(\aleph_1)$ the third class.

Every ordinal number is of the form $\omega\mu + \nu$ ($\nu < \omega$, i.e. ν finite; see § 14, (4)); in particular, a limit number is of the form $\lambda = \omega\mu$, so that we have for its cardinal number

$$\mathfrak{l} = \aleph_0 \mathfrak{m}, \quad \aleph_0 \mathfrak{l} = \aleph_0{}^2 \mathfrak{m} = \aleph_0 \mathfrak{m} = \mathfrak{l}.$$

Since every beginning number is clearly a limit number (an infinite cardinal number cannot be changed by the addition of one element), we have

$$\aleph_0 \aleph_\alpha = \aleph_\alpha$$

for every alef $\aleph_\alpha$, and by the Equivalence Theorem we have, a fortiori,

$$2\aleph_\alpha = \aleph_\alpha + \aleph_\alpha = \aleph_\alpha,$$
$$\mathfrak{x} + \aleph_\alpha = \aleph_\alpha \qquad \text{for } \mathfrak{x} < \aleph_\alpha.$$

If $\mathfrak{x} < \aleph_\alpha$, $\mathfrak{y} < \aleph_\alpha$, then we have $\mathfrak{x} + \mathfrak{y} < \aleph_\alpha$ as well; for, let $\mathfrak{x} \leqq \mathfrak{y}$ and $\mathfrak{y} = \aleph_\eta$ with $\eta < \alpha$ (for finite $\mathfrak{y}$ nothing need be proved), then $\mathfrak{x} + \mathfrak{y} = \mathfrak{x} + \aleph_\eta = \aleph_\eta < \aleph_\alpha$. It follows further that every remainder of ω_α has type ω_α, for otherwise in $\omega_\alpha = \xi + \eta$ ($\aleph_\alpha = \mathfrak{x} + \mathfrak{y}$), $\mathfrak{x}$ as well as $\mathfrak{y}$ would be $< \aleph_\alpha$. Hence we obtain from (1) that

(3) $Z(\aleph_\alpha)$ has type $\omega_{\alpha+1}$ and cardinal number $\aleph_{\alpha+1}$.

For example, $Z(\aleph_0)$ has cardinal number $\aleph_1$, while the corresponding type class $T(\aleph_0)$ has the cardinality $\aleph$ of the continuum, which once again illustrates the inequality $\aleph \geqq \aleph_1$ and the problem of the continuum. Hence by (2) we have

$$\left.\begin{aligned} \omega_\alpha &= \omega_0 + \sum_\xi \omega_{\xi+1} = \omega_0 + \omega_1 + \cdots + \omega_{\xi+1} + \cdots \\ \aleph_\alpha &= \aleph_0 + \sum_\xi \aleph_{\xi+1} = \aleph_0 + \aleph_1 + \cdots + \aleph_{\xi+1} + \cdots \end{aligned}\right\} \quad (\xi < \alpha);$$

for example, $\aleph_\omega = \aleph_0 + \aleph_1 + \aleph_2 + \cdots$; $\aleph_\omega$, in contradistinction to $\aleph$, satisfies the inequality $\aleph_\omega < \aleph_\omega^{\aleph_0}$ (p. 41).

Every power of an alef with finite exponent is equal to this same alef; that is, we have

(4) $$\aleph_\alpha^2 = \aleph_\alpha .$$

For, if the pairs (ξ, η) for which $\xi < \omega_\alpha$ and $\eta < \omega_\alpha$ – they form a set of cardinality $\aleph_\alpha^2$ – are ordered according to the natural sum (p. 80) $\sigma(\xi, \eta) = \zeta$, then[1] $\zeta < \omega_\alpha$, and since only finitely many pairs (ξ, η) correspond to each ζ, we obtain a set of cardinality $\leqq \aleph_0 \aleph_\alpha = \aleph_\alpha$.

Hence $\aleph_\alpha = \aleph_\alpha^2 = \aleph_\alpha^3 = \cdots$. As regards the exponent $\aleph_0$, we know that there are two categories of alefs: those for which $\aleph_\alpha^{\aleph_0} > \aleph_\alpha$ (such as $\aleph_0$ and $\aleph_\omega$) and those for which $\aleph_\alpha^{\aleph_0} = \aleph_\alpha$ (the Alefs of the form $\mathfrak{a}^{\aleph_0}$, as for example, $2^{\aleph_0} = \aleph$). The question as to whether $\aleph_1$ belongs to the first or to the second class, that is, as to which sign holds in $\aleph_1^{\aleph_0} \geqq \aleph_1$, is once again the problem of the continuum, since $\aleph_1^{\aleph_0} = \aleph$ (it follows from $2 < \aleph_1 \leqq \aleph$ that $2^{\aleph_0} \leqq \aleph_1^{\aleph_0} \leqq \aleph^{\aleph_0} = 2^{\aleph_0}$).

It follows from (4) that

III. *A sum of type* $< \omega_{\alpha+1}$ *whose terms are ordinal numbers* $< \omega_{\alpha+1}$ *is itself* $< \omega_{\alpha+1}$.

For, let

$$\sigma = \sum_\eta \alpha_\eta = \alpha_0 + \alpha_1 + \cdots + \alpha_\eta + \cdots \quad (\eta < \beta;\ \beta < \omega_{\alpha+1},\ \alpha_\eta < \omega_{\alpha+1}).$$

Each summand has cardinality $< \aleph_{\alpha+1}$ or $\leqq \aleph_\alpha$, and the same holds for β; therefore σ has cardinality $\leqq \aleph_\alpha \aleph_\alpha = \aleph_\alpha < \aleph_{\alpha+1}$, and hence $\sigma < \omega_{\alpha+1}$.

Another form of this theorem is as follows:

IV. *If a set of ordinal numbers* $< \omega_{\alpha+1}$ *is of type* $< \omega_{\alpha+1}$, *then the next larger ordinal number as well is of type* $< \omega_{\alpha+1}$.

For, if $W = \{\alpha_0, \alpha_1, \ldots, \alpha_\eta, \ldots\}$ is of type β $(\eta < \beta)$, with the same hypotheses as in the proof of III, and if $\sigma = \sum_\eta \alpha_\eta$, then $W < \sigma + 1 < \omega_{\alpha+1}$, so that the smallest number $> W$ is still $< \omega_{\alpha+1}$.

These theorems regulate the size of the segments $W(\omega_{\alpha+1})$, that is, of the classes $Z(\aleph_\alpha)$. For example, if a number α belongs to $Z(\aleph_0)$, then so does its successor $\alpha + 1$, and if an ω-sequence $\alpha_0 < \alpha_1 < \alpha_2 < \cdots$ belongs to $Z(\aleph_1)$, so does its limit; $Z(\aleph_1)$ contains the successor of each of its members, the limit of a ω-sequence whose members belong to it, and also the limit of each ω_1-sequence $\alpha_0 < \alpha_1 < \cdots < \alpha_\omega < \alpha_{\omega+1} < \cdots$ whose members belong to it.

---

[1] If the term $\omega^\gamma z = \omega^\gamma (x + y)$ is the highest term occurring in ζ and if, say, $x > 0$, then $\xi = \omega^\gamma x + \cdots < \omega_\alpha$, so that $\omega^\gamma < \omega_\alpha$, and consequently every multiple of ω^γ is $< \omega_\alpha$, and thus $\zeta < \omega^\gamma (z + 1) < \omega_\alpha$.

Theorems III and IV need not hold for beginning numbers whose subscript is a limit number; for example, the numbers $\omega_0, \omega_1, \omega_2, \cdots$ belong to $W(\omega_\omega)$, but the limit ω_ω of this ω-sequence does not. The beginning numbers for which IV holds are called *regular*: $\omega_{\alpha+1}$ and $\omega_0 = \omega$ are thus regular. No regular beginning numbers whose index is a limit number are known; they would have to be tremendously large.

§ 16. The General Concept of Product

Let $M = \{\ldots, m, \ldots, n, \ldots, p, \ldots\}$ be an ordered set whose elements m correspond to ordered sets A_m; from this set we obtain the as yet unordered product,

$$A = \prod_m^M A_m = (\ldots, A_m, \ldots, A_n, \ldots, A_p, \ldots)$$

as the set of complexes

$$a = (\ldots, a_m, \ldots, a_n, \ldots, a_p, \ldots) \qquad (a_m \varepsilon A_m).$$

Two such complexes a and

$$b = (\ldots, b_m, \ldots, b_n, \ldots, b_p, \ldots)$$

determine the set $M(a, b)$ of those m for which $a_m \neq b_m$; it is non-empty if and only if the two complexes are distinct and in that case is an ordered subset of M. For brevity, let us call M the *argument*, and the elements of $M(a, b)$ the *places of difference* of the pair a, b.

For three complexes a, b, and c we clearly have

$$(1) \qquad M(a, c) \leqq M(a, b) + M(b, c),$$

for, if $a_m \neq c_m$, then at least one of the inequalities $a_m \neq b_m$ and $b_m \neq c_m$ must hold.

We have already indicated at the end of § 10 that, in the case of a *well-ordered*, M a *lexicographic* ordering of the product A is possible. For, in this case the set $M(a, b)$ has a first element m when $a \neq b$, and we can then define $a \lesseqgtr b$, according as $a_m \lesseqgtr b_m$; we shall shortly see that this is actually an ordering, that is, that the $<$ sign is transitive. The above A shall then mean the lexicographically ordered product; we must, to be sure, denote its type by

$$\alpha = \prod_m^{M^*} \alpha_m = \cdots \alpha_p \cdots \alpha_n \cdots \alpha_m \cdots,$$

where the order of the factors (α_m is the type of A_m) is the opposite of the order of the factors in the set product and in M. The inverted argument $M^* = N$ may appropriately be called the *exponent*. When the factors are equal, $A_m = B$, then we obtain from the product the *power* B^M, having the type $\beta^{\mu^*} = \beta^\nu$ (β, μ, and ν are the respective types of B, M, and N). We have already found among others, the power $\omega^{\omega^*} = 1 + \lambda$ (p. 56).

In the case of an *arbitrary* M, which is not necessarily well-ordered, we must define the lexicographic order insofar as it is definable. That is, *if* $M(a, b)$ has a first element m, which we will then denote by $m(a, b)$, and if $a_m \lesseqgtr b_m$, then let $a \lesseqgtr b$. $a < b$ then implies $b > a$, and the transitive law holds: if $a < b$ and $b < c$, then $a < c$. For, let $m = m(a, b)$, $n = m(b, c)$ and $p = \min\,[m, n]$ (i.e., $p = m$ for $m \leqq n$, $p = n$ for $n \leqq m$); then

$$\text{for } l < p, \text{ we have } a_l = b_l,\ b_l = c_l, \text{ so that } a_l = c_l,$$

while

$$a_p \leqq b_p, \quad b_p \leqq c_p$$

with at least one inequality sign; hence $a_p < c_p$. That is, the first element of $M(a, c)$ is p, and we have $a < c$. We can thus formulate the transitive law as follows:

If $a < b$ and $b < c$, then $a < c$ and

$$m(a, c) = \min\,[m(a, b),\quad m(b, c)]. \tag{2}$$

If, for $a \neq b$, $M(a, b)$ has no first element, then we will call a and b lexicographically *incomparable* and denote this by the symbols

$$a \,||\, b, \quad b \,||\, a.$$

Thus, in general, the set product A will only be partially ordered; between two distinct elements there holds one and only one of the relations

$$a < b, \quad a > b, \quad a \,||\, b,$$

which are equivalent with

$$b > a, \quad b < a, \quad b \,||\, a,$$

respectively. Note, moreover, that comparability need not be transitive; we can have $a < b$, $b > c$, and $a \,||\, c$.

If, in this situation, we want to salvage something for the theory of ordered sets, we shall have to restrict ourselves to the *ordered subsets* of A, and since there are many such subsets, we will restrict ourselves to those which are defined in as simple and unarbitrary a way as possible and which retain as many of the characteristics of a set product as possible. For this purpose, we again avail ourselves of the theory of well-ordering.

If, for two complexes, the set $M(a, b)$ of places of differences of a and b is *well-ordered,* the complexes will be called *congruent,* a term borrowed from number theory:

$$a \equiv b \quad \text{or} \quad b \equiv a.$$

The case $M(a, b) = 0$ is also included here: $a \equiv a$. By (1), the transitive law holds: $a \equiv b$ and $b \equiv c$ implies $a \equiv c$. Hence A can be divided into classes in such a way that congruent complexes belong to the same class and incongruent complexes to distinct classes; such a class $A(a)$ – namely the set of complexes congruent to a, and hence to each other – is either identical with $A(b)$ (when $b \equiv a$) or has no element in common with it.

The complexes of any one class are lexicographically comparable, and therefore $A(a)$ is an ordered set. The properties that lend it the character of a product (for instance, the associative law) will not be considered further; we shall merely show that it is a *maximal* ordered subset of A, that is, that it is not capable of being imbedded in a larger ordered subset of A (we are, of course, referring to the lexicographic ordering).

For, if $c \not\equiv a$, then the not well-ordered set $M(a, c)$ splits into two *complements* P and Q, where P is well-ordered and Q is non-empty and has no first element (for example, let Q be the sum of all subsets of $M(a, c)$ that have no first element; then Q has no first element either, and its complement P can have no non-empty subset that has no first element, and hence is well-ordered). If we then define a complex b by

$$b_m = c_m \text{ for } m \varepsilon P, \quad b_m = a_m \text{ for } m \varepsilon M - P,$$

then $M(a, b) = P$ and $M(b, c) = Q$, so that $b \equiv a$ and $b \parallel c$, hence if $c \not\equiv a$, then c is incomparable with at least one complex of the class $A(a)$, and hence $A(a)$ cannot be extended.

An important case is the one in which the *exponent* $N = M^*$ is well ordered (rather than, as was originally the case, the argument M). Every set $M(a, b)$ is now inversely well-ordered; if it is well-ordered also, then it is finite; that is, $a \equiv b$ means that the complexes a and b differ only at finitely many places.

Let us consider, for example, the case

$$N = \{0, 1, 2, \ldots\}, \qquad M = \{\ldots, 2, 1, 0\},$$

where N is of type ω; our complexes then are

$$a = (\ldots, a_2, a_1, a_0), \qquad a_m \varepsilon A_m.$$

To investigate the class $A(a)$ and its type, we let

$$A_m = B_m + \{a_m\} + C_m, \qquad \alpha_m = \beta_m + 1 + \gamma_m$$

be respectively the partition of A_m determined by a_m, and the type of that partition; furthermore, let x_m, y_m, z_m run through the sets A_m, B_m, C_m. The complexes congruent to a then appear in the following order

$$\begin{array}{c}
\vdots \\
(\ldots, a_4, y_3, x_2, x_1, x_0) \\
(\ldots, a_4, a_3, y_2, x_1, x_0) \\
(\ldots, a_4, a_3, a_2, y_1, x_0) \\
(\ldots, a_4, a_3, a_2, a_1, y_0) \\
(\ldots, a_4, a_3, a_2, a_1, a_0) \\
(\ldots, a_4, a_3, a_2, a_1, z_0) \\
(\ldots, a_4, a_3, a_2, z_1, x_0) \\
(\ldots, a_4, a_3, z_2, x_1, x_0) \\
(\ldots, a_4, z_3, x_2, x_1, x_0) \\
\vdots
\end{array}$$

The dots above and below the array denote the further continuation of the array; the dots inside the complexes indicate the presence of elements a_m; every complex except the middle one represents (for $x_m \varepsilon A_m$, $y_m \varepsilon B_m$, $z_m \varepsilon C_m$) a whole set of such complexes, which is to be ordered lexicographically; these sets, considered as summands ordered from above to below, constitute the entire set $A(a)$. We thus obtain as the type of $A(a)$ the expression

$$\begin{aligned}\alpha(a) = \cdots &+ \alpha_0\alpha_1\alpha_2\beta_3 + \alpha_0\alpha_1\beta_2 + \alpha_0\beta_1 + \beta_0 + 1 \\ &+ \gamma_0 + \alpha_0\gamma_1 + \alpha_0\alpha_1\gamma_2 + \alpha_0\alpha_1\alpha_2\gamma_3 + \cdots;\end{aligned}$$

we see how the expression is exhibited by means of a summation extending to both *the left and the right* as, in a certain sense, the limit of the partial products

$$\begin{aligned}
\alpha_0 &= \beta_0 + 1 + \gamma_0 \\
\alpha_0\alpha_1 &= \alpha_0(\beta_1 + 1 + \gamma_1) = \alpha_0\beta_1 + \alpha_0 + \alpha_0\gamma_1 \\
&= \alpha_0\beta_1 + \beta_0 + 1 + \gamma_0 + \alpha_0\gamma_1 \\
\alpha_0\alpha_1\alpha_2 &= \alpha_0\alpha_1\beta_2 + \alpha_0\beta_1 + \beta_0 + 1 + \gamma_0 + \alpha_0\gamma_1 + \alpha_0\alpha_1\gamma_2 \\
&\cdots
\end{aligned}$$

The similarity with the genesis of the Cantor products (§ 14) is unmistakable; in fact, these products are actually included as special cases in our general concept of product. For, if we take all the A_m to be well ordered and let the a_m be their first elements; then we must set $\beta_m = 0$, $\alpha_m = 1 + \gamma_m$, so that

$$\alpha(a) = 1 + \gamma_0 + \alpha_0\gamma_1 + \alpha_0\alpha_1\gamma_2 + \cdots$$

and (assuming all $\alpha_m > 1$, $\gamma_m > 0$) this is, in the sense of Cantor,

$$\alpha_0\alpha_1\alpha_2 \ldots = \lim \alpha_0\alpha_1 \ldots \alpha_m.$$

In general, the Cantor products are the types of our classes $A(a)$ if it is assumed that the exponent N and the sets A_m are well ordered and that the complex a consists of the first elements a_m of the A_m; this fact, which is not difficult to prove, also explains the circumstance (p. 78) that the Cantor products do not have to have the cardinality of the full products A, of which the $A(a)$ are after all only subsets.

We can partition these classes $A(a)$ further, and thus obtain new product-like sets, as long as we take the cardinality of the set $M(a, b)$ into account. Let us write

$$a \equiv b(\omega_\xi)$$

if the set $M(a, b)$ is well-ordered and of type $< \omega_\xi$ (or of cardinality $< \aleph_\xi$) where ω_ξ denotes a beginning number; by (1), this stronger congruence is also transitive and induces a partition into classes $A_\xi(a)$, where for $\xi < \eta$, $A_\xi(a)$ is a subset of $A_\eta(a)$; for sufficiently large ξ these classes coincide with the $A(a)$. The smallest class $A_0(a)$, defined by $a \equiv b(\omega)$, consists of those complexes that differ from a at only finitely many places; for well-ordered exponents this already coincides with $A(a)$. If the argument M is well ordered, then there is only one class $A(a) = A$; but even in this case A can split into smaller classes $A_\xi(a)$. In the case of equal factors $A_m = B$ we obtain corresponding sets, whose *power character*, however, remains adequately preserved only when the complex a is allowed to consist entirely of equal elements $a_m = b$.

Limitations of space forbid further investigation of the generalized concept of product. Nevertheless, we did not wish to be guilty of keeping from the reader the fact that all the various formations of products he has become acquainted with can be subsumed under one overall concept as well as an explanation of how this is done.

CHAPTER V

SYSTEMS OF SETS

§ 17. Rings and Fields

For the sake of clarity, we shall call a set of sets a *system* of sets; we shall denote systems of sets by capital German letters. $M \varepsilon \mathfrak{M}$ thus means that the set M is an element of the system $\mathfrak{M}$. The sets M under consideration are pure sets, without relations (order) between their elements, so that in this respect we have returned to the point of view of the first two chapters; nevertheless the knowledge of ordinal numbers that we have since acquired will be useful to us and, on occasion, indispensable. We shall direct our attention, in particular, to certain largest and smallest systems of sets which, in accordance with rules to be described, can have no elements adjoined to or removed from them.

1. Rings. *A system of sets will be called a ring*[1] *if the sum and the intersection of any two sets of the system are themselves sets of the system.* The same is then true for any finite number of sets of the system. A ring is thus in a sense a largest system of sets — one that cannot be extended by the operations of taking sums and intersections (of a finite number of elements).

Examples. The system of all subsets of a given set is a ring. If $I = [\alpha\beta)$ denotes the interval $\alpha \leqq x < \beta$ of the real axis, then the sums

$$S = I_1 + I_2 + \ldots + I_n$$

of a finite number of disjoint I constitute a ring if the null set is included. For, the intersection of two I is an I or is 0, and it follows from the distributive law that the intersection of two S is an S. If we enclose S in an I, then clearly $I - S$ is an S. From this it follows that $I - (S_1 \dot{+} S_2) = (I - S_1)(I - S_2)$ is an S, and its complement is in I, so that $S_1 \dot{+} S_2$ is also an S. Incidentally, the difference $S - S_1$ of two S is also an S, for if we enclose S in an I then $S(I - S_1) = S - S_1$ is an S.

Given an arbitrary system of sets $\mathfrak{M}$, there exists a uniquely determined smallest ring $\geqq \mathfrak{M}$.

[1] The names ring and field are used because of some slight analogy to the similarly-named concepts of Number Theory.

In the above examples, we could define this ring — that is to say, the sets belonging to it — very easily. But, in anticipation of less elementary cases that will arise later, we give a general existence proof. There certainly do exist rings $\geqq \mathfrak{M}$; for if S is the sum of all the sets $\varepsilon\, \mathfrak{M}$, then the system $\mathfrak{S}$ of all subsets of S is a ring containing $\mathfrak{M}$. Since the intersection of any number of rings is obviously itself a ring, it follows that the intersection $\mathfrak{R}_0$ of all rings $\mathfrak{R}$ for which $\mathfrak{M} \leqq \mathfrak{R} \leqq \mathfrak{S}$ is a ring containing $\mathfrak{M}$. This ring is the smallest ring possible; that is to say, it is contained in *every* ring $\mathfrak{R}$ containing $\mathfrak{M}$, since $\mathfrak{M} \leqq \mathfrak{R}\mathfrak{S} \leqq \mathfrak{S}$ and hence $\mathfrak{R}_0 \leqq \mathfrak{R}\mathfrak{S} \leqq \mathfrak{R}$.

This smallest of the rings containing $\mathfrak{M}$, referred to henceforth as $\mathfrak{R}$, can obviously be constructed as follows: It consists of the finite sums

$$R = D_1 \dot{+} D_2 \dot{+} \ldots \dot{+} D_n,$$

whose summands, in turn, are of the form

$$D = M_1 M_2 \ldots M_m,$$

that is, are intersections of finitely many sets M ($\varepsilon\, \mathfrak{M}$). It is clear that the sets R so defined belong to $\mathfrak{R}$; but they themselves already constitute a ring (which is therefore $\mathfrak{R}$), since it follows from the associative law that the sum of two R is itself an R and from the distributive law that the intersection of two R is itself an R.

It is clear that the operations of sum and intersection can also be applied in the reverse order, so that $\mathfrak{R}$ consists of the intersections

$$R = S_1 S_2 \ldots S_n$$

of finitely many sets S which in turn are sums

$$S = M_1 \dot{+} M_2 \dot{+} \ldots \dot{+} M_m$$

of a finite number of sets M.

2. Fields. *A system of sets will be called a field if the sum, intersection, and difference of two sets of the system are themselves sets of the system.*

In taking the difference, the subtrahend must, as usual, be assumed a subset of the minuend. Furthermore, it would suffice to impose the requirement of the definition only on the sum and the difference, since the intersection can be defined in terms of these two operations (p. 18). A field is a fortiori a ring.

Example. The sums of intervals S in the above example constitute a field, as we have already proved. If, in constructing our example, we had used instead of half-open intervals $I = [\alpha, \beta)$ either open intervals (α, β) or closed intervals $[\alpha, \beta]$, then the sets S would still form a ring but would no longer form a field.

Exactly as in the case of a ring, we can see that there exists a smallest field $\mathfrak{K}$ containing any given system of sets $\mathfrak{M}$; but the construction of its elements is, in this case, not quite so trivial. Since $\mathfrak{K}$ contains the null set if it contains any sets whatever, we begin by assuming that the null set is already contained in $\mathfrak{M}$: furthermore, $\mathfrak{K}$ contains the smallest ring $\mathfrak{R} \geqq \mathfrak{M}$ and is also the smallest field containing $\mathfrak{R}$. Hence we may as well suppose $\mathfrak{M}$ to be a ring that contains the null set. We then consider a finite number of sets $M_1 \geqq M_2 \geqq \cdots \geqq M_n$ or, to simplify our notation, a decreasing sequence of sets M

$$(1) \qquad M_1 \geqq M_2 \geqq M_3 \geqq \cdots$$

with ultimately vanishing terms. The differences $M_1 - M_2, M_2 - M_3, \ldots$ are disjoint. The set

$$(2) \qquad A = (M_1 - M_2) + (M_3 - M_4) + (M_5 - M_6) + \cdots$$

will be called a (finite) *chain of differences* of the system $\mathfrak{M}$. Clearly, all these sets A will be elements of $\mathfrak{K}$; we shall show that as they stand they constitute a field, which is therefore the field $\mathfrak{K}$ we have been looking for.

The complements $M - A$ are themselves sets A. If we write

$$A = MA = (MM_1 - MM_2) + (MM_3 - MM_4) + \cdots,$$

which once more is a representation of the form (2), then we see that the only statement needed for the proof is the following: If $M_0 \geqq M_1$, then $M_0 - A$ is an A. But then

$$(3) \qquad M_0 = (M_0 - M_1) + (M_1 - M_2) + (M_2 - M_3) + \cdots,$$
$$(4) \qquad M_0 - A = (M_0 - M_1) + (M_2 - M_3) + \cdots,$$

and the result is proved. Finally, it should be noted that for every A there exists an $M \geqq A$: for example, M_1.

The intersection of two A's is an A. Here a change of notation is desirable; we set

$$(5) \qquad \begin{cases} A = (M_0 - M_0') + (M_1 - M_1') + \cdots \\ B = (N_0 - N_0') + (N_1 - N_1') + \cdots \\ M_0 \geqq M_0' \geqq M_1 \geqq M_1' \geqq \cdots \\ N_0 \geqq N_0' \geqq N_1 \geqq N_1' \geqq \cdots \end{cases}$$

with ultimately vanishing[1] M_i, M'_i, N_k, N'_k which belong to the system $\mathfrak{M}$.

If we now define

$$(6)\qquad \begin{cases} P_l = \underset{i+k=l}{\mathfrak{S}} \; M_i N_k \\ P'_l = \underset{i+k=l}{\mathfrak{S}} \; (M'_i N_k \dotplus M_i N'_k), \end{cases}$$

that is, $P_0 = M_0 N_0, \quad P_1 = M_0 N_1 \dotplus M_1 N_0, \ldots$

$$P'_0 = M'_0 N_0 \dotplus M_0 N'_0, \ldots$$

(where the subscripts i, k, l range over the integers, 0, 1, 2, . . .), then the P_l, P'_l belong to the ring $\mathfrak{M}$ and ultimately vanish. Furthermore, $P_l \geqq P'_l$, and if we take into account that

$$P_{l+1} = \underset{i+k=l}{\mathfrak{S}} (M_{i+1} N_k \dotplus M_i N_{k+1}),$$

we have $P'_l \geqq P_{l+1}$, so that

$$P_0 \geqq P'_0 \geqq P_1 \geqq P'_1 \geqq \cdots.$$

We shall now show that

$$(7)\qquad AB = (P_0 - P'_0) + (P_1 - P'_1) + \cdots$$

and even that, term by term,

$$(8)\qquad \sum_{i+k=l} (M_i - M'_i)(N_k - N'_k) = P_l - P'_l.$$

Let us denote the sum on the left-hand side of (8) by C_l. If $x \,\varepsilon\, C_l$, then x belongs to one of the summands, say $x \,\varepsilon\, (M_{i_0} - M'_{i_0})(N_{k_0} - N'_{k_0})$, so that $x \,\varepsilon\, M_{i_0} N_{k_0} \leqq P_l$, while, at the same time, $x \,\bar{\varepsilon}\, P'_l$. For if $i + k = i_0 + k_0 = l$, then either $i \geqq i_0$ and $M'_i N_k \leqq M'_{i_0}$ or $i < i_0$, $k > k_0$, and $M'_i N_k \leqq N_{k_0+1} \leqq N'_{k_0}$; thus $x \,\bar{\varepsilon}\, M'_i N_k$, and similarly $x \,\bar{\varepsilon}\, M_i N'_k$. Hence $C_l \leqq P_l - P'_l$. Conversely, if $x \,\varepsilon\, P_l - P'_l \leqq P_l$ and, say, $x \,\varepsilon\, M_i N_k$, then $x \,\bar{\varepsilon}\, M'_i$, since otherwise we should have $x \,\varepsilon\, M'_i N_k \leqq P'_l$ and similarly $x \,\bar{\varepsilon}\, N'_k$, $x \,\varepsilon\, (M_i - M'_i)(N_k - N'_k) \leqq C_l$, so that $P_l - P'_l \leqq C_l$. Thus (8) and (7) are proved; and it follows that AB is an A.

The difference of two A's is an A. For $A \geqq A_1$, we choose $M \geqq A$. Then $A - A_1 = A(M - A_1)$ is an A.

The sum of two A's is an A. For A_1, A_2, we choose sets M_1 and M_2 containing them and let $M = M_1 \dotplus M_2$; then

$$M - (M - A_1)(M - A_2) = A_1 \dotplus A_2$$

is an A.

We have thus proved that the A's constitute a field.

[1] This assumption, however, is not essential here; the infinite chains of differences (2) have the intersection property too.

3. Extended fields. In anticipation of a later application (§ 30, II and III), we wish to extend our chains of differences to infinity. We let Greek letters range over the ordinal numbers $< \omega_\mu$, where ω_μ is a fixed *beginning number*, the first ordinal number of cardinality $\aleph_\mu$. From the system $\mathfrak{M}$, which is again assumed to be a ring containing the null set, we choose sets M to form a decreasing well-ordered sequence of type ω_μ

$$(9) \qquad M_1 \geqq M_2 \geqq \cdots \geqq M_{\omega+1} \geqq M_{\omega+2} \geqq \cdots,$$

whose components are thus denoted by $M_{\xi+1}$ and use them to form the set

$$(10) \quad A = (M_1 - M_2) + (M_3 - M_4) + \cdots + (M_{\omega+1} - M_{\omega+2}) + \cdots = \sum_\xi (M_{2\xi+1} - M_{2\xi+2}),$$

where it must be remembered that the ordinal numbers are either even (2ξ) or odd ($2\xi + 1$), the limit ordinals, in particular, being even. We again call A a *chain of differences* of the system $\mathfrak{M}$, and specifically, a chain of type ω_μ if all the sets (9) are non-empty, and of type $\eta < \omega_\mu$ if $M_{\eta+1}$ is the first vanishing set occurring in (9). Of course, the ordinal type depends not only on the set itself but also on the representation chosen. We now assert:

1. *If the system* $\mathfrak{M}$ (which is a ring containing the null set) *has, in addition, the property that the intersection of less than* $\aleph_\mu$ *sets* M *is an* M, *then the chains of differences (over* $\mathfrak{M}$*) of type* $< \omega_\mu$ *constitute a field.*

Proof: $M - A$ *is also an* A. As above, it suffices to show that $M_0 - A$ is an A for $M_0 \geqq M_1$. In addition, for the limit ordinals $\eta < \omega_\mu$ we define the sets

$$M_\eta = \mathfrak{D}_{\xi<\eta} M_{\xi+1},$$

which are themselves sets M because of the intersection property assumed in our hypothesis. Now the totality of the sets M_ξ constitutes a decreasing well-ordered system

$$M_0 \geqq M_1 \geqq M_2 \geqq \cdots \geqq M_\omega \geqq M_{\omega+1} \geqq \cdots \geqq M_{\omega 2} \geqq \cdots,$$

in which every set whose index is a limit ordinal is the intersection of all the preceding sets. Next we observe that

$$(11) \qquad M_0 = \sum_\xi (M_\xi - M_{\xi+1});$$

for, since the M_ξ are ultimately $= 0$, there is a first M_ζ with $x \bar{\varepsilon} M_\zeta$ for every $x \varepsilon M_0$, where ζ is > 0 and is not a limit ordinal, so that $\zeta = \xi + 1$ and $x \varepsilon M_\xi - M_{\xi+1}$. If we now separate the even and odd indices it follows that

$$(12)\quad M_0 - A = \sum_\xi (M_{2\xi} - M_{2\xi+1}) \\ = (M_0 - M_1) + (M_2 - M_3) + \cdots + (M_\omega - M_{\omega+1}) + \cdots.$$

The Intersection of two A's is itself an A.[1] Once more we write as in (5)

$$(13)\quad \begin{cases} A = \sum_\xi (M_\xi - M'_\xi) \\ B = \sum_\xi (N_\xi - N'_\xi) \\ M_0 \geqq M'_0 \geqq \cdots \geqq M_\omega \geqq M'_\omega \geqq \cdots \\ N_0 \geqq N'_0 \geqq \cdots \geqq N_\omega \geqq N'_\omega \geqq \cdots. \end{cases}$$

In order to generalize (6) we have to make use of the *natural sum.* We define

$$(14)\quad \begin{cases} P_\zeta = \overset{\zeta}{\mathfrak{S}}\, M_\xi N_\eta \\ P'_\zeta = \overset{\zeta}{\mathfrak{S}}\, (M'_\xi N_\eta \dot{+} M_\xi N'_\eta), \end{cases}$$

where $\overset{\zeta}{\mathfrak{S}}$ means that we are to sum over the pairs ξ, η with $\sigma(\xi, \eta) = \zeta$. Since there are at most a finite number of these, the sets P and P' belong to the ring $\mathfrak{M}$. From $\xi < \omega_\mu$ and $\eta < \omega_\mu$ it follows also that $\zeta < \omega_\mu$ (p. 84, footnote), and it is easily seen that P and P' must ultimately vanish provided that M, M' and N, N' do so. Furthermore

$$P_0 \geqq P'_0 \geqq P_1 \geqq P'_1 \geqq \cdots \geqq P_\omega \geqq P'_\omega \geqq \cdots.$$

In fact, $P_\zeta \geqq P'_\zeta$ follows immediately; in addition $P'_{\zeta_0} \geqq P_\zeta$ for $\zeta_0 < \zeta$. For if $x \varepsilon P_\zeta$ and if x is an element of, say, $M_\xi N_\eta$ with $\sigma(\xi, \eta) = \zeta$, then there exists (p. 81) a pair of numbers ξ_0, η_0 with $\sigma(\xi_0, \eta_0) = \zeta_0$ and $\xi_0 \leqq \xi$, $\eta_0 \leqq \eta$; if $\xi_0 < \xi$, then we have $M_\xi \leqq M'_{\xi_0}$, $N_\eta \leqq N_{\eta_0}$ and $x \varepsilon P'_{\zeta_0}$, and similarly for $\eta_0 < \eta$.

Now once again we have

$$(15)\quad AB = \sum_\zeta (P_\zeta - P'_\zeta)$$

and even, term by term,

$$(16)\quad \overset{\zeta}{\Sigma} (M_\xi - M'_\xi)(N_\eta - N'_\eta) = P_\zeta - P'_\zeta;$$

the proof has the same form as the proof of (8), because the natural sum has all the properties of ordinary sums (in particular: if $\sigma(\xi, \eta) = \sigma(\xi_0, \eta_0)$ and $\xi < \xi_0$, then $\eta > \eta_0$).

As in the case of the finite chains of differences, it follows also that the sum and difference of two A's it itself an A. This proves I.

[1] For this it suffices that $\mathfrak{M}$ be a ring; even the hypothesis of the ultimate vanishing of the sets (9) can be dispensed with, and the intersection of two chains of type $\leqq \omega_\mu$ is also such a chain.

For $\omega_\mu = \omega_0 = \omega$, where $\mathfrak{M}$ is only required to be a ring, we again obtain the result of the preceding subsection: The finite chains of differences constitute a field (the smallest field containing $\mathfrak{M}$). For $\omega_\mu = \omega_1 = \Omega$ it follows that chains of differences which are at most countable (of type $< \Omega$) constitute a field, provided that the intersection of countably many M is an M.

If the intersection of any number of M is an M, then all the chains of differences over $\mathfrak{M}$ form a field. For, all these chains of differences (each having a fixed representation) are of type $< \omega_\mu$ provided that ω_μ is taken sufficiently large.

§ 18. Borel Systems

1. The σ and δ processes. We have called a system of sets a ring if it contains the sum and intersection of two (or any finite number of) sets of the system. If we now extend this to the sum and intersection of a *countable* number of sets, we arrive at the concept of a *Borel System.* But the simple method that enabled us to construct the smallest ring containing a given system of sets $\mathfrak{M}$ does not allow of generalization to the present case. For if we were to try, as in the earlier situation (p. 90), to form the intersections

$$D = M_1 M_2 M_3 \ldots$$

of sequences of sets M ($\varepsilon\, \mathfrak{M}$) and to form from them the sums

$$R = D_1 \dot{+} D_2 \dot{+} D_3 \dot{+} \cdots$$

of sequences of sets D, these R would nevertheless by no means form a Borel system: for the sum of a countable number of R is certainly itself an R, by the associative law, but the intersection of a countable number of R, written as a sum by means of the distributive law, is a sum of an *uncountable* number of D and so in general is not an R.

This complication makes it seem advisable, as a first step, to separate the conditions imposed on sums from those on intersections.

A system of sets will be called a $\begin{Bmatrix} \sigma\text{-system} \\ \delta\text{-system} \end{Bmatrix}$ *if the* $\begin{Bmatrix} \text{sum} \\ \text{intersection} \end{Bmatrix}$ *of every sequence of sets of the system is a member of the system.*

We begin with some remarks about σ-systems which are then easily applied to δ-systems. In a σ-system the sum

$$A \dot{+} B \dot{+} A \dot{+} B \dot{+} \cdots = A \dot{+} B$$

of two sets as well as of a finite number of sets of the system also belongs to the system.

The smallest σ-system over a given system of sets $\mathfrak{M}$ (whose existence we deduce in the same way as we did that of the smallest ring) will be called $\mathfrak{M}_\sigma$. It is formed by the sets

$$(1) \qquad M_\sigma = M_1 \dotplus M_2 \dotplus M_3 \dotplus \cdots = \mathfrak{S} M_n \qquad (M_n \,\varepsilon\, \mathfrak{M}),$$

that is, by the sums of sequences of sets $M \,\varepsilon\, \mathfrak{M}$. For the M_σ must belong to $\mathfrak{M}_\sigma$, while at the same time they themselves already constitute a σ-system (transformation of a double sequence into a simple sequence).

If $\mathfrak{M}$ is a ring, then $\mathfrak{M}_\sigma$ is also a ring; for, by the distributive law, the intersection of two M_σ is an M_σ. Furthermore, in this case the M_σ can be written as sums of *increasing* sequences of sets M, for it follows from (1) that

$$M_\sigma = \mathfrak{S} S_n, \quad S_n = M_1 \dotplus M_2 \dotplus \cdots \dotplus M_n,$$

where the S_n are themselves sets M, and $S_1 \leqq S_2 \leqq \cdots$.

In a δ-system, the intersection of a finite number of sets of the system also belongs to the system. The smallest δ-system $\mathfrak{M}_\delta$ over $\mathfrak{M}$ is formed by the sets

$$(2) \qquad M_\delta = M_1 M_2 M_3 \ldots = \mathfrak{D} M_n \qquad (M_n \,\varepsilon\, \mathfrak{M});$$

the M_δ are intersections of sequences of sets $M \,\varepsilon\, \mathfrak{M}$. If $\mathfrak{M}$ is a ring, then $\mathfrak{M}_\delta$ is a ring, and the M_δ can be represented as intersections of *decreasing* sequences of sets M:

$$M_\delta = \mathfrak{D} D_n, \qquad D_n = M_1 M_2 \cdots M_n.$$

A system of sets which is at one and the same time a σ-system and a δ-system will be called a $(\sigma\delta)$-system, or a Borel system.

For a given system of sets there exists once more a smallest Borel system $\mathfrak{B} = \mathfrak{M}_{(\sigma\delta)}$ containing it. The sets B belonging to it are called the *Borel sets* generated by $\mathfrak{M}$, or by the sets $M \,\varepsilon\, \mathfrak{M}$.

We can represent these sets in the following way. Let $i, k, l, m, \ldots$ range over the natural numbers, and define

$$S = \mathfrak{S}_i D_i, \quad D_i = \mathfrak{D}_k S_{ik}, \quad S_{ik} = \mathfrak{S}_l D_{ikl}, \quad D_{ikl} = \mathfrak{D}_m S_{iklm}, \ldots,$$

with the proviso that for every sequence of natural numbers $i, k, l, m, \ldots$ the corresponding sequence of sets $D_i, S_{ik}, D_{ikl}, S_{iklm} \ldots$ is ultimately to contain only sets M.

Similarly, we begin the alternate formation of sums and intersections with the latter, and we let

$$D = \mathfrak{D}_i S_i, \quad S_i = \mathfrak{S}_k D_{ik}, \quad D_{ik} = \mathfrak{D}_l S_{ikl}, \quad S_{ikl} = \mathfrak{S}_m D_{iklm}, \ldots$$

and require that every sequence $S_i, D_{ik}, S_{ikl}, D_{iklm}, \ldots$ ultimately contain only sets M. Then the sets S, as well as the sets D, are the Borel sets generated by $\mathfrak{M}$.

For since the D_i of the first group of formulas are arbitrary sets D of the second group, it follows that every D_σ (the sum of a sequence of sets D) is an S and vice versa and that, in particular, every $D = D \dotplus D \dotplus \ldots$ is itself an S. Similarly, the S_δ are identical with the D, and every S is a D. Hence the S are identical with the D and form a Borel system that contains the sets $M\,(S = D_i = S_{ik} = \ldots = M)$; the smallest Borel system $\mathfrak{B}$ is contained in it; that is, every set B is an S.

Conversely, every S is also a B. For if the S were not a B, there would have to be at least one D_i which is not a B, then at least one S_{ik}, one D_{ikl}, and so forth, so that there would have to be at least one sequence of integers $i, k, l, \ldots$ for which no B occurred in the sequence $D_i, S_{ik}, D_{ikl}, \ldots$. But this would contradict the requirement that the sequence is ultimately to contain only sets M.

The representation thus obtained, which yields all the Borel sets at one stroke, does not, however, give us as clear an idea of these sets as we should like, and we shall therefore try to give a stepwise construction of the Borel system $\mathfrak{B}$. If the notation of (1) and (2) is to be extended in a natural way, then $\mathfrak{B}$ must in any case contain the following sets.

(3)
- the sets M $(\varepsilon\, \mathfrak{M})$,
- the sums M_σ of sequences of sets M,
- the intersections $M_{\sigma\delta}$ of sequences of sets M_σ,
- the sums $M_{\sigma\delta\sigma}$ of sequences of sets $M_{\sigma\delta}$,
- etc.,

where we alternate the formation of sums and intersections, since — to take one example — the sets $M_{\sigma\sigma}$, which are sums of sequences of sets M_σ, are identical with the sets M_σ. Similarly, if we begin with intersections instead of sums, we must include in our Borel System the following sets

(4)
- the sets M $(\varepsilon\, \mathfrak{M})$,
- the intersections M_δ of sequences of sets M,
- the sums $M_{\delta\sigma}$ of sequences of sets M_δ,
- the intersections $M_{\delta\sigma\delta}$ of sequences of sets $M_{\delta\sigma}$,
- etc.

The systems formed by these sets ought to be denoted by

$$\mathfrak{M}, \mathfrak{M}_\sigma, \mathfrak{M}_{\sigma\delta}, \mathfrak{M}_{\sigma\delta\sigma}, \ldots \text{ or } \mathfrak{M}, \mathfrak{M}_\delta, \mathfrak{M}_{\delta\sigma}, \mathfrak{M}_{\delta\sigma\delta}, \ldots$$

(hence the parentheses in the notation $\mathfrak{B} = \mathfrak{M}_{(\sigma\delta)}$ may not be omitted).

By way of example, we remark that the upper and lower limits (p. 22)

$$\overline{M} = \overline{\text{Lim}}\ M_n = S_1 S_2 S_3 \ldots, \qquad S_n = M_n \dotplus M_{n+1} \dotplus M_{n+2} \dotplus \cdots$$
$$\underline{M} = \underline{\text{Lim}}\ M_n = D_1 \dotplus D_2 \dotplus D_3 \dotplus \cdots, \qquad D_n = M_n M_{n+1} M_{n+2} \cdots$$

are Borel sets generated by the sets M_n $(\varepsilon\, \mathfrak{M})$; the sets S_n and D_n are sets M_σ and M_δ, the upper limit $\overline{M}$ is an $M_{\sigma\delta}$, the lower $\underline{M}$ an $M_{\delta\sigma}$; the limit of a convergent sequence is both of these simultaneously.

Even though we have now formed all the sets (3) or (4) having a finite number of indices, σ and δ, the Borel system is by no means yet complete. In continuation of the procedure of, say, (3) we must next adjoin the intersections

$$N = M M_\sigma M_{\sigma\delta} M_{\sigma\delta\sigma} \cdots,$$

then the N_σ, $N_{\sigma\delta}$, $N_{\sigma\delta\sigma}$, ..., and finally again,

$$P = N N_\sigma N_{\sigma\delta} N_{\sigma\delta\sigma} \cdots,$$

and so on. To give this "and so on" a precise meaning we avail ourselves of the *ordinal numbers.*

2. The construction of the Borel System $\mathfrak{B}$. Let ξ and η be ordinal numbers $< \Omega$, where $\Omega = \omega_1$ is the beginning number of the class $Z(\aleph_1)$. We again distinguish between even ordinals 2ξ and odd ordinals $2\xi + 1$. We now assign to each ξ a system $\mathfrak{A}^\xi$ of sets A^ξ by means of the following inductive rule:

(α) *The sets A^0 are the sets M $(\mathfrak{A}^0 = \mathfrak{M})$;*
The sets A^η are the sums of sequences of sets A^ξ $(\xi < \eta)$ if $\eta > 0$ is odd and the intersections if ξ is even.

Then the systems of all sets A^ξ so defined is the smallest Borel system $\mathfrak{B}$ containing $\mathfrak{M}$.

It is clear that all the sets A^ξ must belong to $\mathfrak{B}$. It only remains to show that these sets do indeed constitute a Borel System. If a sequence of sets A^{ξ_1}, A^{ξ_2}, ... is now given, let ξ be the ordinal number immediately following $\xi_1, \xi_2, \ldots$ (because of § 15, IV, we have $\xi < \Omega$). One of the numbers ξ, $\xi + 1$ is even and the other odd, and so both the sum and the intersection of the given sequence occur among the sets A^ξ, $A^{\xi+1}$. From this we see that there would have been no point in extending the definition to $\xi \geqq \Omega$ (for then we should have found $\mathfrak{A}^\Omega = \mathfrak{A}^{\Omega+1} = \cdots = \mathfrak{B}$).

The systems $\mathfrak{A}^\xi$ increase with increasing index; that is, $\mathfrak{A}^\xi \leqq \mathfrak{A}^\eta$ for $\xi < \eta$. For since $M = M \dot{+} M \dot{+} \ldots = MM \ldots$, every A^ξ is also an $A^{\xi+1}$, $A^{\xi+2}$,.... From this it follows that the $A^{\xi+1}$ could also have been defined as sums or intersections (depending on whether ξ is even or odd) of sequences of sets A^ξ; for a limit ordinal η the A^η are intersections of sequences of sets A^ξ $(\xi < \eta)$.

Thus, the sets (3) begin the induction; the

$$A^0, \quad A^1, \quad A^2, \quad A^3, \ldots$$

are identical with the $\quad M, \; M_\sigma, \; M_{\sigma\delta}, \; M_{\sigma\delta\sigma}, \ldots;$

then we get the A^ω as intersections of sequences of preceding sets, the $A^{\omega+1}$ as sums of sequences of sets A^ω, and so forth. We call the $\mathfrak{A}^\xi$ *Borel classes* and say that a set belongs *exactly* to the class $\mathfrak{A}^\eta$ if it belongs to that class but not to any class preceding it — that is, if it is an A^η but not an A^ξ (for $\xi < \eta$). (It is generally customary, although for us somewhat inconvenient, to take the classes as disjoint, that is, to call $\mathfrak{A}^\eta - \underset{\xi<\eta}{\mathfrak{S}} \mathfrak{A}^\xi$ a class.)

A slightly different way of generating $\mathfrak{B}$ is derived from the above by interchanging the roles played by sum and intersection, so that the system $\mathfrak{B}^\xi$ of sets B^ξ are defined as follows:

(β) *The sets B^0 are the sets M $(\mathfrak{B}^0 = \mathfrak{M})$;*
The sets B^η are the intersections, if η is odd, and the sums, if $\eta > 0$ is even, of sequences of sets B^ξ $(\xi < \eta)$.

All the sets B^ξ also form the smallest Borel system $\mathfrak{B}$ containing $\mathfrak{M}$. The $B^{\xi+1}$ are the intersections or sums (depending on whether ξ is even or odd) of sequences of sets B^ξ. The induction this time starts with the sets (4); that is, the sets

$$B^0, \quad B^1, \quad B^2, \quad B^3, \ldots$$

are identical with the sets $M, \; M_\delta, \; M_{\delta\sigma}, \; M_{\delta\sigma\delta}, \ldots$.

These systems of sets, too, are called Borel classes. It is easy to see that every A^ξ is a $B^{\xi+1}$ and every B^ξ an $A^{\xi+1}$; the $A^1 = M_\sigma$, for example, occur among the $B^2 = M_{\delta\sigma}$ and the $B^1 = M_\delta$ among the $A^2 = M_{\sigma\delta}$.

It may happen, of course, that not *all* the sets A^ξ or B^ξ are really needed to complete the Borel System; that is, it may happen that some $\mathfrak{A}^\xi$ is, as it stands, the whole Borel system. This depends on the given system $\mathfrak{M}$: if, for instance, $\mathfrak{M}$ itself happens to be a Borel system, then $\mathfrak{A}^0 = \mathfrak{B}$ to begin with, and every extension is superfluous. We shall see later (§ 33, I), however, that it is just in the most important cases that every step gives rise to new sets and all the A^ξ are required for the formation of $\mathfrak{B}$. One additional remark: If for any $\xi \geqq 1$ it should happen that $\mathfrak{A}^\xi = \mathfrak{A}^{\xi+1}$, then $\mathfrak{A}^\xi = \mathfrak{B}$. For of the two systems $\mathfrak{A}^\xi$ and $\mathfrak{A}^{\xi+1}$, the one is a σ-system, and the other a δ-system; when they coincide, we have a Borel system.

3. Representation of Borel sets. We have seen (to continue with the second form) that every $B^{\xi+1}$ is an intersection, for even ξ, and a sum for odd ξ, of a sequence of sets B^ξ. If η is a limit ordinal, then

$$(5) \qquad B^\eta = C_1 \dot{+} C_2 \dot{+} \cdots \qquad (C_n \text{ a } B^{\xi_n} \text{ with } \xi_n < \eta);$$

but this form suffers from a certain lack of definiteness in that the ξ_n may depend on the set B^η which is to be represented, and we should like to transform it in such a way as to make the ξ_n a fixed sequence depending only on η (as was the case for $\eta = \xi + 1$, where we were able to choose $\xi_n = \xi = \eta - 1$). By way of example, we should like to transform a set B^ω, which is given, to begin with, in the form $B^\omega = B^{\xi_1} \dot{+} B^{\xi_2} \dot{+} \cdots$ with arbitrary finite indices ξ_n, into the special form $B^\omega = B^1 \dot{+} B^2 \dot{+} \cdots$, where $\xi_n = n$. If we choose a fixed sequence of ordinal numbers

$$1 \leqq \eta_1 < \eta_2 < \eta_3 < \cdots, \quad \lim \eta_n = \eta,$$

which depends only on the limit ordinal η, then we must show that every B^η can be represented in the special form

$$(6) \qquad B^\eta = B_1 \dot{+} B_2 \dot{+} \cdots \qquad (B_n \text{ a } B^{\eta_n}).$$

To transform (5) into (6) we can first make the indices ξ_n greater, since B^ξ is some $B^{\xi+1}$, etc.; and since for every $\xi < \eta$ there exists an n for which $\xi \leqq \eta_n$, we can choose the natural numbers $p < q < r < \ldots$ in such a way as to have $\xi_1 \leqq \eta_p$, $\xi_2 \leqq \eta_q$, $\xi_3 \leqq \eta_r$, ... If we then set $C_1 = B_p$, $C_2 = B_q$, $C_3 = B_r$, ..., we obtain in place of (5)

$$B^\eta = B_p \dot{+} B_q \dot{+} B_r \dot{+} \cdots,$$

where, for those n that occur in the formula, every B_n is a B^{η_n}. In order to arrive at the form (6) we still have to interpolate suitable summands B_n for the indices $n = 1, \ldots, p-1, p+1, \ldots$ that are still missing. Now every B^ξ for which $\xi \geqq 1$ certainly contains a subset of the form $M_\delta = B^1$. For the property of containing such a subset always carries over from an arbitrary set N to the sets N_σ and N_δ (N_δ contains a subset of the form $M_{\delta\delta} = M_\delta$) and thus carries over from the sets B^1 to the subsequent B^ξ. If, therefore, B is a subset of B^η of the form B^1, then the B_n that are to be interpolated may all be chosen equal to B; for since B_n is a B^1, it is also some B^{η_n}. This gives the form (6).

Let us now suppose that a unique set

(7) $$X = \Phi(M_1, M_2, M_3, \ldots)$$

is made to correspond, by some rule or other, to every sequence of sets $M_1, M_2, \ldots$ (say, for example, $X = M_1 M_2 M_3 \ldots$ or $X = M_1 + M_2 \dotplus M_3 \dotplus \ldots$), so that Φ denotes a single-valued function of the sets M_n. If the sets M_n are chosen from a given system of sets $\mathfrak{M}$ in every possible way, then X ranges over some system of sets $\mathfrak{X}$. Then we assert:

I. *For every $\xi \geqq 1$ a function Φ_ξ, depending only on ξ, can be determined in such a way that*

(8) $$X = \Phi_\xi(M_1, M_2, M_3, \ldots) \qquad (M_n \varepsilon \mathfrak{M})$$

represents precisely the Borel sets B^ξ generated by $\mathfrak{M}$.

The statement that X represents precisely the B^ξ is of course supposed to mean that X represents all the B^ξ and no other sets, or that X ranges over the system of sets

The proof is very simple. If we set

(9) $$\Phi_1(M_1, M_2, M_3, \ldots) = M_1 M_2 M_3 \ldots,$$

then $X = \Phi_1$ represents precisely the $M_\delta = B^1$.

If, further, the function Φ_ξ is already defined, then corresponding to the formation of the $B^{\xi+1}$ from the B^ξ we obtain a suitable function $\Phi_{\xi+1}$ in the following way. We divide the set of natural numbers into a countable number of subsets by means, say, of the dyadic scheme of p. 34. For odd ξ we then set

(10) $$\begin{cases} \Phi_{\xi+1}(M_1, M_2, M_3, \ldots) \\ = \Phi_\xi(M_1, M_3, M_5, \ldots) + \Phi_\xi(M_2, M_6, M_{10}, \ldots) \\ \qquad \dotplus \Phi_\xi(M_4, M_{12}, M_{20}, \ldots) \dotplus \cdots \end{cases}$$

and for even ξ

(11) $$\begin{cases} \Phi_{\xi+1}(M_1, M_2, M_3, \ldots) \\ = \Phi_\xi(M_1, M_3, M_5, \ldots)\, \Phi_\xi(M_2, M_6, M_{10}, \ldots)\, \Phi_\xi(M_4, M_{12}, M_{20}, \ldots) \ldots \end{cases}$$

For a limit ordinal η, finally, we set

(12) $$\begin{cases} \Phi_\eta(M_1, M_2, M_3, \cdots) \\ = \Phi_{\eta_1}(M_1, M_3, M_5, \ldots) \dotplus \Phi_{\eta_2}(M_2, M_6, M_{10}, \ldots) \\ \qquad \dotplus \Phi_{\eta_3}(M_4, M_{12}, M_{20}, \ldots) \dotplus \cdots \end{cases}$$

in conformity with the representation (6).

The functions Φ_ξ have now been defined by induction, and it is clear that they do the required job, for the separation of the indices on the right-hand side of the last three formulas — for example, in (10) and (11) — permits of each Φ_ξ being made into a pre-assigned B^ξ independently of the rest, so that $\Phi_{\xi+1}$ does in fact represent *all* the sets $B^{\xi+1}$; the same is true of (12). For instance

$$\Phi_2(M_1, M_2, M_3, \ldots)$$
$$= (M_1 M_3 M_5 \ldots) \dot{+} (M_2 M_6 M_{10} \ldots) \dot{+} (M_4 M_{12} M_{20} \ldots) \dot{+} \cdots$$

gives precisely the sets $M_{\delta\sigma} = B^2$ for $M_n \varepsilon \mathfrak{M}$.

Now the functions, inductively defined in (9) through (12), that occur here are all[1] of a special form. They are all *sums of intersections of subsequences of the sequence of sets* $M_1, M_2, \ldots$. These special functions Φ are thus formed as follows: We let the intersection

$$M_\nu = M_{n_1} M_{n_2} M_{n_3} \ldots$$

correspond to the sequence of increasing natural numbers

$$\nu = (n_1, n_2, n_3, \ldots);$$

then we let N be a set of such sequences and let

$$X = \mathfrak{S}_\nu^N M_\nu = \Phi(M_1, M_2, M_3, \ldots), \tag{13}$$

where the function symbol Φ and the set N correspond to one another. We call these frequently occurring functions *δs-functions.* If, as before, we now denote the formation of sums and intersections of *countably* many sets by σ and δ and of *arbitrarily* many sets by s and d, then in (13) every summand M_ν is some M_δ, the sum itself is an $M_{\delta s}$ (in case N is countable, an $M_{\delta\sigma}$; in case N contains only a single element, an M_δ). By interchanging the roles of sum and intersection we get, analogously, the *σd-functions,* the intersections of sums of subsequences of a sequence of sets; the complements of the sets (13) are an example of such functions.

Since we have made the claim that the functions Φ_ξ are δs-functions as in (13), we have to prove the following: For every $\xi \geqq 1$ there exists a set N_ξ depending only on ξ such that

[1] The sets B^0 could have been included in Theorem I using

$$\Phi_0(M_1, M_2, M_3, \ldots) = M_1,$$

but what follows below would not apply to them.

$$(14) \qquad \Phi_\xi(M_1, M_2, M_3, \ldots) = \mathfrak{S}_{\nu}^{N_\xi} M_\nu .$$

For example, N_1 consists of the single sequence $(1, 2, 3, \ldots)$; N_2 of the sequences $(1, 3, 5, \ldots)$, $(2, 6, 10, \ldots)$, $(4, 12, 20, \ldots)$, $\ldots$; and so forth. Let us now assume that (14) is true for some particular ξ; then

$$\Phi_\xi(M_1, \ M_3, \ M_5, \ldots) = \mathfrak{S}_{\alpha}^{A_\xi} M_\alpha ,$$
$$\Phi_\xi(M_2, \ M_6, \ M_{10}, \ldots) = \mathfrak{S}_{\beta}^{B_\xi} M_\beta ,$$
$$\Phi_\xi(M_4, \ M_{12}, \ M_{20}, \ldots) = \mathfrak{S}_{\gamma}^{\Gamma_\xi} M_\gamma ,$$
$$\ldots\ldots\ldots\ldots\ldots\ldots ,$$

where a sequence $\alpha = (2n_1 - 1, 2n_2 - 1, 2n_3 - 1, \ldots)$ consisting entirely of odd numbers corresponds to each $\nu = (n_1, n_2, n_3, \ldots)$, and thus a fixed set A_ξ to the set N_ξ; β, B_ξ, γ, Γ_ξ, $\ldots$ are to be understood analogously. If, then, (10) is valid, we have

$$\Phi_{\xi+1}(M_1, M_2, M_3, \ldots) = \mathfrak{S}_{\nu}^{N_{\xi+1}} M_\nu , \qquad N_{\xi+1} = A_\xi + B_\xi + \Gamma_\xi + \cdots ,$$

and the set N_η is determined analogously in the case of formula (12). In the formation of the intersections (11) there appears first, by the distributive law, the sum[1]

$$\mathfrak{S}\, M_\alpha M_\beta M_\gamma \ldots ,$$

and the summation extends over $\alpha \varepsilon A_\xi$, $\beta \varepsilon B_\xi$, $\gamma \varepsilon \Gamma_\xi$, $\ldots$; that is, the sequence $(\alpha, \beta, \gamma, \ldots)$ of sequences ranges over the set product $(A_\xi, B_\xi, \Gamma_\xi, \ldots)$. Any sequence of sequences determines a single sequence ν simply by the uniting of the disjoint sequences α, β, γ, $\ldots$, and the product determines in this sense a set $N_{\xi+1}$ of sequences ν, whence it then follows that

$$\Phi_{\xi+1}(M_1, M_2, M_3, \ldots) = \mathfrak{S}_{\nu}^{N_{\xi+1}} M_\nu .$$

We have thus proved the following, more precise, version of Theorem I:

II. *For every $\xi \geqq 1$, a set N_ξ depending only on ξ, whose elements $\nu = (n_1, n_2, n_3, \ldots)$ are increasing sequences of natural numbers, can be found for which the δs-function*

---

[1] The set of summands is already uncountable in the case of the B^3.

$$(15)\qquad X = \mathop{\mathfrak{S}}_{\nu}^{N_\xi} M_\nu = \mathop{\mathfrak{S}}_{\nu}^{N_\xi} M_{n_1} M_{n_2} M_{n_3} \ldots$$
$$= \Phi_\xi (M_1, M_2, M_3, \ldots) \qquad (M_n \varepsilon \mathfrak{M})$$

represents precisely the Borel sets B^ξ *generated by* $\mathfrak{M}$.

Of course, the Borel sets A^ξ (p. 99) permit of analogous treatment; the Φ_ξ would then be intersections of sums — rather than sums of intersections — of subsequences of the sequence M_n, that is, σd-functions.

§ 19. Suslin Sets

Theorem II of the preceding section immediately suggests the question whether there is not perhaps a *fixed* δs-function or a fixed set N of sequences of increasing natural numbers $\nu = (n_1, n_2, \ldots)$ such that the set

$$(1)\quad X = \mathop{\mathfrak{S}}_{\nu}^{N} M_\nu = \mathop{\mathfrak{S}}_{\nu}^{N} M_{n_1} M_{n_2} M_{n_3} \ldots = \Phi (M_1, M_2, M_3, \ldots) \qquad (M_n \varepsilon \mathfrak{M})$$

ranges *precisely* over *all* the Borel sets generated by $\mathfrak{M}$. This question has to be answered in the negative. If, however, we are willing to strike out the word "precisely," an affirmative answer becomes possible: there is a representation (1) that produces all the Borel sets, but in general it gives other sets as well. We shall return to this point toward the end of the section and shall first discuss the sets in question in terms of a different symbolism in which, instead of the sets M_n, there appear sets with multiple indices — indices which, however, vary independently of each other.

This time we assign sets $M_{n_1}, M_{n_1 n_2}, M_{n_1 n_2 n_3}, \ldots$, not to the natural numbers, but to the *finite complexes* (n_1), (n_1, n_2), (n_1, n_2, n_3), ... of natural numbers (these, too, are a countable collection); except for external form, this is nothing but a sequence of sets. We indicate some of these sets (omitting the dots that denote additional sets, in order not to clutter up the scheme);

$$(2)\qquad \begin{cases} M_1 & & & & M_2 & & & \\ M_{11} & & M_{12} & & M_{21} & & M_{22} & \\ M_{111} & M_{112} & M_{121} & M_{122} & M_{211} & M_{212} & M_{221} & M_{222}. \end{cases}$$

After this, we assign to each sequence

$$(3)\qquad \nu = (n_1, n_2, n_3, \ldots)$$

of natural numbers, which this time do not need to be pairwise distinct, the intersection

(4) $$M_\nu = M_{n_1} M_{n_1 n_2} M_{n_1 n_2 n_3} \cdots$$

constructed from the sets which correspond to the finite sections of the sequence ν; we then form the sum

(5) $$X = \mathfrak{S}_\nu M_\nu$$

taken over *all* the sequences ν.

This, then, is a function $\Phi(M_1, M_{11}, M_2, \ldots)$ of the generating sets (2). If these sets are taken in all possible ways from a system of sets $\mathfrak{M}$, then X ranges over a system of sets $\mathfrak{X}$, and these sets X are called the *Suslin sets* generated by $\mathfrak{M}$ (or, generated by the sets $M \varepsilon \mathfrak{M}$). The summands M_ν are then indeed sets M_δ, but there are uncountably many, just as was the case for the Borel sets B^ξ for $\xi \geqq 3$. In addition, it should be observed that X does not coincide with the intersection

$$\mathfrak{S} M_{n_1} \cdot \mathfrak{S} M_{n_1 n_2} \cdot \mathfrak{S} M_{n_1 n_2 n_3} \cdots$$

(which is an $M_{\sigma\delta}$), for this latter, developed by means of the distributive law, is the same as

$$\mathfrak{S} M_{a_1} M_{b_1 b_2} M_{c_1 c_2 c_3} \cdots,$$

where all the indices range over all the natural numbers independently of each other, while in our case we ought to have $a_1 = b_1 = c_1 = \ldots = n_1$, etc.

Let us call the Suslin sets generated by $\mathfrak{M}$ the sets M_S and let us call the system formed by them $\mathfrak{M}_S$.

Every M_σ and M_δ is an M_S; thus the Suslin formula embraces the formation of sums and intersections of sequences. For if a sequence of sets $M^1, M^2, \ldots$ is given and if we set $M_{n_1 n_2 \ldots n_k} = M^{n_1}$, then $M_\nu = M^{n_1}$ and $X = \mathfrak{S} M^{n_1}$; if, on the other hand, we set $M_{n_1 n_2 \ldots n_k} = M^k$, then every M_ν and consequently X itself equals $\mathfrak{D} M^k$.

The truly fundamental property of the Suslin sets, however, is given by the following theorem:

I. *The Suslin sets generated by Suslin sets M_S are themselves sets M_S.*

Or in brief: Every set M_{SS} is merely a set M_S (just as every $M_{\sigma\sigma}$ is an M_σ). The Suslin process is so comprehensive that its iteration produces nothing new.

The proof looks difficult only because there are so many indices, but it is really quite simple. Let

$$P = \mathfrak{S}_\nu N^{n_1} N^{n_1 n_2} N^{n_1 n_2 n_3} \cdots$$

be a Suslin set whose generating sets are themselves also Suslin sets:

$$
\begin{aligned}
N^{n_1} &= \underset{\alpha}{\mathfrak{S}} M^{n_1}_{a_1} \quad M^{n_1}_{a_1 a_2} \quad M^{n_1}_{a_1 a_2 a_3} \cdots \\
N^{n_1 n_2} &= \underset{\beta}{\mathfrak{S}} M^{n_1 n_2}_{b_1} \quad M^{n_1 n_2}_{b_1 b_2} \quad M^{n_1 n_2}_{b_1 b_2 b_3} \cdots \\
N^{n_1 n_2 n_3} &= \underset{\gamma}{\mathfrak{S}} M^{n_1 n_2 n_3}_{c_1} \, M^{n_1 n_2 n_3}_{c_1 c_2} \, M^{n_1 n_2 n_3}_{c_1 c_2 c_3} \cdots, \\
&\cdots
\end{aligned}
$$

where $\nu = (n_1, n_2, \ldots)$, $\alpha = (a_1, a_2, \ldots)$, $\beta = (b_1, b_2, \ldots), \ldots$ range independently of each other through all the sequences of natural numbers. It is to be shown that P can be formed as a Suslin set from the sets M themselves. By the distributive law, P is the sum of all intersections

$$
(6) \qquad M^{n_1}_{a_1} M^{n_1}_{a_1 a_2} M^{n_1}_{a_1 a_2 a_3} \cdots M^{n_1 n_2}_{b_1} M^{n_1 n_2}_{b_1 b_2} \cdots M^{n_1 n_2 n_3}_{c_1} \cdots,
$$

where the summation extends over all the sequences $\nu, \alpha, \beta, \ldots$ or all the natural numbers $n_k, a_k, b_k, \ldots$. Again using, say, the dyadic scheme, we transform the sequence of sequences $\nu, \alpha, \beta, \gamma, \ldots$ into a single sequence $\mu = (m_1, m_2, \ldots)$; that is, we do so in such a way that the matrices

$$
\begin{array}{llll|llll}
n_1 & n_2 & n_3 & \cdots & m_1 & m_3 & m_5 & \cdots \\
a_1 & a_2 & a_3 & \cdots & m_2 & m_6 & m_{10} & \cdots \\
b_1 & b_2 & b_3 & \cdots & m_4 & m_{12} & m_{20} & \cdots \\
c_1 & c_2 & c_3 & \cdots & m_8 & m_{24} & m_{40} & \cdots \\
\cdot & \cdot & \cdot & \cdots & \cdot & \cdot & \cdot & \cdots
\end{array}
$$

become equal to one another. In this way (6) goes over into

$$
\begin{aligned}
(7) \quad & M^{m_1}_{m_2} M^{m_1}_{m_2 m_6} M^{m_1}_{m_2 m_6 m_{10}} \cdots M^{m_1 m_3}_{m_4} M^{m_1 m_3}_{m_4 m_{12}} \cdots M^{m_1 m_3 m_5}_{m_8} \cdots \\
&= M(1)\, M(3) \quad M(5) \quad \cdots M(2) \;\; M(6) \;\; \cdots \quad M(4) \quad \cdots,
\end{aligned}
$$

where $M(k)$ denotes a set depending only on $m_1, m_2, \ldots, m_{2k}$ (though not, in general, on all these numbers) and where k runs through all the natural numbers once; for it is easy to see that the superscripts $m_1, m_3, \ldots, m_{2h-1}$ on which a set in (7) depends have smaller indices than the subscripts, which begin with m_{2h}, and that thus the largest m_k on which the set depends is of even index. If, finally, we set up a one-to-one correspondence between the pairs of numbers (m_{2k-1}, m_{2k}) and the natural numbers p_k and define the set

$$
M_{p_1 p_2 \ldots p_k} = M(k),
$$

depending on $p_1, \ldots, p_k$ or $m_1, \ldots, m_{2k}$, then (7) goes over into

$M_{p_1} M_{p_1 p_2} M_{p_1 p_2 p_3} \ldots$, and P is the sum of these intersections taken over all sequences $(p_1, p_2, p_3, \ldots)$ of natural numbers, that is, it is a Suslin set formed from the sets M.

This proves I. The sets $N = M_S$ generate no new Suslin sets; every N_S is an N. Thus, in particular, every N_σ and N_δ is an N, and the sets N form a Borel system $\mathfrak{N}$ containing $\mathfrak{M}$; the smallest Borel system $\mathfrak{B}$ is therefore contained in $\mathfrak{N}$: *all the Borel sets generated by $\mathfrak{M}$ are also Suslin sets.* The converse is not true in general, as we shall see later (§ 33, I).

Finally, we can return easily from the Suslin formula (5), (4) to a representation of the form (1) and in so doing answer the question raised at the beginning of this section. All we have to do is to produce a one-to-one correspondence between the natural numbers p and the finite complexes of natural numbers $(n_1, n_2, \ldots, n_k)$, for instance the one arising from the dyadic representation

$$p = 2^{n_1 - 1} + 2^{n_1 + n_2 - 1} + \cdots + 2^{n_1 + n_2 + \cdots + n_k - 1}. \tag{8}$$

Then we set

$$M^p = M_{n_1 n_2 \cdots n_k}.$$

To every sequence $\nu = (n_1, n_2, n_3, \ldots)$ of arbitrary natural numbers there corresponds, then, a sequence $\pi = (p_1, p_2, p_3, \ldots)$ of increasing natural numbers of the form

$$p_1 = 2^{n_1 - 1}, \quad p_2 = 2^{n_1 - 1} + 2^{n_1 + n_2 - 1},$$
$$p_3 = 2^{n_1 - 1} + 2^{n_1 + n_2 - 1} + 2^{n_1 + n_2 + n_3 - 1}, \ldots$$

(that is, the numbers $p_1, p_2 - p_1, p_3 - p_2, \ldots$ are a subsequence of $1, 2, 4, 8, \ldots$). If Π is the set of all these sequences π, then (5) goes over into

$$X = \overset{\Pi}{\underset{\pi}{\mathfrak{S}}} M^{p_1} M^{p_2} M^{p_3} \ldots .$$

If we return to the notation of (1), this proves the theorem:

II. *There exists a fixed set N of sequences of increasing natural numbers $\nu = (n_1, n_2, n_3, \ldots)$ such that the δs-function*

$$X = \overset{N}{\underset{\nu}{\mathfrak{S}}} M_\nu = \overset{N}{\underset{\nu}{\mathfrak{S}}} M_{n_1} M_{n_2} M_{n_3} \ldots \tag{1}$$
$$= \Phi(M_1, M_2, M_3, \ldots) \qquad (M_n \in \mathfrak{M})$$

represents precisely the Suslin sets generated by $\mathfrak{M}$.

CHAPTER VI

POINT SETS

§ 20. Distance

We have until now dealt in part with pure sets, in part with sets in which there are relations among the elements (ordered sets). It is to the second of these classes that the sets we are about to study belong: sets in which any two elements have a *distance* from each other.

1. Metric spaces. Let E be a set, whose elements we now refer to as *points*. To each pair of points (x, y) we assign a real number xy, the *distance* between the two points,[1] that is, a real function $xy = f(x, y)$ defined in (E, E). We require of this function that the following *distance axioms*, or *postulates*, be satisfied:

(α) $xx = 0$;
(β) $xy = yx > 0$ for $x \neq y$;
(γ) $xy + yz \geqq xz$.

The axiom (γ), the most important among them, is called the *triangle inequality* or triangle axiom (the sum of two sides of a triangle is at least as great as the third side). The set E is called a metric set, a *point set*, or a *metric space*. In the case of the last of these terms we have in mind the relation of E and its subsets and points, in the first two, of the inclusion of E in some containing space.

The example closest to hand is the set of real numbers E_1, where distance is defined as the absolute value $|x - y|$ of the difference of the two numbers. Next comes *n-dimensional Euclidean space*, E_n; its elements are the complexes

$$x = (x_1, x_2, \ldots, x_n)$$

of n real numbers; equality has the usual meaning ($x = y$ means $x_1 = y_1, \ldots, x_n = y_n$), and distance is defined by

$$xy = \sqrt{(x_1 - y_1)^2 + (x_2 - y_2)^2 + \cdots + (x_n - y_n)^2},$$

[1] Whenever there is the possibility of confusion with a product, a notation other than xy will have to be chosen.

where we take the positive root. The postulates (α) and (β) are satisfied, and we shall return to the proof of (γ) later on.

If two spaces can be mapped on each other *one-to-one* and *with preservation of distance* (that is, if the points x correspond one-to-one to the points ξ in such a way that $xy = \xi\eta$), then they are said to be *isometric*. For example, E_1 is isometric with the set of points $(x, 0)$ of E_2. Isometry, fundamentally nothing but the congruence of elementary geometry, is a concept for metric sets analogous to equivalence for pure sets and to similarity for ordered sets (another, more important, analogue is that of homeomorphism, § 38) ; it is unnecessary, however, to introduce names corresponding to cardinal number and ordinal type. Two isometric spaces each thought of in relation to its subsets and its points may be regarded simply as identical (two isometric sets in a containing space, however, may not).

A space isometric with E_n is called an *n-dimensional Euclidean space*; $x_1, \ldots, x_n$ are called the rectangular Cartesian coordinates of the point ξ that corresponds to the complex x. The isometric mapping can be done in infinitely many ways (coordinate transformation, orthogonal substitution). Ordinary space, idealized from our everyday experience and observation, is a three-dimensional Euclidean space, whose planes and lines are two-dimensional and one-dimensional Euclidean spaces, respectively. It is here that the familiar geometrical expressions originate (also used for E_n, and for other spaces as well).

2. Linear spaces. The points of Euclidean space were finite complexes of real numbers. This lends itself to immediate generalization: we assign to each element m of an arbitrary set

$$M = \{m, n, \ldots\}$$

a real number x_m (or, we define a real function in M) ; we thus obtain the complex, or *point*,

$$x = (x_m, x_n, \ldots)$$

whose "coordinates" are $x_m, x_n, \ldots$. Equality of points will mean equality of all the coordinates ($x = y$ means $x_m = y_m$ for all $m \varepsilon M$). The point

$$0 = (0, 0, 0, \ldots)$$

is called the *origin*. We define the multiplication of a point by a real number α, and the addition of points, by

$$\alpha x = (\alpha x_m, \alpha x_n, \ldots)$$

$$x + y = (x_m + y_m, \ x_n + y_n, \ldots),$$

so that it is clear what we mean by such symbols as $-x$, $x - y, \alpha x + \beta y$, and $\alpha x + \beta y + \gamma z$.

We say that three points, x, y, z lie on a straight line, or that they are *collinear,* if there exist three numbers α, β, γ, not all zero, such that

$$\alpha x + \beta y + \gamma z = 0, \quad \alpha + \beta + \gamma = 0.$$

Here γ cannot be zero except when $x = y$ (for then *every* point z lies on a straight line with x and y) ; for $x \neq y$, we can choose $\gamma = -1$, since only the ratios $\alpha : \beta : \gamma$ matter, and thus from

$$(1) \qquad z = \alpha x + \beta y, \quad \alpha + \beta = 1$$

we get all the points z collinear with x and y, the set of such points being called the *line* determined by x and y; z depends on a real variable α or β. If we impose on (1) the restriction that $\alpha \geqq 0$, $\beta \geqq 0$, then we get the (closed) *segment* or *interval* $[x, y]$ determined by x and y.

This process can be continued. Let us say that $k + 1$ points $x_0, x_1, \ldots$, x_k are *linearly dependent* if there exists a relation

$$\alpha_0 x_0 + \alpha_1 x_1 + \cdots + \alpha_k x_k = 0, \quad \alpha_0 + \alpha_1 + \cdots + \alpha_k = 0,$$

where $\alpha_0, \alpha_1, \ldots, \alpha_k$ are real numbers that do not all vanish simultaneously; otherwise, we say that the points are linearly *independent.* If $x_0, x_1, \ldots, x_k$ are linearly dependent but $x_1, \ldots, x_k$ linearly independent, then α_0 cannot be 0; and, setting $\alpha_0 = -1$, we obtain all the points x_0 linearly dependent on $x_1, \ldots, x_k$ in the form

$$x_0 = \alpha_1 x_1 + \ldots + \alpha_k x_k, \quad \alpha_1 + \cdots + \alpha_k = 1;$$

these points are determined by $k - 1$ real parameters and, in the usual terminology, they form the $(k-1)$-*dimensional space* R_{k-1} determined by $x_1, \ldots, x_k$ and, if the α_i are restricted to non-negative values, the $(k-1)$-*dimensional simplex* S_{k-1} determined by those points. (R_1 is the line, R_2 the plane, S_1 the line-segment, S_2 the triangle, and S_3 the *tetrahedron.*)

A set of points x will be called *linear*[1] if whenever it contains two points x, y it contains the whole line determined by x and y; it is called *convex* if it contains the segment $[x, y]$. Hence the set R_{k-1} defined above is

[1] Cantor and others call the subsets of E_1 linear sets.

linear, S_{k-1} convex; a linear space is also obtained by taking all the points whose coordinates satisfy a system of linear equations. Clearly, the intersection of any number of linear or convex sets is itself linear or convex. If E is a linear or convex space and $A \leqq E$, then the intersection K of all the convex sets containing A is the smallest convex set containing K and is called *the convex hull* of A.[1] Whenever K contains any linearly independent points of A, it contains the whole simplex determined by them and is simply the sum of all these simplexes.

If a is a particular point, then

$$\text{(2)} \qquad \xi = x + a, \qquad x = \xi - a$$

defines a one-to-one mapping of the points x on each other; this relation is called a *translation,* or a displacement. Under such a correspondence, every linear space goes over into another and, in particular, can be made into a (homogeneous, linear) space *containing the origin,* and we shall now assume this to have been done. Such a space E, if it contains a point x, also contains the points $\alpha x = \alpha x + (1 - \alpha) \cdot 0$, and if it contains the pair of points x, y, also contains all the linear combinations $\alpha x + \beta y$ (and not only those for which $\alpha + \beta = 1$). The translations (2) transform E into itself, provided that a is a point of E. We shall now make E into a metric space in such a way as to make the translations isometric mappings, that is, so that the points x, y have the same distance as $x + a$, $y + a$ and, in particular, the same as $x - y$, 0 or 0, $y - x$. All distances are referred back, in this way, to distances from the origin; if the distance of x from the origin is denoted by $|x|$ and is called the *absolute value* or *norm* of x, then $xy = |x - y|$ is the distance between any two points. An ordered pair of points (x, y) is also called a *vector,* and equality of two vectors (x, y) and (ξ, η) is defined by $y - x = \eta - \xi$. Thus pairs of points that yield equal vectors have equal distance (called the norm, or length, of the vector).

Now the real function $|x|$ of x must satisfy the three *norm axioms,* corresponding to the distance axioms:

$$(\alpha_0) \qquad |0| = 0;$$
$$(\beta_0) \qquad |x| = |-x| > 0 \quad \text{for} \quad x \neq 0;$$
$$(\gamma_0) \qquad |x + y| \leqq |x| + |y|.$$

[1] Smallest sets $\geqq A$ are called *hulls,* largest sets $\leqq A$ are called *kernels* of A with a suitable identifying adjective (convex, complete, closed hull; open or dense-in-itself kernel). The existence of such largest and smallest sets having a given property has to be proved, of course, in any given case.

The last of these, which we call the *addition axiom*, follows from the triangle inequality by replacement of x, y, z by $x, 0, -y$. Conversely, if $|x|$ satisfies these norm axioms, then

$$xy = |x - y| \tag{3}$$

satisfies the distance axioms; (γ) follows from (γ_0) because

$$|x - z| = |(x - y) + (y - z)| \leqq |x - y| + |y - z|.$$

The norms occurring in the next subsection will satisfy, in addition, the condition

$$|\alpha x| = |\alpha||x|$$

(α a real number); that is, they will be positive homogeneous functions of the first degree in the coordinates. In this case, the straight lines of our space will be isometric with E_1 or with the Euclidean straight lines no matter how the norm is defined. This is so because for two points

$$z = x + \beta(y - x)$$

of the line (1) we have

$$z_1 - z = (\beta_1 - \beta)(y - x), \quad |z_1 - z| = |\beta_1 - \beta||y - x|,$$

so that the points z are in isometric relation to the numbers $c\beta$ ($c = |y - x|$ is constant).

3. Examples of linear spaces. The Euclidean space E_n is formed by the assignment to the point

$$x = (x_1, x_2, \ldots, x_n) \tag{4}$$

of the norm

$$|x| = (x_1^2 + x_2^2 + \cdots + x_n^2)^{\frac{1}{2}} \tag{5}$$

The proof of the addition axiom is obtained most quickly by a well-known argument: since the quadratic form in the real variables u, v

$$\Sigma(x_k u + y_k v)^2 = a u^2 + 2b uv + c v^2$$

with

$$a = \Sigma x_k^2, \quad b = \Sigma x_k y_k, \quad c = \Sigma y_k^2$$

is non-negative, its determinant is $\geqq 0$,

$$\begin{aligned} b^2 &\leqq ac, \\ b &\leqq a^{\frac{1}{2}} c^{\frac{1}{2}}, \\ a + 2b + c &\leqq (a^{\frac{1}{2}} + c^{\frac{1}{2}})^2, \\ (a + 2b + c)^{\frac{1}{2}} &\leqq a^{\frac{1}{2}} + c^{\frac{1}{2}}, \end{aligned}$$

and this is the inequality that was to be proved.

If n is allowed to increase without limit, then the addition inequality states first that when $x_1^2 + x_2^2 + \cdots$ and $y_1^2 + y_2^2 + \cdots$ converge then $(x_1 + y_1)^2 + (x_2 + y_2)^2 + \cdots$ also converges. Therefore, if we now consider sequences of real numbers

$$(6) \qquad x = (x_1, x_2, \ldots),$$

that is, complexes with the index sets $M = \{1, 2, \ldots\}$, and if H is the set of those x for which the *sum of the squares converges*, then H is a linear space (when x and y belong to it, then so do $x + y$ and $\alpha x + \beta y$), and this becomes a metric space if the norm is defined by

$$|x| = (x_1^2 + x_2^2 + \cdots)^{\frac{1}{2}}$$

with a corresponding definition (3) of distance. It is called *Hilbert space*, and it is in a certain sense an $\aleph_0$-dimensional Euclidean space. Incidentally, another space can be inserted between the Euclidean spaces E_n and Hilbert space, one formed by the sequences of numbers x in which only *finitely many* numbers $x_1, x_2, \ldots$ differ from zero; this space can be denoted by $E_1 \dotplus E_2 \dotplus \ldots$, provided the set of sequences

$$(x_1, \ldots, x_n, 0, 0, \ldots)$$

isometric with E_n is identified with E_n.

This process can be extended to the use of any set M whatsoever as an index set for the complexes, and if, moreover, we do not distinguish between isometric spaces, the result depends only on the cardinality of M. We keep only those $x = (x_m, \ldots)$ in which only a *finite number* of x_m or an *at most countable number* – in the latter case, with *sum of squares convergent* – are different from zero, and then define the norm $|x|$ as above. These two spaces can be considered Euclidean spaces whose dimension is the cardinality of M.

If the passage to the limit $n \to \infty$ is carried out not on the sum of the squares $x_1^2 + \cdots + x_n^2$ but rather on the mean square $\frac{1}{n}(x_1^2 + \cdots + x_n^2)$, then we obtain *integrals*.

If, for example, M denotes the interval $a \leqq t \leqq b$, then the set of functions continuous on this interval

$$(8) \qquad x = x(t)$$

becomes a metric linear space if the norm is defined by

$$(9) \qquad |x| = \left[\int_a^b x(t)^2\,dt\right]^{\frac{1}{2}}$$

and the corresponding definition of distance (3) is made. If this is extended to integrals of discontinuous functions – at first, say, to proper

Riemann integrals – we encounter a phenomenon that later on will occasionally appear again: it can happen that $|x| = 0$ without x being $= 0$ in the sense (p. 110) originally defined ($x(t) = 0$ in the whole interval). In order to preserve the axioms (β) and (β_0), we have to modify the original definition and define the equality $x = y$ precisely by $xy = 0$. In other words, if we call a function for which $|x| = 0$ a *null* function, then two functions differing only by a null function represent the same point of the metric function space.

Euclidean space, whose variants and limiting cases we have been examining thus far, was based on the definition (5) of the norm. The exponent 2 in this definition, which derives from the Pythagorean Theorem, can be replaced by any exponent $p > 1$ (which need not be an integer), and the norm of the complex

(4) $$x = (x_1, x_2, \dots, x_n)$$

can be defined by

(10) $$|x| = (|x_1|^p + |x_2|^p + \cdots + |x_n|^p)^{\frac{1}{p}} \qquad (p > 1).$$

The addition inequality, here called *Minkowski's inequality*, is proved as follows. For positive x, ξ, Taylor's Formula

$$x^p = \xi^p + p\,\xi^{p-1}(x - \xi) + \frac{p(p-1)}{2}\,\xi_1^{p-2}(x - \xi)^2$$

(ξ_1 between x and ξ) gives, on leaving out the non-negative remainder,

$$\frac{x^p}{\xi^{p-1}} \geqq \xi + p(x - \xi) = px - (p-1)\,\xi.$$

If, for positive y and η, we substitute $\dfrac{x}{x+y}$ for x and $\dfrac{\xi}{\xi+\eta}$ for ξ in this inequality, then we get

$$\frac{x^p}{\xi^{p-1}} \geqq \frac{(x+y)^p}{(\xi+\eta)^{p-1}}\left[p\,\frac{x}{x+y} - (p-1)\,\frac{\xi}{\xi+\eta}\right].$$

If we interchange x, ξ and y, η and add, then

$$\frac{x^p}{\xi^{p-1}} + \frac{y^p}{\eta^{p-1}} \geqq \frac{(x+y)^p}{(\xi+\eta)^{p-1}}.$$

Setting x_k, y_k ($k = 1, 2, \dots, n$) for x, y, and also setting

$$\xi^p = \Sigma\, x_k^p, \quad \eta^p = \Sigma\, y_k^p$$

and summing for k, we obtain

$$(\xi + \eta)^p \geqq \Sigma (x_k + y_k)^p ,$$

or

$$(\Sigma x_k^p)^{\frac{1}{p}} + (\Sigma y_k^p)^{\frac{1}{p}} \geqq (\Sigma (x_k + y_k)^p)^{\frac{1}{p}} .$$

This is valid for positive and, of course, also for non-negative x_k, y_k; for any x_k, y_k whatsoever we obtain, by virtue of

$$| x_k | + | y_k | \geqq | x_k + y_k | ,$$

$$(\Sigma | x_k |^p)^{\frac{1}{p}} + (\Sigma | y_k |^p)^{\frac{1}{p}} \geqq (\Sigma | x_k + y_k |^p)^{\frac{1}{p}} ,$$

and we thus have the inequality to be proved.

The space defined by the norm (10) should perhaps be called the *pseudo-Euclidean* n-dimensional space E_n^p.

The number p, thus far taken to be > 1, may also be taken $= 1$, thus giving a norm defined by

(11) $$| x | = | x_1 | + | x_2 | + \cdots + | x_n | .$$

At the other extreme, it can be said that the definition

(12) $$| x | = \max [| x_1 |, \ | x_2 |, \ldots, | x_n |]$$

for the norm corresponds to the limiting case $p = \infty$; if this largest of the absolute values $| x_k |$ is denoted by ξ, then it follows from (10) that $\xi \leqq | x | \leqq n^{\frac{1}{p}} \cdot \xi$, so that if $p \to \infty$ then $| x | \to \xi$. The addition inequality for these last two norms, incidentally, is trivial.

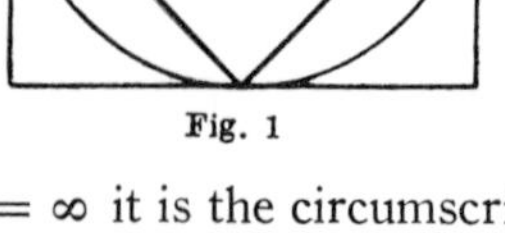

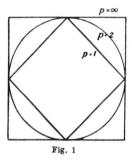

Fig. 1

If we interpret x_1, x_2 as rectangular coordinates in the Euclidean plane, so that E_2^p is mapped on it one-to-one – but isometrically only in the case $p = 2$ – then it is not without interest to visualize the "calibration curve" $| x_1 |^p + | x_2 |^p = 1$, the image of the "unit circle" $| x | = 1$. For $p = 2$ it is the Euclidean unit circle; for $p = 1$, it is an inscribed square with corners $(\pm 1, 0)$ and $(0, \pm 1)$; and for $p = \infty$ it is the circumscribed square with the corners $(\pm 1, \pm 1)$. For the remaining p, the curve stays in the corresponding intermediate regions.

For $n = 3$, we note that $p = 2$ gives the Euclidean unit sphere, $p = 1$ an octahedron inscribed in it, and $p = \infty$ a cube circumscribed about it.

The spaces corresponding to the limiting process $n \to \infty$ are found just as in the case $p = 2$; thus, we have the pseudo-Hilbert space l^p as the space of sequences of numbers for which $|x_1|^p + |x_2|^p + \cdots$ converges, with norm defined by

$$(13) \qquad |x| = (|x_1|^p + |x_2|^p + \cdots)^{\frac{1}{p}},$$

the space of continuous functions $x = x(t)$ with norm defined by

$$(14) \qquad |x| = \left(\int_a^b |x(t)|^p \, dt\right)^{\frac{1}{p}}$$

etc.; for $p = \infty$ the appropriate re-interpretation of (12) is: the space of *bounded* sequences of numbers with

$$(15) \qquad |x| = \sup |x_n|;$$

and this can be extended without further ado to complexes with arbitrary index set.

So far we have taken all our norms to be symmetric functions of the coordinates; if we are willing to sacrifice this feature, the field of possible examples is greatly extended. Thus, it is possible to assign to the bounded sequences $x = (x_1, x_2, \ldots)$ the norms

$$|x| = c_1 |x_1| + c_2 |x_2| + \cdots,$$

where $c_1 + c_2 + \ldots$ is a fixed convergent series of positive numbers. Or, we may define the norm of a (real) $m \times n$ matrix

$$x = \begin{pmatrix} x_{11} & \cdots & x_{1n} \\ \cdot & \cdots & \cdot \\ x_{m1} & \cdots & x_{mn} \end{pmatrix}$$

as follows: We let

$$v_i = \sum_k x_{ik} u_k \qquad (i = 1, \ldots, m; \; k = 1, \ldots, n)$$

and set $|x|$ equal to the maximum of $(\Sigma v_i^2)^{\frac{1}{2}}$ under the condition that $\Sigma u_k^2 = 1$. It is easy to see that the axioms for the norm are satisfied by this $|x|$, so that the distance $|x - y|$ makes this collection of matrices (of mn elements each) into a metric space. The exponent 2 may again be replaced by p, and we may again go over to infinite matrices.

4. Baire spaces. If $x = (x_1, x_2, \ldots)$ is a sequence of real numbers or, possibly, of elements of arbitrary sets $x_n \in A_n$, and if $m(x, y)$ is the first place in the sequence at which the two sequences $x \neq y$ actually differ, that is, if m is the natural number defined by

$$x_m \neq y_m, \quad x_n = y_n \text{ for } n < m,$$

then an admissible definition of distance is obtained by setting

$$(16) \qquad xx = 0, \qquad xy = 1 : m(x, y) \quad \text{for} \quad x \neq y.$$

Here the triangle inequality actually takes on the stronger form

$$xz \leqq \max\,[xy, yz].$$

For under the assumption that all three sequences are different (otherwise there is nothing to prove), we have

$$m(x, z) \geqq \min\,[m(x, y), m(y, z)],$$

because, setting the right-hand side equal to m, we have $x_n = y_n$ and $y_n = z_n$ for $n < m$, so that $x_n = z_n$; and hence $m(x, z) \geqq m$. These spaces are called *Baire spaces*; in particular, the *Baire null space* is obtained if the x_n are allowed to range over all the natural numbers.

5. The *p*-adic space. Let p be a natural prime number and ϑ a number in the interval $0 < \vartheta < 1$, both taken as fixed. Then it is possible to assign to every rational number x a norm or — more precisely, since we must be careful to avoid confusion here — a "valuation" $||\, x \,||$, in the following way:

$$(17) \qquad ||\, 0 \,|| = 0, \quad ||\, x \,|| = \vartheta^{m(x)} \text{ for } x \neq 0,$$

where $m(x)$ is that integer $m\,(\gtreqless 0)$ for which x is exactly divisible by p^m, that is, $x = p^m x_0$, and x_0 is the quotient of two integers neither of which is divisible by p. The addition axiom again holds, in the stronger form,

$$||\, x + y \,|| \leqq \max\,[||\, x \,||, ||\, y \,||];$$

for if $x, y, x + y \neq 0$ (otherwise there is nothing to be proved), then

$$m(x + y) \geqq \min\,[m(x), m(y)];$$

if $x = p^m x_0$, $y = p^n y_0$ and, without loss of generality, $m \leqq n$, then $x + y = p^m (x_0 + p^{n-m} y_0)$, where the second factor can be represented with a denominator (the product of the denominators of x_0 and y_0) not divisible by p, and therefore $x + y$ is exactly divisible by p^m or by an even higher power. The distance $||\, x - y \,||$ converts the set of rational numbers into a metric space; the completion (§ 21) of this space leads to the p-adic numbers created by Hensel, which are of great significance for the theory of algebraic number fields.

6. Products of metric spaces. Suppose that x ranges over a metric space A and y over a metric space B; then the pair of points $z=(x, y)$ ranges (§ 4) over the set $C=(A, B)$, which can itself be made into a metric space in an infinite number of ways, say by

$$z_1 z_2 = [(x_1 x_2)^p + (y_1 y_2)^p]^{\frac{1}{p}} \qquad (p \geqq 1) \tag{18}$$

or

$$z_1 z_2 = \max\,[x_1 x_2, y_1 y_2]. \tag{19}$$

If, for example, we take $p=2$, then the product (E_m, E_n) of two Euclidean spaces becomes isometric with the Euclidean space E_{m+n}. The x belonging to some $z=(x, y)$ is called the *projection of the point z on the space A*, and the projections of all the points z of a set $Z \subseteqq C$ form the projection X of Z. The distance between two points is at least as great as the distance between their projections: $z_1 z_2 \geqq x_1 x_2$. This construction can be extended immediately to any finite number of factors.

§ 21. Convergence

1. Let $(x_1, x_2, \ldots)$ be a sequence of points of the metric space E. If E contains a point x such that the distance xx_n converges to 0 as $n \to \infty$,

$$\lim xx_n = 0 \quad \text{or} \quad xx_n \to 0,$$

then we say that the sequence is *convergent in E* and that x is its *limit* (limit point), and we write

$$\lim x_n = x \qquad \text{or} \qquad x_n \to x.$$

There can only be one such point, of course, for from $xx_n \to 0$ and $yx_n \to 0$ it follows, by use of the triangle inequality, that $xy=0$ and $x=y$. More generally, for two sequences $x_n \to x$ and $y_n \to y$ convergent in E we have

$$x_n y_n \to xy. \tag{1}$$

For, the triangle inequality gives

$$\begin{aligned} x_n y_n &\leqq x_n x + xy + y y_n, \\ xy &\leqq x x_n + x_n y_n + y_n y, \\ |x_n y_n - xy| &\leqq x x_n + y y_n, \end{aligned}$$

from which, letting $n \to \infty$, (1) follows. In a terminology that the reader will readily understand, we express (1) as follows: xy is a *continuous function* of x and y.

The sequence of points $(x_1, x_2, \ldots)$ is called a *fundamental sequence,* or Cauchy sequence, if for every ε (no matter how small) there is a point x_m in the sequence whose distance is $< \varepsilon$ from all the points following it:

$$x_m x_n < \varepsilon \quad \text{for} \quad n > m.$$

Every convergent sequence is clearly a fundamental sequence. The converse cannot be true in general, since the definition of a fundamental sequence involved only the sequence itself, whereas convergence in E depends on the space E. If, for example, E is the space of rational numbers, then a sequence of rational numbers which converges to an irrational number is a fundamental sequence but is not convergent in E. *If every fundamental sequence in E converges in E, then E is said to be a complete space* (a complete point set). Thus, the set of rational numbers is not complete, whereas that of the real numbers is. As a matter of fact, the convergence of every fundamental sequence of real numbers is precisely what is stated in the so-called *general convergence criterion* of Cauchy, which is familiar to the reader from his elementary work.

2. Examples of complete and incomplete spaces. Every Euclidean space, including Hilbert space, is complete; let us prove this for the latter. The norm of a point x

$$|x| = (x_1^2 + x_2^2 + \cdots)^{\frac{1}{2}}$$

is at least equal to the norm of a coordinate $|x| \geqq |x_k|$; hence the distance $|x - y| \geqq |x_k - y_k|$. If, then, the points[1]

$$x^n = (x_1^n, x_2^n, \ldots, x_k^n, \ldots)$$

form a fundamental sequence, then all the more so do their k-th coordinates, which thus have a limit

$$x_k = \lim_n x_k^n;$$

let us then set

$$x = (x_1, x_2, \ldots, x_k, \ldots).$$

For a preassigned $\varepsilon > 0$ we have $|x^n - x^m| < \varepsilon$ for a suitable m and for every $n > m$, so that

$$\sum_{k=1}^{\infty} (x_k^n - x_k^m)^2 < \varepsilon^2,$$

and, a fortiori, for every natural number l

$$\sum_{k=1}^{l} (x_k^n - x_k^m)^2 < \varepsilon^2,$$

[1] n and m are superscripts, not exponents.

so that for $n \to \infty$,

$$\sum_{k=1}^{l} (x_k - x_k^m)^2 \leqq \varepsilon^2;$$

and from this it follows, for $l \to \infty$, that

$$\sum_{k=1}^{\infty} (x_k - x_k^m)^2 \leqq \varepsilon^2.$$

From the convergence of the series on the left, we infer that $x - x^m$, and therefore x as well, belongs to the Hilbert space. Furthermore $|x - x^m| \leqq \varepsilon$, which, combined with $|x^n - x^m| < \varepsilon$ gives $|x - x^n| < 2\varepsilon$ for $n > m$; and this means that $|x - x^n| \to 0$ or $x^n \to x$.

The space $E = \mathfrak{S}E_n$ (p. 114) lying between the Euclidean spaces and Hilbert space is incomplete: for if $x = (x_1, x_2, \ldots)$ is a point of Hilbert space, then the points

$$x^n = (x_1, x_2, \ldots, x_n, 0, 0, \ldots)$$

belonging to E converge to x and constitute a fundamental sequence; but in case infinitely many coordinates x_n are $\neq 0$, this fundamental sequence does not converge in E.

The space of the functions continuous in $[a, b]$ with norm defined by

$$|x| = \left(\int_a^b x(t)^2\, dt\right)^{\frac{1}{2}}$$

is not complete. For every integrable (Riemann integrable and bounded) function ξ a sequence of continuous functions x_n with $|x_n - \xi| \to 0$ can be given; if at the same time there were to be a continuous function x with $|x_n - x| \to 0$, so that $|x - \xi| = 0$, then the null function $x - \xi$ would have to vanish at its points of continuity, and x would have to agree with ξ at the points at which ξ is continuous. The simplest examples show that such a continuous function x need not exist: for example, let $\xi(t)$ have a single jump at c between a and b with $\xi(c - 0) \neq \xi(c + 0)$, and let it be continuous everywhere else. Even the space of Riemann-integrable functions is not complete. (Indeed, only the space of those functions for which $x(t)$ and its square are Lebesgue-integrable[1] will be complete.)

The pseudo-Euclidean spaces and pseudo-Hilbert space are also complete; in particular, this is true of the space of bounded sequences of numbers with norm given by

---

[1] The Lebesgue theory of measure and integration is not discussed in this book, and acquaintance with it is not assumed. The reader who does not understand the above allusion to the Riesz-Fischer Theorem should simply forget it was mentioned.

$$|x| = \sup |x_n|$$

that corresponds to the limiting case $p = \infty$. The space of continuous functions also is complete if the norm is given by

$$|x| = \max_{a \leqq t \leqq b} |x(t)|,$$

for then a fundamental sequence of continuous functions converges *uniformly* to a limit function $x(t)$, which consequently is itself continuous.

The sequences of real numbers $x = (x_1, x_2, \ldots)$ with norm defined by

$$|x| = \inf_k \left(x_1^2 + x_2^2 + \cdots + x_k^2 + \frac{1}{k^2}\right)^{\frac{1}{2}}$$

– which we leave to the reader to prove an admissible definition – constitute a complete space in which convergence $x^n \to x$ is equivalent with the convergence of all the coordinates separately ($x_1^n \to x_1$, $x_2^n \to x_2, \ldots$).

The Baire space (p. 117) of sequences of elements

$$x = (x_1, x_2, \ldots)$$

is complete, provided that the x_k range independently of one another over all the elements of the given sets A_k. For if the points

$$x^n = (x_1^n, x_2^n, \ldots)$$

form a fundamental sequence, then for every natural number k, $x^n x^m < \frac{1}{k}$ for some suitable m and every $n > m$; but this, together with our definition of distance, implies that $x_k^m = x_k^{m+1} = x_k^{m+2} = \cdots$. If we call this element x_k and form the sequence

$$x = (x_1, x_2, \ldots),$$

then x^n agrees with x in its first k elements, where the number k goes to infinity simultaneously with n; that is, $xx^n \to 0$.

3. Completion of spaces. Just as, in § 11, we took the Dedekind theory of irrational numbers as our model in filling up the gaps in ordered sets, so we now use the Cantor-Méray theory, which defines the irrational numbers in terms of fundamental sequences of rationals, as our guide in extending every metric space E to a complete space E, whose elements are to be the fundamental sequences

$$\xi = (x_1, x_2, \ldots, x_n, \ldots)$$

of points of E. We note first:

(α) For two fundamental sequences ξ, η, $\lim x_n y_n$ always exists.

In fact,

$$x_m y_m \leqq x_m x_n + x_n y_n + y_n y_m,$$
$$| x_m y_m - x_n y_n | \leqq x_m x_n + y_m y_n,$$

whence it follows immediately that the real numbers $x_n y_n$ form a fundamental sequence and converge.

(β) If one of two sequences ξ, η is a fundamental sequence and if $x_n y_n \to 0$, then the other is also a fundamental sequence.

This follows from

$$|y_m y_n - x_m x_n| \leqq x_m y_m + x_n y_n.$$

In accord with (α) we define the distance between ξ and η by

$$\xi\eta = \lim x_n y_n.$$

From $x_n y_n + y_n z_n \geqq x_n z_n$ the triangle inequality $\xi\eta + \eta\zeta \geqq \xi\zeta$ follows. In order to preserve the distance axiom (β) (p. 109) we define equality of two fundamental sequences to be equivalent with $\xi\eta = 0$, deviating from our earlier definition of equality for complexes (cf. the remark on p. 115 about discontinuous functions).

The constant sequences

$$(x, x, x, \ldots)$$

are certainly fundamental sequences; the distance between two of them is xy, so that E corresponds isometrically to a subset of E. These constant sequences may safely be identified with the points x themselves, so that E becomes simply a subset of E. The distance between $x = (x, x, \ldots)$ and $\xi = (x_1, x_2, \ldots)$ is $x\xi = \lim x x_n$. In particular, the distance between ξ and one of its own points x_m is

$$x_m \xi = \lim_n x_m x_n.$$

This converges to 0 for $m \to \infty$; for if m is chosen so that for $n > m$ we always have $x_m x_n < \varepsilon$, then $x_m \xi \leqq \varepsilon$, $x_n \xi < 2\varepsilon$ for $n > m$. Hence for every ξ it is possible to find an x that makes $x\xi$ arbitrarily small (E is dense in E, § 25).

For the sake of clarity, let us for the time being use the French *suite* to denote sequences of elements ξ. If $(\xi_1, \xi_2, \ldots)$ is a fundamental suite, then for each ξ_n we determine some x_n with $x_n \xi_n < \frac{1}{n}$; by the remark

(β), the x_n then form a fundamental suite in E or a fundamental sequence $\xi = (x_1, x_2, \ldots)$ in E. Hence $\xi x_n \to 0$, and moreover $x_n \xi_n \to 0$, so that $\xi \xi_n \to 0$ by the triangle inequality; that is, ξ_n converges to ξ, and the space E is complete.

Let us now refer to the set E, in its dependence on E, as $\overline{E}$ (the set of the fundamental sequences of elements of E). For a complete space V we have $V = \overline{V}$. If E is contained in the complete space V then $\overline{E} \leqq \overline{V} = V$, so that $\overline{E}$ is also contained in V: $\overline{E}$ is *the smallest complete space containing* E and will be called the *complete hull*[1] of E. Of course in doing this we have made an identification of the points x of E with the constant sequences $(x, x, \ldots)$ or, as a result of our definition of equality for fundamental sequences, with all the sequences $(x_1, x_2, \ldots)$ convergent to x. If we wish to avoid this confounding of isometric spaces we might say the following: If V is a complete space $\geqq E$, then all fundamental sequences in E converge to points x of V, and the set $\overline{E}$ of these points is called a *complete hull* of E; all the complete hulls of E are isometric, and the isometry is such, moreover, that the points of E are mapped onto themselves.

4. Compact sets. Let x_p be a subsequence of the sequence x_n; more explicitly, let $(x_{p_1}, x_{p_2}, \ldots)$ be a subsequence of $(x_1, x_2, \ldots)$, where $p_1 < p_2 < \ldots$ is an increasing sequence of natural numbers. If x_n has a convergent subsequence $x_p \to x$, then x is called a *point of accumulation* of the whole sequence x_n. For this to obtain, it is necessary and sufficient that, for every $\varepsilon > 0$, xx_n become $< \varepsilon$ *infinitely many times* (whereas for $x_n \to x$ the condition is that $xx_n < \varepsilon$ *ultimately*.) *Necessity*: Ultimately $xx_p < \varepsilon$, and therefore $xx_n < \varepsilon$ an infinite number of times. *Sufficiency*: There is some p_1 for which $xx_{p_1} < 1$, some $p_2 > p_1$ for which $xx_{p_2} < \frac{1}{2}$, some $p_3 > p_2$ for which $xx_{p_3} < \frac{1}{3}$, etc., and thus $x_p \to x$.

We now make the following definitions:

A subset A of the space E is said to be compact in E if every sequence of points $x_n \in A$ has a convergent subsequence in E, i.e., a point of accumulation in E.

A set A will be said to be conditionally compact if every sequence of points $x_n \in A$ has a fundamental sequence as a subsequence.

A set E that is compact in itself is complete. Let E be compact in itself, that is, in E; every fundamental sequence in E has a point of accumulation in E which, in this case, is the limit of the whole sequence.

[1] Compare this with the footnote on p. 112.

A set which is compact in the space E is conditionally compact. Conversely, a conditionally compact set A is compact in some suitable space $E \geqq A$, for example in a complete space E (say the complete hull $\bar{A}$); for, every fundamental sequence will have a limit in that space and thus every sequence of points $x_n \varepsilon A$ will have a point of accumulation. More precisely, we have:

I. *Every conditionally compact subset of E is compact in E if and only if E is complete.*

For if E is not complete and x_n is a fundamental sequence without a limit, where we may clearly suppose the x_n to be pairwise distinct, then the set $A = \{x_1, x_2, \ldots\}$ is indeed conditionally compact, but not compact in E.

The conditionally compact sets, therefore, are those that are compact in suitable spaces.

In order to characterize the conditionally compact sets, we set up some additional definitions:

A set A is said to be bounded if the distances between any pairs of its points have a finite least upper bound; this is called the diameter d(A) of A.

A set A is said to be totally bounded if for every $\delta > 0$ it can be represented as the sum of a finite number of sets each with diameter $\leqq \delta$.

Every totally bounded set is, a fortiori, bounded. In Euclidean space E_p bounded sets are totally bounded as well; for by division of its edges into n equal portions, a cube may be divided into n^p smaller cubes whose diameters become arbitrarily small with increasing n. In Hilbert space, however, the set of points

$$\begin{array}{c}(1, 0, 0, 0, \ldots)\\(0, 1, 0, 0, \ldots)\\(0, 0, 1, 0, \ldots)\\\ldots\end{array}$$

to take one example, is bounded but not totally bounded; for the distance between two points is always $\sqrt{2}$ and for $\delta < \sqrt{2}$ the set cannot be represented as the sum of a finite number of sets of diameter $\leqq \delta$.

II. *Conditionally compact and totally bounded sets are identical.*

Let A be conditionally compact and let ϱ be an arbitrarily small positive number. We choose a point a_1 of A, then a second a_2, with $a_1 a_2 \geqq \varrho$, a third a_3 with $a_1 a_3$, $a_2 a_3 \geqq \varrho$, etc. In short, we look *as long as it is possible to do so* for points whose pairwise distance is $\geqq \varrho$. There can be at most a finite number of such points, say $a_1, a_2, \ldots, a_n$, since otherwise we should end with a sequence none of whose subsequences can possibly be a fundamental sequence. Now every point $x \varepsilon A$ has a distance $< \varrho$ from at least one of these points a_k, since otherwise the point x could have been adjoined to the points a_k. If, therefore, A_k is the set of the points $x \varepsilon A$ for which $xa_k < \varrho$, then $A = A_1 \dot{+} A_2 \dot{+} \ldots \dot{+} A_n$, and every set A_k has a diameter $\leqq 2\varrho$. A is therefore totally bounded.

Conversely, let A be totally bounded. If we then represent A as a sum of a finite number of sets A_k with diameters $\leqq \delta$ and if x_n is a sequence of points belonging to A, then at least one summand A_k must contain infinitely many x_n. Thus we can assert that *every sequence of points has a subsequence x_p of arbitrarily small diameter* $\leqq \delta$ (that is, a subsequence in which the distance between two points is $\leqq \delta$). Then we form from the x_n a subsequence

$$x_{p_1} x_{p_2} x_{p_3} \ldots$$

of diameter $\leqq 1$, from these x_p a subsequence

$$x_{q_1} x_{q_2} x_{q_3} \ldots$$

of diameter $\leqq \frac{1}{2}$, from these a subsequence

$$x_{r_1} x_{r_2} x_{r_3} \ldots$$

of diameter $\leqq \frac{1}{3}$, etc. Now since $p_1 = q_1 < q_2 \leqq r_2 < r_3 \leqq \ldots$, we can form the *diagonal sequence*

$$x_{p_1} x_{q_2} x_{r_3} \ldots$$

which from the k-th element on is a subsequence of the k-th of the preceding sequences, and in which therefore the k-th element has a distance $\leqq \frac{1}{k}$ from all the elements following. Thus it is a fundamental sequence contained in the arbitrarily chosen subsequence x_n, and A is conditionally compact. This proves II.

In Euclidean space E (which is complete), bounded sets, totally bounded sets, conditionally compact sets, and sets compact in E are all identical. The reader knows this as the Bolzano-Weierstrass Theorem: *Every bounded sequence of points in Euclidean space has a point of accumulation.* In general, however, it is not boundedness but rather total boundedness that is the true equivalent of conditional compactness; this, which is a property of the set A itself, must be supplemented with a suitable condition on the space E – completeness certainly being sufficient – in order to make A into a set compact in E.

§ 22. Interior Points and Border Points

We next consider points and subsets of a fixed metric space E. If x is a point and ϱ a positive number, then the set of points y whose distance from x is $< \varrho$ is called a *neighborhood* of x and ϱ is its *radius*. It will be denoted by U_x or, more precisely, by $U_x(\varrho)$.

In terms of the concept of neighborhood the fact that a point is a *limit point (point of accumulation)* of the sequence x is expressed by saying: *Every neighborhood U_x contains almost all (infinitely many) points of the sequence x_n.* For, in fact, for every $\varrho > 0$ we have *ultimately (infinitely often)* $xx_n < \varrho$, or $x_n \varepsilon U_x(\varrho)$.

Let A be a point set. If a point x is such that there exists a neighborhood $U_x \leqq A$, then it is called an *interior point*, otherwise it is called a *border point* of A. Let A_i be the set of interior points, A_b the set of border points. Then we have a decomposition

$$A = A_i + A_b$$

of A into disjoint summands. Let us call A_i the *open kernel* (for a reason which will become clear later) or *interior* of A, and A_b the *border* of A. *A set that consists entirely of interior points will be called an open set* $(A_b = 0)$; *one that consists entirely of border points* $(A_i = 0)$ *will be called a border set.*[1]

We give some examples taken from the Euclidean plane with a rectangular coordinate system, x_1, x_2.

Let A be a circular disc including the circumference, e.g., $x_1^2 + x_2^2 \leqq 1$. The points of the circumference $(x_1^2 + x_2^2 = 1)$ are border points; the rest, interior points.

Let A be a circular disc without its circumference, $x_1^2 + x_2^2 < 1$; this is an open set.

Let A be the circumference of a circle, $x_1^2 + x_2^2 = 1$; this is a border set.

Let A be the set of "rational points," that is, those points whose coordinates are rational; and let $E - A$ be the set of "irrational points," that is, points having at least one coordinate irrational; both are border sets.

Let $f(x_1, x_2)$ be a continuous function. The set $[f > 0]$, which denotes the set of points x at which $f(x_1, x_2) > 0$, is open. An example is the interior of an ellipse, $1 - \dfrac{x_1^2}{a_1^2} - \dfrac{x_2^2}{a_2^2} > 0$.

---

[1] In both cases the null set is to be included.

This is true for any space. If we assign to each point x of E a unique point $y = f(x)$ in another metric space (or in the same metric space) then this function is said to be *continuous at the point* x if one of the following equivalent conditions is satisfied:

(1) If x_n converges to x, then $y_n = f(x_n)$ converges to $y = f(x)$.

(2) If $y = f(x)$, $\eta = f(\xi)$, then $y\eta$ can be made *arbitrarily* small by making $x\xi$ *sufficiently* small; that is, for every $\sigma > 0$, it is possible to find some $\varrho > 0$ such that, if $x\xi < \varrho$, then $y\eta < \sigma$. x is considered constant throughout.

If $f(x)$ is continuous at every point x, then we say simply that $f(x)$ is *continuous*. We shall later consider *continuous* functions in more detail. Meanwhile, however, we can say:

1. *If $f(x)$ is real and continuous, then the set* $[f > 0]$ *is open.*

For if $y = f(x) > 0$, then for given $\sigma > 0$ a suitable $\varrho > 0$ can be found such that for $x\xi < \varrho$ we have at the same time $|y - \eta| < \sigma$, and consequently (if we choose $\sigma < y$), we have $\eta > y - \sigma > 0$. This means that there exists some neighborhood $U_x(\varrho)$ at whose points ξ the inequality $f(\xi) > 0$ holds; thus x is an interior point of the set $[f > 0]$.

We shall now try to convince ourselves that all the open sets can be obtained by this method. For a point x and a non-empty set B let us define a *lower distance*

$$\delta(x, B) = \inf_{y \varepsilon B} xy,$$

the greatest lower bound of the distances of the point x from the points y of B. From $xy \leqq \xi y + x\xi$, it follows that

$$\delta(x, B) \leqq \delta(\xi, B) + x\xi$$

if, for $y \varepsilon B$, we take the greatest lower bound on both sides. Interchanging x and y we obtain

$$|\delta(x, B) - \delta(\xi, B)| \leqq x\xi.$$

This states that *$\delta(x, B)$ is a continuous function of x.* If we let $A = E - B$ denote the complement of B, then the inequality $\delta(x, B) > 0$ is obviously equivalent to the statement that x has a neighborhood free of points of B, that is, a neighborhood (of radius $\varrho = \delta(x, B)$) that is completely in A, so that x is an interior point of A. Thus for the continuous function $f(x) = \delta(x, B)$ the set $[f > 0]$ is identical with A_i and, if $A = A_i$ is open, identical with A. In the exceptional case $B = 0$, $A = E$, we can use the constant function $f(x) = 1$. Therefore we have:

II. *For every open set A there exists a function $f(x)$ continuous in E such that the set $[f > 0]$ is identical with A.*

From I it follows that the *neighborhoods are open sets*; for $\varrho - ax$ is a continuous function of x and is positive in the set $U_a(\varrho)$.

If $A \leqq B$, then of course $A_i \leqq B_i$; A_i is a "*monotone*" function of A.

The set A_i is always open, since we represented it above as a set $[f > 0]$ for some continuous $f(x)$. If B is an open subset of A then $B = B_i \leqq A_i$; therefore A_i is the *greatest open subset* of A, whence the name *open kernel* of A, in conformity with the convention established on p. 112.

The set A_b is always a border set.

If $A, B, \ldots$ are any number of sets, not necessarily a finite number, and if

$$S = A \dot{+} B \dot{+} \cdots, \quad D = A B \cdots$$

are their sum and intersection, then the property of monotonicity implies in either case that

$$S_i \geqq A_i \dot{+} B_i \dot{+} \cdots, \quad D_i \leqq A_i B_i \cdots.$$

For a finite number of sets, however, a stronger result holds which, in the case of two sets, can be written

$$\text{if} \quad D = AB, \quad \text{then} \quad D_i = A_i B_i.$$

For, $x \,\varepsilon\, A_i B_i$ has a neighborhood $U \leqq A$ and a neighborhood $V \leqq B$; the smaller of the two neighborhoods then belongs to D, and so $x \,\varepsilon\, D_i$. Therefore $A_i B_i \leqq D_i$; but, on the other hand, we already had $D_i \leqq A_i B_i$.

From this, it follows immediately that:

III. *The sum of any number of open sets and the intersection of a finite number are themselves open sets.*

For with the notation above we have $S_i \geqq S$, and thus $S_i = S$ and $D_i = D$.

The intersection of infinitely many open sets need not be open. In the Euclidean plane the intersection of concentric open circular discs with radii $\varrho + \frac{1}{n}$ $(n = 1, 2, \ldots)$ is the disc of radius ϱ inclusive of the circumference; every point is the intersection of its neighborhoods of radius $1/n$.

A sum of any number of neighborhoods is open, and every non-empty open set can be represented as such a sum — say, as the sum of all the neighborhoods it contains.

Let B be the complement of $A : E = A + B$. The interior points of

B are also called *exterior points* of[1] A, and conversely. The union of the borders of sets yields the *boundary*, or *frontier*, of A and of B:

$$A_f = A_b + B_b = B_f.$$

If, for example, A is a circular disc in the plane, with or without its circumference or with only part of its circumference, then the boundary is in each case the whole circumference. If A is the set of rational points then A_f is the whole plane.

The boundary of an open set reduces to the border of the complement ($A_f = B_b$) and is therefore a border set. The boundary of the whole space, as well as that of the null set, is the null set.[2]

§ 23. The α, β, and γ Points

Let A be a point set in the space E and x a point of E (not necessarily of A). We make the following definition: x is called an

α-point,		at least one point,
β-point,	of A if every neighborhood U_x contains	infinitely many points,
γ-point		non-denumerably many points

of A. The sets of the α, β, and γ points will be denoted by A_α, A_β, A_γ.

The β-points are also called *points of accumulation*, the γ-points *points of condensation*, and the set A_β the *derived set* of A.

(Points of accumulation are often called *limit points* or *cluster points.*)

It is thus required that the intersection AU_x have, for each U_x, at least the cardinalities $1, \aleph_0, \aleph_1$; this scale, of course, could be extended. In order that we can be concise in what follows, we introduce the notation

$$k_\alpha = 1, \quad k_\beta = \aleph_0, \quad k_\gamma = \aleph_1$$

and say: x is a λ-point of A if each AU_x has at least the cardinality k_λ; we let A_λ be the set of λ-points ($\lambda = \alpha, \beta, \gamma$).

An accumulation point x of A could also have been defined by the condition that every neighborhood U_x contain at least one point of A different from x.

[1] The preposition "of" is used here, and in other cases as well, for points that do not belong to A. While this may be questionable grammatical usage, it is now quite customary.

[2] Usage in connection with the terms "boundary," "border," and "frontier" is unfortunately quite variable.

Examples in the Euclidean plane E:

A, a circular disc without circumference: $A_\alpha = A_\beta = A_\gamma =$ circular disc with its circumference.

A, the set of rational points: $A_\alpha = A_\beta = E$, $A_\gamma = 0$.

A, the set of irrational points: $A_\alpha = A_\beta = A_\gamma = E$.

A, the set of points with integer coordinates: $A_\alpha = A$, $A_\beta = A_\gamma = 0$.

Let A be the set (Fig. 2) of the points $(x_1, x_2) = \left(\frac{m}{n}, \frac{1}{n}\right)$, where n ranges over the numbers 1, 2, 4, 8, . . . and m over all the integers, positive, negative, and zero. Then A_β is the line $x_2 = 0$, $A_\alpha = A + A_\beta$, $A_\gamma = 0$.

Using the concept of limit instead of the concept of neighborhood, we can define the λ-points as follows:

The α-points are clearly just the limit points $x = \lim a_n$ of the convergent sequences of points of A $(a_n \varepsilon A)$ – convergent, that is, in E; the β-points are those among them that can be represented with $x \neq a_n$. Or: the β-points are those points that are α-points of every set obtainable from A by leaving out a finite number of points, and vice versa; the γ-points are those points that are α-points of every set obtainable from A by leaving out a finite or a denumerably infinite number of points, and vice versa. Points of accumulation of sequences of points of A (p. 124) are not necessarily points of accumulation of A but are, in any event, α-points.

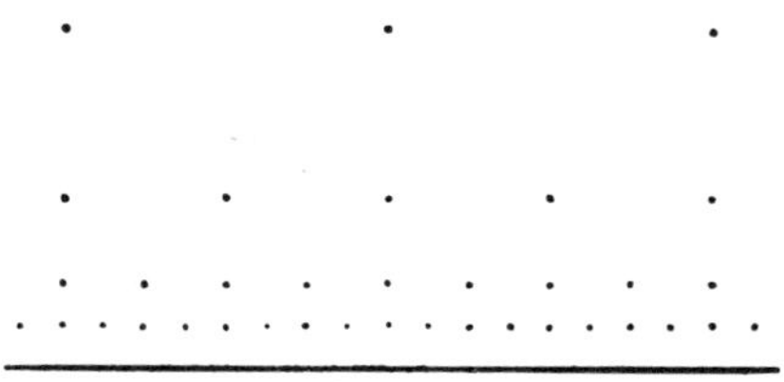

Fig. 2

In connection with the sets A_λ, we wish to introduce some further notation, the abundance of which will perhaps confuse the reader least if we take the radical step of introducing at this point even those members of the system that will not actually be needed until later. We shall be concerned here with the intersections of the A_λ with A and with the complements of these intersections in A, where A_α may be left out of consideration, since $AA_\alpha = A$. We set

$$(1) \quad \begin{cases} A_a = AA_\beta, & A_c = AA_\gamma, \\ A = A_a + A_h = A_c + A_j. \end{cases}$$

A_a and A_c are thus the sets of points of accumulation and points of condensation belonging to A itself; A_h and A_j are their respective complements. Since it is not a point of accumulation, a point a of A_h has a neighborhood that contains only a finite number of points of A, and so it also has one that contains no points of A at all except a itself. Hence a

is called an *isolated* point of A, and the set A_h of the isolated points is called the *isolated part* of A. Cantor also calls A_h the *adherence* and A_a the *coherence* of A. Since it is not a condensation point, a point of A_j has a neighborhood that contains at most a countable number of points of A. It is called an *uncondensed* point of A, and A_j the *uncondensed part* of A. We shall return to the sets A_j and A_c later (§ 25).

In addition to the trivial relations

$$A_\alpha \geqq A, \quad A_\alpha \geqq A_\beta \geqq A_\gamma, \quad A \geqq A_a \geqq A_c$$

we have, as is equally easy to see,

$$A_\alpha = A \dot{+} A_\beta, \tag{2}$$

from which we obtain the relation

$$A_\alpha = (A - A_a) + A_\beta = A + (A_\beta - A_a) \tag{3}$$

in which the summands are disjoint; thus the isolated part of A is

$$A_h = A - A_a = A_\alpha - A_\beta, \tag{4}$$

while

$$A_\alpha - A = A_\beta - A_a$$

is the set of those points of accumulation of A that do not belong to A.

The set A is said to be

isolated	if $A_a = 0$, $A_h = A$,
dense-in-itself	if $A_h = 0$, $A_a = A$,

that is, if it consists entirely of isolated points or entirely of points of accumulation. (We write dense-in-itself hyphenated because, according to a later definition (§ 25), every set is dense in itself.)

Examples. In the plane, the set of the rational points is dense-in-itself and the set of the integral points, isolated; every set that has no point of accumulation at all — and, in particular, every finite set — is isolated. The set of numbers $\{1, 1/2, 1/3, \ldots\}$ is isolated, since its only point of accumulation 0 does not belong to it; the same is true of the set A of Fig. 2.

The set A_h cannot contain a point of accumulation of itself (which would also be a point of accumulation of A), and it is thus an isolated set. A_a, however, can contain isolated points of itself (which are then not isolated points of A), and therefore it need not be dense-in-itself. For the set of numbers $A = \{1, 1/2, 1/3, \ldots, 0\}$, $A_a = \{0\}$ is even an isolated set. If we use several subscripts, which are to be read from left to right so that, for instance, $A_{ha} = (A_h)_a$ and $A_{ah} = (A_a)_h$, then we have

$$A_{hh} = A_h, \qquad A_{ha} = 0,$$

whereas neither $A_{aa} = A_a$ nor $A_{ah} = 0$ need be true.

The condition for a set to be dense-in-itself may be expressed by writing $A \leqq A_\beta$. This gives rise to further definitions, as follows: We say that the set A is

dense-in-itself if $A \leqq A_\beta$,
closed if $A \geqq A_\beta$,
perfect if $A = A_\beta$,

that is, if every point of A is a point of accumulation, if every point of accumulation of A is a point of A itself, and if both hold at the same time. This can also be expressed, by means of (2), in the form of equations, inasmuch as A_α becomes equal to one of the summands A, A_β, or both: the set A is

dense-in-itself if $A_\alpha = A_\beta$,
closed if $A_\alpha = A$,
perfect if $A_\alpha = A_\beta = A$.

Once more we cite the simplest examples of planar sets.

A, a circular disc without circumference: dense-in-itself.

A, a circular disc including its circumference and a single external point: closed.

A, a circular disc including its circumference: perfect.

Sets without points of accumulation ($A_\beta = 0$) – in particular, finite sets – count, of course, as closed sets. The null set is everything: isolated, dense-in-itself, closed, perfect (open set, border set).

Whenever $A \leqq B$ we also have of course $A_\lambda \leqq B_\lambda$ $(\lambda = \alpha, \beta, \gamma)$, $A_a \leqq B_a$, $A_c \leqq B_c$; these sets behave monotonically; their complements A_h and A_j, however, do not.

Furthermore, we have (for the meaning of multiple subscripts, see above):

(5) $$A_{\lambda\alpha} = A_\lambda \qquad (\lambda = \alpha, \beta, \gamma)$$

(6) $$A_{\alpha\beta} = A_\beta.$$

Proof of (5). If $x \,\varepsilon\, A_{\lambda\alpha}$, then each U_x contains a point $y \,\varepsilon\, A_\lambda$, but since U_x is open, there exists some $U_y \leqq U_x$; U_y, and therefore U_x, contains at least k_λ points of A, so that $x \,\varepsilon\, A_\lambda$. Hence $A_{\lambda\alpha} \leqq A_\lambda$; but we already had $A_{\lambda\alpha} \geqq A_\lambda$.

(5) says that: *The sets A_λ are closed.* For every closed set $B \geqq A$, we have $B = B_\alpha \geqq A_\alpha$: *$A_\alpha$ is thus the smallest closed set containing A, the closed hull of A* (p. 112).

Proof of (6). If $x \varepsilon A_{\alpha\beta}$, then each U_x contains a point $y \varepsilon A_\alpha$ different from x. We choose a neighborhood $U_y < U_x$ that does not contain x; U_y contains a point $z \varepsilon A$. Therefore every U_x contains a point $z \varepsilon A$ different from x, and x is a β-point of A. Hence $A_{\alpha\beta} \leqq A_\beta$; but we already had $A_\beta \leqq A_{\alpha\beta}$.

From (6) it follows that: *The sets A and A_α have the same isolated points.* For,

$$A_h = A_\alpha - A_\beta = A_{\alpha\alpha} - A_{\alpha\beta} = A_{\alpha h}.$$

If A is dense-in-itself, then A_α is perfect, and vice versa.

If, again, $A, B, \ldots$ are any number of sets (not necessarily a finite number), and if

$$S = A \dot{+} B \dot{+} \ldots, \qquad D = AB \ldots$$

are their sum and intersection respectively, then it follows from the monotonicity that

$$S_\lambda \geqq A_\lambda \dot{+} B_\lambda \dot{+} \cdots, \quad D_\lambda \leqq A_\lambda B_\lambda \cdots, \qquad (\lambda = \alpha, \beta, \gamma).$$

For a finite number of sets we have a stronger result; for two sets, for example:

(7) If $S = A \dot{+} B$, we have $S_\lambda = A_\lambda \dot{+} B_\lambda$. $(\lambda = \alpha, \beta, \gamma)$.

It is only necessary to prove that $S_\lambda \leqq A_\lambda \dot{+} B_\lambda$ or that a point x that does not belong to $A_\lambda \dot{+} B_\lambda$ does not belong to S_λ either. Now if x is a λ-point neither of A nor of B, then there are neighborhoods U_x and V_x such that AU_x and BV_x are of cardinality $< k_\lambda$, and if U_x, say, is the one having the smaller radius, then $SU_x = AU_x \dot{+} BU_x$ also has cardinality $< k_\lambda$ so that x is not a λ-point of S either.

From this it follows that:

I. *The sum of a finite number of closed sets and the intersection of an arbitrary number of closed sets is closed.*

This theorem means exactly the same thing as Theorem III, § 22, because:

II. *Open and closed sets are the complements of one another.*

For if $E = A + B$ and if x is a point, then *either* (i) every U_x contains a point of A $(x \varepsilon A_\alpha)$ *or* (ii) there exists some U_x with $AU_x = 0$, $U_x \leqq B$ $(x \varepsilon B_i)$. Thus

(8) If $E = A + B$, we have $E = A_\alpha + B_i = A_i + B_\alpha$.

II follows from this. *The boundary of every set is closed*; for, $A_f = A_b + B_b$ is a complement of the open set $A_i + B_i$ or, $A_f = A_\alpha B_\alpha$ is the intersection of two closed sets.

As a result, the closed sets can be characterized, as the open sets were (§ 22, I, II), by real *continuous functions* $f(x)$ (continuous in the space E). The sets $[f > 0]$, $[f < 0]$ and their sum $[f \neq 0]$ are open; their complements, the sets $[f \leqq 0]$, $[f \geqq 0]$ and the intersection $[f = 0]$ of these sets are closed; all the open and closed sets can be found in this way. For $f(x) = \delta(x, A)$, we have $[f = 0] = A_\alpha$, and therefore $= A$ in case A is closed. The curves and surfaces of analytical geometry are closed sets insofar as they are defined by setting equal to zero one (or more) continuous functions of the coordinates. The same is not true of *parametric representations* (which belong to the material of Chapter VIII). A curve of the x_1x_2-plane represented by means of continuous functions of the form

$$x_1 = \varphi_1(t), \qquad x_2 = \varphi_2(t)$$

or, more generally,

$$f(x_1, x_2, t) = 0, \qquad g(x_1, x_2, t) = 0$$

(where t ranges over all the real numbers) is not necessarily closed. This does not contradict what we have just said: these equations do define a closed set in the x_1x_2t-space, but its projection A into the x_1x_2-plane need not be closed. An example of an A that is not closed can be obtained from the simple case $x_1 = \dfrac{t}{1 + |t|}$, $x_2 = 0$, in which the curve becomes the open interval $(-1, 1)$ of the x_1-axis.

A second and no less important relation between open and closed sets is contained in the theorem:

III. *Every closed set is the intersection of a sequence of open sets; every open set is the sum of a sequence of closed sets.*

For let A be any set; we enclose every point $x \varepsilon A$ in a neighborhood $U_x(\varrho)$ with a fixed radius ϱ. The sum of these neighborhoods of points

$$U(A, \varrho) = \mathfrak{S}_x^A U_x(\varrho) \tag{9}$$

may appropriately be called a *neighborhood of the set A of radius* ϱ. It is an open set consisting of the points y for which there can be found at least one point $x \varepsilon A$ such that $xy < \varrho$. We now state that

$$A_\alpha = U(A, 1)\, U(A, \tfrac{1}{2})\, U(A, \tfrac{1}{3}) \ldots, \tag{10}$$

which represents A_α, and consequently every closed set, as the intersection of a sequence of open sets. For, the intersection on the right — which is also, incidentally, the intersection of all the $U(A, \varrho)$ with $\varrho > 0$ — is exactly the set of those points y for which a point $x \varepsilon A$ with $xy < \varrho$

exists for every $\varrho > 0$; that is, it is the set of all the α-points of A. The second half of Theorem III follows from the first by taking complements.

The theorem can also be deduced directly from the identities ($n = 1, 2, 3, \ldots$)

$$[f > 0] = \mathfrak{S}_n \left[f \geqq \frac{1}{n} \right]$$
$$[f \leqq 0] = \mathfrak{D}_n \left[f < \frac{1}{n} \right]$$

– valid for every real function $f(x)$ – if we let $f(x)$ be a continuous function. The second of the equations is nothing but (10) with $\delta(x, A)$ set equal to $f(x)$.

It follows from the earlier formula

$$S = A \dotplus B \dotplus \cdots, \quad S_\lambda \geqq A_\lambda \dotplus B_\lambda \dotplus \cdots$$

with $\lambda = \beta$, that

IV. *The sum of any number of dense-in-itself sets is dense-in-itself.*

This allows us to form the sum of all the dense-in-itself subsets of A (to which the null set certainly belongs) and this, in turn, is dense-in-itself and is therefore the *greatest dense-in-itself subset*, or the *dense-in-itself kernel*, of A. We call this kernel A_k; and we call the points not belonging to the dense-in-itself kernel *separated points* and the totality A_s of these points the *separated part* of A. We have thus obtained a new, and final, decomposition of A

$$A = A_k + A_s \tag{11}$$

into disjoint summands. A set consisting entirely of separated points ($A_k = 0$) is called a *separated* set, and we now have still another counterpart to dense-in-itself: A is

dense-in-itself	if $A_s = 0$, $A_k = A$,
separated	if $A_k = 0$, $A_s = A$.

Clearly, the set A_s of separated points is itself a separated set, just as the set A_h of the isolated points was an isolated set (the names separated part and isolated part are thus justified grammatically). Obviously, we have

$$A_h \leqq A_s, \quad A_a \geqq A_k, \tag{12}$$

since an isolated point of A surely cannot belong to a dense-in-itself subset of A; every subset of A that is dense-in-itself belongs to the coherence A_a. But then it must also belong to the second coherence A_{aa}, to the third coherence A_{aaa}, and so forth. We shall see later (§ 30) how transfinite repetition of the construction of the coherence enables us finally to attain the dense-in-itself kernel. We may also say: Not only does the isolated part A_h of A belong to the separated part A_s, but also so do the isolated part A_{ah} of A_a the isolated part A_{aah} of A_{aa} (the first, second, and third adherences of A), and so on.

Example. Let A be the set of numbers $\frac{1}{p}+\frac{1}{q}+\frac{1}{r}$, where p, q, r run through the natural numbers. Then A_a is the set of numbers $\frac{1}{p}+\frac{1}{q}$ (which, in the form $\frac{1}{p}+\frac{1}{2q}+\frac{1}{2q}$ belong to A, the only additional points of accumulation of A being 0); A_{aa} is the set of numbers $\frac{1}{p}$, $A_{aaa}=0$, and thus $A_k=0$, and the set A is separated.

As a supplement to the formulas concerning the behavior of the λ-points under formation of sums and intersections, we add the following, which concerns the intersection of A with an *open* set.

We have

(13) $$(AG)_\lambda \geqq A_\lambda G \qquad (G \text{ open}) \quad (\lambda=\alpha,\beta,\gamma),$$

while of course the trivial formula $(AG)_\lambda \leqq A_\lambda G_\lambda$ also holds. For if $x \,\varepsilon\, A_\lambda G$ and U_x is a neighborhood, then GU_x is open, and there exists a neighborhood $V_x \leqq GU_x$; this neighborhood contains at least k_λ points of A which, however, also belong to G and consequently to AG. Thus every U_x contains at least k_λ points of AG, and $x \,\varepsilon\, (AG)_\lambda$.

Some applications of this result follows.

V. *The intersection of an open set with a set that is dense-in-itself is dense-in-itself.*

For from $A_\beta \geqq A$ it follows, using (13), that $(AG)_\beta \geqq A_\beta G \geqq AG$.

We remark that, in contrast to IV and V, even the intersection of two dense-in-itself sets need not be dense-in-itself.

Example: Two intersecting lines of the Euclidean plane.

VI. *An open set that contains no isolated point of the space is dense-in-itself.*

For if G is open and contained in E_β, then $G_\beta=(EG)_\beta \geqq E_\beta G = G$. The necessary condition for a set to be dense-in-itself — that it be contained in E_β — is thus, for open sets, a sufficient condition as well.

If A is a set containing no isolated points of the space, then A_i is dense-in-itself, and as a result,

(14) $$A_i \leqq A_k, \quad A_b \geqq A_s.$$

If A is once again arbitrary, then between the isolated and the separated parts there subsists the relation

$$(15) \qquad A_h \leqq A_s \leqq A_{h\alpha},$$

the first half of which we already know from (12). The second half states that every point $x \varepsilon A_s$ is an α-point of A_h. If this were not the case, then x would have a neighborhood U with $A_h U = 0$; since U is open, (13) would imply that

$$AU = A_a U \leqq A_\beta U \leqq (AU)_\beta$$

and AU would be dense-in-itself, whence $AU \leqq A_k$, in contradiction to $x \varepsilon A_s$. Therefore A_s consists of the isolated part and (certain) accumulation points thereof; this is a more precise formulation of the fact that A_s vanishes whenever A_h does (because A is then dense-in-itself).

As a counterpart to VI we prove another theorem:

VII. *A closed set that contains no isolated points of the space is a derived set.*

This condition is thus both necessary and sufficient, for every derived set A_β is closed and $\leqq E_\beta$. We base our proof on an auxiliary theorem:

VIII. *If H is the boundary of the open set G, then H can be represented as the derived set A_β of an isolated set $A \leqq G$.*[1]

We assume H to be non-empty. (If $H = 0$, then A may be taken to be zero.) $H = G_\alpha - G$ is a closed set consisting of those accumulation points of G that are not in G (or the boundary $F - F_i$ of the complement $F = E - G$).

For every point $x \varepsilon G$, the lower distance from H is positive,

$$\delta(x) = \delta(x, H) > 0.$$

Now let A be a *greatest* subset of G, that is, one that cannot be extended,[2] such that for any two distinct points in A,

$$(16) \qquad xy \geqq \tfrac{1}{2}\,\delta(x) + \tfrac{1}{2}\,\delta(y).$$

It follows that $A_\beta \leqq H$. To see this, let x be a point of accumulation of A; x can be represented as the limit $x = \lim x_n$ of a sequence of points

[1] *An example from the Euclidean plane*: G, the half-plane $x_2 > 0$; H, the line $x_2 = 0$; A, the set of Fig. 2.

[2] The existence of such a subset can hardly be proved without a well-ordering of G. To every set $B < G$ we assign (§ 12) as differential element a point of $B - G$ that has the relation (16) with all the points of B, whenever the assignment is possible. A segment of the resultant well-ordering yields a set A having the required property.

$x_n \varepsilon A$ which are pairwise distinct. The continuity of the function $\delta(x)$ then implies that $\delta(x_n) \to \delta(x)$, and since in

$$x_n x_{n+1} \geqq \tfrac{1}{2}\,\delta(x_n) + \tfrac{1}{2}\,\delta(x_{n+1})$$

the left-hand side converges to 0 and the right-hand side to $\delta(x)$, we have $\delta(x) = 0$. Thus x is a point of accumulation of G without belonging to G, which is to say, it is a point of $H: A_\beta \leqq H$.

On the other hand, $H \leqq A_\beta$. Let $h \varepsilon H$ and $y \varepsilon G$ with arbitrarily small $hy < \delta$. If $y \varepsilon A$, there is nothing to prove; if not, then there is at least one $x \varepsilon A$ that fails to satisfy (16) for this y, for the set A could otherwise be extended by adjunction of y. Next we infer that:

$$\begin{aligned} xy &< \tfrac{1}{2}\,\delta(x) + \tfrac{1}{2}\,\delta(y) \leqq \tfrac{1}{2}\,hx + \tfrac{1}{2}\,hy, \\ hx &\leqq hy + xy < \tfrac{1}{2}\,hx + \tfrac{3}{2}\,hy, \\ hx &< 3\,hy < 3\,\delta. \end{aligned}$$

In either case there are therefore points $x \varepsilon A$ with arbitrarily small distance ($< 3\delta$) from h, whence $H \leqq A_\beta$, and we have proved that $H = A_\beta$.

The proof of VII now proceeds as follows. Let $F = F_b + F_i = H + F_i$ be closed, so that H is the boundary of the open set $G = E - F$ and therefore $H = A_\beta$ with $A \leqq G$. Since $F \leqq E_\beta$ it follows, using VI, that F_i is dense-in-itself and $F_i \leqq F_\beta$. Therefore we have

$$\begin{aligned} F &= F_i + H \leqq F_\beta \dot{+} H \leqq F \dot{+} H = F, \\ F &= F_\beta \dot{+} H = F_\beta + A_\beta = (F + A)_\beta; \end{aligned}$$

F is the derived set of $F + A$.

IX. *The sum of a finite number of separated sets is separated.*

It suffices to consider two separated sets and to show that their sum $S = A \dot{+} B$, if dense-in-itself, is empty. (The same applies to any subset of S; S is separated.) Since $G = E - A_\alpha$ is open, V implies that $SG = BG$ is dense-in-itself and therefore empty; $S \leqq A_\alpha$, $S_\alpha = A_\alpha$, $A \leqq S \leqq S_\beta = A_\beta$, A is dense-in-itself, so that $A = 0$ and also $B = 0$.

§ 24. Relative and Absolute Concepts

The sets and properties defined in the last two sections (A_α, A_i, closed, open, etc.) depend, of course, not only on the set A but also on the containing space E; they have a *relative* character. This fact must on occasion be indicated more explicitly; for example, by writing $A_\alpha(E)$ instead of A_α and, in case $A = A_\alpha(E)$, by saying that *A is closed in E*.

(Similarly, in § 21, it was said that a sequence is convergent 'in E' or that A is compact 'in E.') A point set may be closed, open, a boundary set or the like, in one space E without having the same property in another space E'. The set of irrational numbers between 0 and 1 is closed in the space of irrational numbers but not in the space of the reals. A circular disc excluding its circumference is open as a planar set but is a boundary set in three-dimensional space. Every set is both closed and open in that set itself.

Such concepts, properties, and relations as are independent of the containing space are called *absolute.* Thus, a set is called *absolutely closed* if it is closed in *every* space $E \geqq A$. The statement 'A is dense-in-itself' is of absolute character, since it says: For every point $a \in A$ and every $\varrho > 0$ there exist infinitely many points of A whose distance from a is $< \varrho$; in this statement it is only A itself, and not the containing space, that comes into question.

The statement 'x is a λ-point of A' means that for every $\varrho > 0$ there are at least k_λ points $a \in A$ for which $ax < \varrho$ (p. 130); it does presuppose that x and A belong to some metric space E, but it does not depend on this space and is of absolute character. If A and D are subsets of E, then the set

$$A_\lambda(D)$$

of the λ-points of A belonging to D is defined absolutely, and independently of E. It is obvious that

$$A_\lambda(D) = D A_\lambda(E), \tag{1}$$

where the right-hand side only seemingly depends on E. If we now return to the original notation and once again suppress the argument E, so that the sets A_λ and the concepts closed and open refer to the space E, then

$$A_\lambda(D) = D A_\lambda. \tag{2}$$

The set A is *closed in D* if $A = A_\alpha(D)$, so that

$$A = D A_\alpha. \tag{3}$$

Those sets that are closed in D are the intersections of D with closed sets.

For, on the one hand, (3) is such an intersection; on the other hand, if

$$A = DF \tag{4}$$

is the intersection of A with a closed set F, then it follows from $A \leqq A_\alpha \leqq F$ by forming the intersection with D that $A \leqq D A_\alpha \leqq A$, and so we have (3).

If $A + B = D$, then the open kernel $B_i(D)$ of B in the space D has to be defined as the complement $D - A_\alpha(D)$. According to (2), this yields the set $D(E - A_\alpha)$ or

$$(5) \qquad B_i D = D B_i^*,$$

where $B^* = E - A$ is the complement of A in E and B_i^* is its open kernel relative to E.[1] The set B is *open in* D if

$$(6) \qquad B = D B_i^*.$$

The sets open in D are the complements in D of the sets closed in D or the intersections.

$$(7) \qquad B = DG$$

of D with the open sets. (7) follows from (4) if $G = E - F$ denotes the open complement of F.

That A is closed in D is equivalent to the statement that $A \leqq D$ and that $D - A$ contains no point of accumulation of A: $A_\alpha(D - A) = A_\beta(D - A) = 0$.

The dense-in-itself kernel A_k of A is closed in A. For if $A - A_k$ contained an accumulation point a of A_k, then $A_k + \{a\}$ would be dense-in-itself and A_k could not be the greatest dense-in-itself set $\leqq A$. *The dense-in-itself kernel of a closed set is perfect.*

Since (2) depends only on A and D and not on the containing space E, it follows that, in particular, the sets

$$(8) \qquad A_\lambda(A) = A A_\lambda$$

depend only on A and are of absolute character. The sets

$$A_a = A A_\beta, \qquad A_c = A A_\gamma$$

and their complements

$$A_h = A - A_a, \qquad A_j = A - A_c$$

are all determined by A alone. Hence *dense-in-itself* and *isolated* are absolute concepts, and so the dense-in-itself kernel A_k as well as its complement $A_s = A - A_k$ depend only on A. Once more bringing together all the sets thus far defined:

$A_i, A_b, A_f, A_\alpha, A_\beta, A_\gamma$	depend on the space E;
$A_a, A_h, A_c, A_j, A_k, A_s$	do not depend on the space E.

[1] Thus, on the right-hand side of (5) we do not have DB_i, as analogy to (3) might have led us to suspect.

Of course, we call *A perfect in D* if A is dense-in-itself and closed in D. $A = DA_\alpha$ is in this case the intersection of D with a perfect set; but the converse does not hold, since such an intersection need not be dense-in-itself. A_k is perfect in A.

If E is a *complete* space, then obviously

$$A_\alpha = A_\alpha(E) = \bar{A} \tag{9}$$

is a *complete hull* (p. 124) of A. *The closed hull of A in a complete space is a complete hull of A; the sets that are closed in a complete space are complete.* This $\bar{A}$ depends essentially (to within the notation chosen for the elements of $\bar{A} - A$) only on A, since all the complete hulls are isometric in the sense given on p. 124. In this sense, $\bar{A}$ is the *greatest closed hull* of A; for if $A \leqq D$ and E is a complete space $\geqq D$ (which can be obtained, for example, by completing D), then $A_\alpha(D)$ is a subset of $A_\alpha(E) = \bar{A}$. If A itself is complete, then $A = \bar{A} = A_\alpha$, A is closed in E and all the more so in $D(A = DA = DA_\alpha)$; this means that *complete sets are absolutely closed* (closed in every space $D \geqq A$), *and conversely*; for an absolutely closed set is closed, in particular, in every complete space and is therefore complete.

The two remaining sets $A_\lambda = A_\lambda(E)$ $(\lambda = \beta, \gamma)$ as well depend essentially only on A when E is complete, and each is the largest set possible of its kind.

The natural counterpart of the absolutely closed sets would seem to be the absolutely open sets, that is, sets open in every containing space. However, it is easy to see that, apart from the null set, such sets cannot exist. For, any set can be imbedded in some space E in such a way as to make it contain boundary points or even consist entirely of such points — say, in the same way that the Euclidean plane is imbedded in three-dimensional space. This may be done simply by forming (p. 119) the product (A, B) of A with the set B of the real numbers; in this space, whose points are (x, y), every 'layer' $y =$ constant is isometric with A and consists entirely of boundary points.

Compactness, also, is a relative concept; we said that A was to be called *compact in E* if every sequence of points of A had at least one subsequence convergent in E. We can also say: *A is compact in E if and only if every infinite subset of A has at least one point of accumulation in E.*

The sets that are *compact in themselves* are complete or absolutely closed (p. 124); they may also be called *absolutely compact* (in every containing space). If A is compact in any space E whatever, then A is already compact considered as a subset of its closed hull A_α, and this latter is compact in itself; if A is both compact and closed in E, then A is compact in itself.

The concepts of completeness and compactness, on the other hand, and of closure, on the other hand, are of completely different character, as must be emphasized because present-day usage is so unsettled. The former require, in certain cases, the *existence* of α-points or points of accumulation; the latter requires that *in the event they exist* they belong to the set under consideration. In the case of the concepts of closure and compactness, the difference appears very clearly in the inferences to be drawn when $A \leqq B \leqq C$: if A is closed in C, then it is also closed in B; if A is compact in B, then it is also compact in C.

The considerations of the present section were essential to our understanding of the concepts discussed. This will not, however, prevent us in what follows from using relative concepts such as closed, open, and compact, as well as the names A_α and so on, without qualification; they will be assumed in each case to refer to the containing space. In particular, it goes without saying that two relative concepts occurring in one context are to refer to the *same* space; if we speak, for instance, of a closed compact set, this is to mean that the set is closed in E and compact in E.

§ 25. Separable Spaces

In this section and in the one following, questions of cardinality will play the principal role. The cardinality (of the space and of certain of its subsets) will be at first bounded from above and later on, from below. As a preliminary example of how this is to be done, we recall how the cardinality of the real numbers is determined. It is *at most* equal to $\aleph = \aleph_0^{\aleph_0}$, because every x can be represented as $\lim r_n$ of rational numbers and the countable set R of the rationals is "dense in E"; it is *at least* equal to $\aleph$ because, conversely, each $\lim r_n$ is a real number x — that is, E is the complete hull of R or is itself complete.

Let us consider once more only points and subsets of a fixed metric space E. We say *A is dense to B* if

$$A_\alpha \geqq B.$$

This means: Every point $b \varepsilon B$ is an α-point of A or, can be represented as $b = \lim a_n$ $(a_n \varepsilon A)$; or, Every neighborhood U_b contains at least one point of A; or, For each b there exists some a whose distance from b is arbitrarily small. The last formulation, or the notation $B = BA_\alpha = A_\alpha(B)$, states, incidentally, that this property is independent of the containing space E. The fact that A is dense to B yields an upper bound for the cardinality $\mathfrak{b}$ of B in terms of the cardinality $\mathfrak{a}$ of A, namely

$$\mathfrak{a}^{\aleph_0} \geqq \mathfrak{b}.$$

For there are only $\mathfrak{a}^{\aleph_0}$ sequences $(a_1, a_2, \ldots)$ of points of A and thus at most that many that are convergent (in E), so that A_α has a cardinality $\leqq \mathfrak{a}^{\aleph_0}$.

The inequalities $A_\alpha \geqq B$ and $A_\alpha \geqq B_\alpha$ are equivalent. We consider two sets *dense to one another* ($A_\alpha = B_\alpha$) to be in the same *density class*; in every such class there exists exactly one closed set ($F = A_\alpha = B_\alpha = \ldots = F_\alpha$), the greatest set of the class.

If A is dense to B and is, at the same time, a subset of B, then we say that *A is dense in B*. Then $A_\alpha = B_\alpha$, and both sets belong to the same density class.

Every set A is dense in A_α and, in particular, in its complete hull $\bar{A}$. The isolated part A_h is dense in the separated part A_s because of § 23, (15). In the Euclidean space E, the set R of the rationals, as well as the set J of the irrationals, are dense; both are dense to one another ($R_\alpha = J_\alpha = E$).

Let us consider all the sets *A dense in the space E*; $A_\alpha = E$. (This means: The complement $B = E - A$ is a border set; $B_i = 0$). If we ignore the finite spaces (the spaces consisting of only a finite number of points), then A is infinite. Among the cardinalities of all these A there is a *smallest*, $\aleph_\mu$; the space then has cardinality $\leqq \aleph_\mu^{\aleph_0}$.

The simplest and most important case is that in which a countable set R is dense in E; $E = R_\alpha$ is then of at most the cardinality of the continuum $\aleph_0^{\aleph_0} = \aleph$. *A set in which a countable set is dense is called separable,* an expression due to Fréchet which, although not exactly suggestive, happens to be generally accepted. A set which is finite or separable will be called *at most separable.*

Examples. We have already mentioned that the Euclidean space E_n is separable; the set R of the points $r = (r_1, r_2, \ldots, r_n)$ with rational coordinates r_n is dense in E_n, since for each $x = (x_1, x_2, \ldots, x_n)$ there exists an r whose distance from x is arbitrarily small. R is countable and of cardinality $\aleph_0^n = \aleph_0$. Hilbert space, too, is separable; a set dense in Hilbert space is the set R of the points

$$r = (r_1, r_2, \ldots, r_n, 0, 0, \ldots)$$

with only a finite number of non-zero rational coordinates. For corresponding to each $x = (x_1, x_2, \ldots)$ with the sum of its squares Σx_n^2

convergent, there exists some $(x_1, x_2, \ldots, x_n, 0, 0, \ldots)$ and, corresponding to this, some r, with arbitrarily small distance from x. The space of the functions $x(t)$ continuous in $a \leqq t \leqq b$ with norm defined by $|x| = \max |x(t)|$ and with the corresponding definition of distance $|x-y|$ is separable; the set R of polynomials

$$r(t) = r_0 + r_1 t + \cdots + r_n t^n$$

with rational coefficients is dense in this space. For it follows from the Weierstrass Approximation Theorem that there is a polynomial arbitrarily close to $x(t)$ and a polynomial with rational coefficients arbitrarily close to the first. This is all the more true for the distance derived from $|x| = \left(\int_a^b x(t)^2\, dt\right)^{\frac{1}{2}}$. As in the case of Hilbert space, R has the cardinality $\aleph_0 + \aleph_0^2 + \aleph_0^3 + \cdots = \aleph_0$.

Non-separable spaces can also be constructed readily. Let us make an arbitrary set $M = \{m, n, \ldots\}$ into a metric space by assigning the distance 1 to any two distinct elements; clearly, no set properly contained in M is dense in M, and if M has cardinality $\mathfrak{m} > \aleph_0$, we obtain a non-separable space. If this M or, more generally, any set M in which two different points have a distance $\geqq \varrho$ from each other (ϱ a fixed positive number) lies in a space E, then a set dense in E never has cardinality less than $\mathfrak{m}$. For corresponding to every $m \varepsilon M$, it must contain a point x_m with $m x_m < \frac{1}{2}\varrho$, and these points are pairwise distinct since, for $m \neq n$,

$$x_m x_n \geqq mn - m x_m - n x_n > \varrho - \tfrac{1}{2}\varrho - \tfrac{1}{2}\varrho = 0.$$

This observation can also be used for constructing in any space E a dense set of smallest possible cardinality. Let us call a set $E(\varrho)$ a ***net*** of the space E if any two distinct points of the set have a distance $\geqq \varrho$ from each other and if it *cannot be extended.*[1] Then every set dense in E has a cardinality at least that of every net. If $E(\varrho)$ is a net, then for $\sigma < \varrho$ it is obviously possible to form a net $E(\sigma)$ that contains $E(\varrho)$ as a subset. For every point x of E there exists a point y of $E(\varrho)$ with $xy < \varrho$ (otherwise the net could be extended by adjoining x). If we form the sequence of nets $E(1), E(½), \ldots$, then it follows that

$$R = E(1) \dot{+} E(½) \dot{+} \ldots \tag{1}$$

is dense in E and if, in addition, each net is chosen so as to contain as a subset the one preceding it, then the cardinality of an arbitrary set dense

[1] The construction of such a set is accomplished by the well-ordering of E, as at the end of § 23.

in E is at least equal to that of R. For if $\mathfrak{a}_n$ is the cardinality of $E(1/n) - E(1/(n-1))$, $\mathfrak{a}_1$ the cardinality of $E(1)$,

$$\mathfrak{m}_n = \mathfrak{a}_1 + \cdots + \mathfrak{a}_n$$

the cardinality of $E(1/n)$, then $\mathfrak{a}_1 + \mathfrak{a}_2 + \ldots$ is the cardinality of R and is the smallest cardinal number $\geqq \mathfrak{m}_n$ for all n.

We have already made use of nets in the discussion of totally bounded sets on p. 125, where the nets were finite and where R consequently was at most countable. Hence: *Every totally bounded — that is, conditionally compact — set is finite or separable.*

Let us now suppose E separable, and let the countable set R be dense in E. For every point $r \,\varepsilon\, R$ we consider the neighborhoods $U_r(\varrho)$ with *rational* radii ϱ and call them *special neighborhoods*. The collection of all special neighborhoods is countable. Hence we can denote these neighborhoods by $V_1, V_2, \ldots$, and on occasion a particular special neighborhood by V and, if it contains the point x, by V_x.

For every neighborhood U_x there exists some $V_x \leqq U_x$. For if U_x has the radius σ, then there exists some r with $xr < \frac{1}{2}\sigma$ and a rational number ϱ with $xr < \varrho < \frac{1}{2}\sigma$. Therefore $U_r(\varrho)$ is some V_x and is contained in U_x; for from $ry < \varrho$ it follows that $xy \leqq xr + ry < 2\varrho < \sigma$.

For every point x of an open set G there exists some $V_x \leqq G$.

Every subset of a separable space is at most separable.

Let V_p $(p = p_1, p_2, \ldots)$ be those of the V_n that contain points of A, and choose a point $a_p \,\varepsilon\, AV_p$. The points a_p constitute an at most countable set dense in A. For if $x \,\varepsilon\, A$ and U_x is a neighborhood and $V_x \leqq U_x$, then V_x is some V_p, and U_x contains the point a_p. The statement just proved is not completely trivial, since a set R dense in E is offhand merely dense *to* A.

Let us recall the earlier notation of § 23, (1)

$$(2) \qquad A_c = AA_\gamma, \qquad A = A_c + A_j,$$

concerning the splitting of A into points of condensation and of non-condensation. If A is at most countable, then $A_\gamma = 0$ in every space. We can now prove a stronger converse to this:

I. *If the space is separable and $A_c = 0$, then A is at most countable.*

For since a point $x \,\varepsilon\, A$ is not a point of condensation, it has a neighborhood U_x with at most countable AU_x; let $V_x \leqq U_x$. Then $\mathfrak{S}_x^A A V_x = A$ is at most countable, since the sum contains at most a countable number of different summands each of which is at most countable.

This theorem, or even one that follows from it and therefore has, formally, a poorer content:

If $A_\gamma = 0$, then A is at most countable;
If $A_\beta = 0$, then A is at most countable;

characterizes the (finite or) separable spaces; if, for example, the last of these holds for every $A \leqq E$, then E is at most separable. This follows immediately from (1), where every net $E(\varrho)$, being a set without points of accumulation, is at most countable.

We now consider the three decompositions

$$A = A_a + A_h = A_k + A_s = A_c + A_j$$

of A into points of accumulation and isolated points, kernel and separated points, and points of condensation and of non-condensation. According to I, A_j is at most countable, since it contains no condensation point of A, not to mention A_j. But then A_c is dense-in-itself, for

$$A_{j\gamma} = 0, \quad A_\gamma = A_{j\gamma} \dotplus A_{c\gamma} = A_{c\gamma},$$
$$A_c \leqq A_\gamma = A_{c\gamma} \leqq A_{c\beta}.$$

Hence

(3) $$A_c \leqq A_k \leqq A_a, \qquad A_j \geqq A_s \geqq A_h,$$

and whenever A_j is at most countable, so are the sets A_s and A_h. Hence:

II. *The isolated, separated, and uncondensed parts of every set of a separable space are each at most countable.*

In particular, isolated, separated, and uncondensed sets are at most countable. If A is uncountable, then A_a, A_k, A_c, A_α, A_β, and A_γ are uncountable. A set having an at most countable derived set A_β is at most countable; if A_γ is at most countable, then A is at most countable, and hence, as a matter of fact, $A_\gamma = 0$.

In addition to the generally valid iteration formulas that we learned in § 23, (5) and (6),

(4) $$\begin{cases} A_{\alpha\alpha} = A_\alpha, \quad A_{\beta\alpha} = A_\beta, \quad A_{\gamma\alpha} = A_\gamma, \\ \qquad\qquad\quad A_{\alpha\beta} = A_\beta, \end{cases}$$

we now obtain in addition

(5) $$\begin{cases} A_{\gamma\alpha} = A_{\gamma\beta} = A_{\gamma\gamma} = A_\gamma \\ \qquad A_{\alpha\gamma} = A_{\beta\gamma}. \end{cases}$$

For we had $A_\gamma = A_{c\gamma} \leqq A_{\gamma\gamma} \leqq A_{\gamma\beta} \leqq A_{\gamma\alpha} = A_\gamma$, and the second line follows from the fact that $A_\alpha - A_\beta = A_h$ is at most countable. The first contains the statement that A_γ is perfect.

III. *A system of disjoint open sets of a separable space is at most countable.*

For corresponding to each of these (non-empty) open sets G we choose a point $x \varepsilon G$ and some $V_x \leqq G$; the V assigned to the different G are different, and there exists at most a countable number of them.

IV. *In a separable space there exist exactly* $\aleph$ *open sets (and the same number of closed sets).*

A non-empty open set G can be represented as a sum of special neighborhoods $V_x \leqq G$ $(x \varepsilon G)$ and can thus be put in the form

$$G = V_{m_1} \dot{+} V_{m_2} \dot{+} \cdots$$

with a suitably chosen set of natural numbers $m_1, m_2, \ldots$. Therefore there exist at most as many sets G as there are sets of natural numbers $(2^{\aleph_0} = \aleph)$. But also there exist at least as many (which, in the case of Euclidean space, for example, is trivial, since the neighborhoods of a point depend one to one on the radius to begin with). Let A, say, be some countable isolated set; such sets exist, for if the whole space is not itself such a set then let $x \varepsilon E_\beta$ and let $A = \{a_1, a_2, \ldots\}$ be a countable set of points $a_n \neq x$ which converge to x. If we enclose each point a_n in a neighborhood U_n that contains no other point of A, then to every subset B of A there corresponds one-to-one an open set $G = \mathfrak{S}_{a_n}^{B} U_n$ whose intersection with A is exactly B, and the set of these G has the cardinality $2^{\aleph_0} = \aleph$.

V. *If the dense-in-itself kernel of the separable space E is non-empty, then E contains exactly* $\aleph$ *perfect sets.*

We may replace E by E_k (the sets perfect in E are identical with those perfect in E_k, since E_k is closed in E); that is, we may assume that E itself is dense-in-itself (perfect). Let $x \varepsilon E$ and, just as above, let $A = \{a_1, a_2, \ldots\}$ be a set of points $a_n \neq x$, $a_n \to x$. The U_n used above may be assumed *disjoint*; we need only halve their radii. Then not only does $G = \sum_{a_n}^{B} U_n$ have exactly the intersection B with A but so does G_α also; for if a_1, for instance, does not belong to B, then $GU_1 = 0$, and a_1 cannot be an α-point of G either. The G, however, are dense-in-themselves and the G_α perfect. Moreover, the G_α corresponding to the countable sets B contain the point x; thus there are also exactly $\aleph$ perfect sets that contain a fixed point of the perfect space.

VI. *A system of open sets of a separable space may be replaced, without changing its sum, by a subsystem that is at most countable.*

For if $G = \mathfrak{S} G_m$, where the sum is extended over an arbitrary set, we look for the (at most countably many) different special neighborhoods V_p contained in the summands G_m and choose for each p a certain $G_{mp} \geqq V_p$. Then we have

$$G = \mathfrak{S}_p V_p \leqq \mathfrak{S}_p G_{mp} \leqq \mathfrak{S}_m G_m = G,$$

so that $G = \mathfrak{S}_p G_{mp}$. Taking complements yields:

VII. *A system of closed sets of a separable space may be replaced by a subsystem that is at most countable, without changing its intersection.*

§ 26. Complete Spaces

1. The Intersection Theorems. Just as the cardinality of the continuum appeared in the preceding section as an upper bound for certain sets, so will it appear in the present section as a lower bound. The foundation for this is laid in the second of the following intersection theorems, which we preface, by way of contrast, with a first one and certain of its corollaries. The latter theorem refers to sets compact in themselves, the former to bounded complete sets.

I. (FIRST INTERSECTION THEOREM). *A decreasing sequence $A_1 \geqq A_2 \geqq \ldots$ of non-empty, closed, compact sets has a non-empty intersection.*

In each set A_n we choose a point a_n. The sequence $(a_1, a_2, \ldots)$, considered as a sequence of points in A_1, has a convergent subsequence with the limit x, which is also a point of accumulation of every sequence of the form $(a_n, a_{n+1}, \ldots)$. Therefore x is an α-point of every set A_n; that is, it is a point of A_n; $x \varepsilon A_1 A_2 \ldots$.

The space E is quite arbitrary here; instead of closed compact[1] sets we might as well have spoken of sets compact in themselves.

II. (BOREL'S THEOREM).[2] *If a compact closed set is contained in the sum of a sequence of open sets, then it is contained in the sum of merely a finite number of these open sets.*

Suppose that: $A \leqq S = G_1 \dotplus G_2 \dotplus \ldots$, A compact and closed, G_n open. The theorem then states: There exists an n for which

$$A \leqq S_n = G_1 \dotplus \cdots \dotplus G_n.$$

[1] This is, of course, supposed to mean compact *in* E and closed *in* E; compare the last statement in § 24.

[2] Or: The Borel Covering Theorem. A set A is said to be *covered* by a collection of open sets when every point of A lies in at least one set of the collection. The reader will find it suggestive to rephrase Theorems II and III in terms of this concept. [*Ed.*]

In fact, the compact closed sets $A(E-S_n)$ form a decreasing sequence with the intersection $A(E-S)=0$; therefore, by I, they cannot all be different from zero, and there exists some n for which $A(E-S_n)=0$; that is, $A \leqq S_n$.

In conjunction with § 25, VI, we obtain a stronger form of the Borel Theorem (for separable spaces):

III. *If a compact closed set of a separable space is contained in the sum of an arbitrary system of open sets, then it is contained in the sum of merely a finite number of these open sets.*

The First Intersection Theorem, too, may be strengthened by means of § 25, VII:

IV. *If the space is separable, then a system of compact closed sets has a non-empty intersection in case every finite collection of sets of the system has a non-empty intersection.*

For, the intersection of the whole system may be represented as the intersection $A_1A_2 \ldots$ of a sequence of sets of the system, that is, as the intersection of the decreasing, non-empty, compact closed sets

$$A_1 \geqq A_1 A_2 \geqq \cdots.$$

V. (SECOND INTERSECTION THEOREM). *In a complete space, a decreasing sequence $A_1 \geqq A_2 \geqq \cdots$ of bounded, closed, non-empty sets whose diameters converge to zero has exactly one point in common.*

Once more, we choose $a_n \,\varepsilon\, A_n$; the sequence $(a_1, a_2, \ldots)$ is then a fundamental sequence, since the distance of a_n from all of the following points (which also belong to A_n) is $\leqq d(A_n)$. Therefore $x = \lim a_n$ exists and, as in I, we see that $x \,\varepsilon\, A_1A_2 \ldots$, and this intersection can contain only a single point, because $d(A_n) \to 0$.

Dependence on the space E could have been avoided in this case also, and we could have spoken simply of complete sets A_n. Neither of the two intersection theorems is a consequence of the other; the second admits bounded rather than compact sets, but to make up for this it has the condition on diameters. This condition is indispensable, as is shown by the example $A_n = \{x_n, x_{n+1}, \ldots\}$, where $x_1, x_2, \ldots$ denote points whose pairwise distance is unity. In Euclidean spaces, where bounded sets and compact sets are identical, the First Intersection Theorem has the greater content; the simplest case of the theorem, to the effect that a decreasing sequence of closed intervals $[a_n, b_n]$ – a sequence, that is, for which $a_n \leqq a_{n+1} < b_{n+1} \leqq b_n$ – has as its intersection a closed interval or a single point, is familiar to the reader from his elementary work.

2. Dyadic sets. Suppose that there is given, in a complete space E, a system of *closed, bounded, non-empty* sets $V_p, V_{pq}, V_{pqr}, \ldots$ whose indices take on the possible values 1 and 2; then we have two sets V_1 and V_2 with a single index, four sets $V_{11}, V_{12}, V_{21}, V_{22}$ with two indices and, in general, 2^n sets with n indices. For every dyadic sequence (that is, a sequence formed from the numerals 1 and 2) we require in addition that

$$V_p \geqq V_{pq} \geqq V_{pqr} \geqq \cdots \tag{1}$$

and that the diameters of these sets converge to zero; according to V, the intersection $V_p V_{pq} V_{pqr} \cdots$ consists of a single point x. The set of all such points

$$D = \mathfrak{S} V_p V_{pq} V_{pqr} \cdots, \tag{2}$$

where the sum is extended over all the dyadic sequences, will be called a *dyadic set*. The name refers only to the form of the representation; as regards the actual nature of these sets themselves, we shall see in a moment that dyadic sets and sets compact in themselves are identical.

Now,

$$D = \mathfrak{S} V_p \cdot \mathfrak{S} V_{pq} \cdot \mathfrak{S} V_{pqr} \cdots \tag{3}$$

holds, so that the set D proves to be closed (in the complete space E) and thus to be complete. In fact, the set (2) is contained in (3) to begin with. Conversely, let x be a point of the set (3), say

$$x \varepsilon V_{p_1} V_{p_2 q_2} V_{p_3 q_3 r_3} \cdots.$$

Among the sets V that appear here the same first index $p_n = p$ must occur infinitely often, among these V, also infinitely often, the same second index $q_n = q$, among these V, infinitely often, the same third index $r_n = r$, and so on. But then $x \varepsilon V_p V_{pq} V_{pqr} \cdots$, and x is a point of the set (2).

The convergence of the diameters to zero required of the sets (1) is uniform for all the dyadic sequences of numerals. This means that if δ_n is the greatest diameter of the sets V with n indices, where obviously $\delta_1 \geqq \delta_2 \geqq \cdots$, then $\delta_n \to 0$. For let $V_{p_1}, V_{p_2 q_2}, V_{p_3 q_3 r_3}, \ldots$ be sets with diameters $\delta_1, \delta_2, \delta_3, \ldots$; we then conclude, as above, that $p_n = p$ infinitely often, then $q_n = q$, then $r_n = r$, and so on. Hence it is impossible that $\delta_n \geqq \delta > 0$, since otherwise $V_p, V_{pq}, V_{pqr}, \ldots$ would have diameters $\geqq \delta$.

It therefore follows from § 21, 4 that the set D is totally bounded; furthermore it was complete, and consequently it is compact in itself.

Before we represent sets compact in themselves, conversely, as dyadic sets, we generalize the latter as follows. Suppose that there is given, in the complete space E, a system of closed, bounded, non-empty sets

$W_i, W_{ik}, W_{ikl}, \ldots$, where this time each index ranges over a finite set which may possibly depend on the preceding indices but which contains at least two numerals. In W_i, that is, we let $i = 1, 2, \ldots, m$; in W_{ik} we let $k = 1, 2, \ldots, m_i$; in W_{ikl} we let $l = 1, 2, \ldots, m_{ik}$; and so on. $(m, m_i, m_{ik}, \ldots \geqq 2.)$ For every sequence $(i, k, l, \ldots)$ of numerals formed in this way, let

$$W_i \geqq W_{ik} \geqq W_{ikl} \geqq \cdots$$

with diameters converging to zero, so that the intersection of the sets consist of a single point; the sum

$$P = \mathfrak{S} W_i W_{ik} W_{ikl} \cdots \tag{4}$$

will be called a *polyadic* set. We conclude, as we did above, that

$$P = \mathfrak{S} W_i \cdot \mathfrak{S} W_{ik} \cdot \mathfrak{S} W_{ikl} \cdots$$

and that the convergence of the diameters to zero is uniform. In actual fact, P is really only a dyadic set, as we shall now see.

The sets $W_i, W_{ik}, \ldots$ we denote in general by W; the sets derived from some set W by adjoining another index we denote by $W^1, W^2, \ldots$ (for example, for $W = W_{ik}$: $W^l = W_{ikl}$). Next we form sets $V_p, V_{pq}, \ldots$ with dyadic indices (1 or 2) which, again, we denote in general by V. The sets derived from the sets V by adjoining a further index, we call V^1, V^2. In this construction we shall require either that V equal some particular W

$$V = W, \tag{α}$$

or that V be the sum of several W with *equally many* indices

$$V = W_{\mathrm{I}} \dot{+} W_{\mathrm{II}} \dot{+} \cdots, \tag{β}$$

where the summands are to be written in an order corresponding to the lexicographic order of the indices. We begin the definition with

$$V_1 = W_1 \dot{+} W_3 \dot{+} \cdots, \quad V_2 = W_2 \dot{+} W_4 \dot{+} \cdots$$

and continue it by induction by defining V^1, V^2 whenever V has already been defined. In the case (α), we let

$$V^1 = W^1 \dot{+} W^3 \dot{+} \cdots, \quad V^2 = W^2 \dot{+} W^4 \dot{+} \cdots;$$

and in the case (β), we let

$$V^1 = W_{\mathrm{I}} \dot{+} W_{\mathrm{III}} \dot{+} \cdots, \quad V^2 = W_{\mathrm{II}} \dot{+} W_{\mathrm{IV}} \dot{+} \cdots.$$

As an example, if the first sets W are

$$\begin{array}{lll} W_1 & W_2 & W_3 \\ W_{11}W_{12}W_{13} & W_{21}W_{22}W_{23}W_{24} & W_{31}W_{32} \end{array}$$

the first sets V would be derived as follows:

$$\begin{array}{llll} V_1 = W_1 \dot{+} W_3 & & V_2 = W_2 & \\ V_{11} = W_1 & V_{12} = W_3 & V_{21} = W_{21} \dot{+} W_{23} & V_{22} = W_{22} \dot{+} W_{24} \\ V_{111} = W_{11} \dot{+} W_{13} & V_{112} = W_{12} & V_{121} = W_{31} & V_{122} = W_{32} \\ V_{211} = W_{21} & V_{212} = W_{23} & V_{221} = W_{22} & V_{222} = W_{24} \\ V_{1111} = W_{11}, & V_{1112} = W_{13}. & & \end{array}$$

We can now see directly that every V is some W or the sum of a finite number of W, and is therefore closed, bounded, and non-empty. Also $V \geqq V^1$, $V \geqq V^2$, so that the inequalities (1) are satisfied for every dyadic sequence of numerals. If V is of type (β) then V^1, V^2 are sums of fewer terms than V, and after the adjunction of sufficiently many indices, some V of type (α) always recurs. Every sequence $V_p, V_{pq}, V_{pqr}, \ldots$ has a subsequence $W_i, W_{ik}, W_{ikl}, \ldots$ and therefore has diameters that converge to zero, where the intersections

$$V_p V_{pq} V_{pqr} \cdots = W_i W_{ik} W_{ikl} \cdots$$

are simultaneously identical. Conversely, every W is equal to a certain V, and every sequence

$$W_i, W_{ik}, W_{ikl}, \ldots$$

determines a sequence

$$V_p, V_{pq}, V_{pqr}, \ldots$$

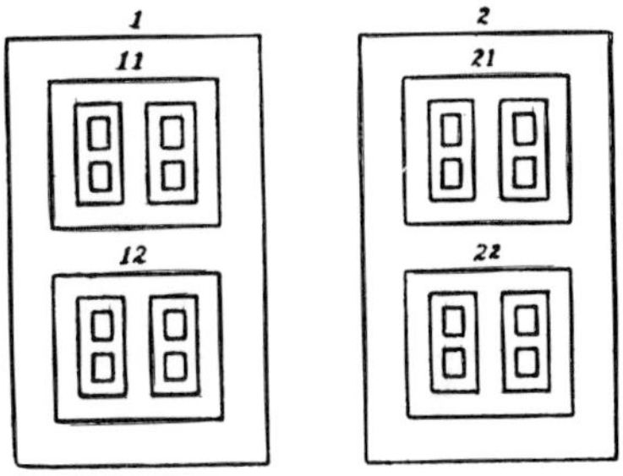

Fig. 3

of which it is a subsequence (for example, the sequence $W_1, W_{13}, \ldots$ determines the sequence $V_1, V_{11}, V_{111}, V_{1112}, \ldots$). Hence the polyadic set P generated by the W is the same as the dyadic set D generated by the V.

A set P compact in itself can be represented as a polyadic set. For it is the sum of a finite number of sets W_i of arbitrarily small diameters $\leqq \delta_1$, where each of these sets may be taken to be be closed (in P) and thus to be compact in itself and where the number of these sets can be taken to be $\geqq 2$. Continuing, we find that

$$P = \mathfrak{S}_i W_i, \quad W_i = \mathfrak{S}_k W_{ik}, \quad W_{ik} = \mathfrak{S}_l W_{ikl}, \ldots,$$

where the W are compact in themselves (and thus complete and bounded), and where the diameters of the sets with n indices are $\leqq \delta_n$, with $\delta_n \to 0$; P is the polyadic set (4) generated by the sets W.

Dyadic sets and sets compact in themselves are therefore identical.

We next consider in particular a dyadic set where V_1 and V_2 are *disjoint*[1] and, similarly V_{p1} and V_{p2}, V_{pq1} and V_{pq2}, ... are disjoint; in general for every n the sets with n indices are to be pairwise disjoint. Such a set

$$D = \Sigma V_p V_{pq} V_{pqr} \cdots = \Sigma V_p \cdot \Sigma V_{pq} \cdot \Sigma V_{pqr} \cdots$$

will be called a *dyadic discontinuum.*[2] It is equivalent to the set of dyadic sequences of numerals and is therefore of the cardinality $2^{\aleph_0} = \aleph$ of the continuum; furthermore it is *perfect* and, even more precisely,

$$D = D_\alpha = D_\beta = D_\gamma;$$

every point of D is a condensation point. For if a finite number of initial numerals are held constant, we obtain the sets DV_p, DV_{pq}, DV_{pqr}, ... (for instance DV_1 = the set of points $x \varepsilon D$ for which $p = 1$) which are all of cardinality $\aleph$ and have diameters convergent to 0; if x is the point in which these sets intersect, then every neighborhood U_x contains $\aleph$ points of D.

A polyadic discontinuum (where the sets W with n indices are disjoint, for every n) is identical with a dyadic one.

The classical example of a dyadic discontinuum is the following which, because of its relation to the triadic fractions, is also referred to as *Cantor's triadic* (or *ternary*) *set*, or *Cantor's discontinuum.* Let V be the closed

Fig. 4

interval [0, 1] in the set E of real numbers; furthermore (forming the dyadic sequences with the numerals 0, 2 instead of 0, 1, for a reason that

[1] Fig. 3 illustrates the case of closed rectangular areas V only the circumferences of which are shown, the interiors being left unshaded.

[2] The name will become clear in § 29, XVI. In § 36, 1 we shall introduce as a counterpart the dyadic continuum.

will soon become apparent), let $V_0 = \left[0, \frac{1}{3}\right]$ be the left-hand third of V and $V_2 = \left[\frac{2}{3}, 1\right]$ the right-hand third and, similarly, let V_{p0} be the left-hand third of V_p and V_{p2} the right-hand third, and so on. In this case, the intersection $V_p V_{pq} V_{pqr} \ldots$ consists, as a moment's reflection will show, of the number

$$x = \frac{p}{3} + \frac{q}{3^2} + \frac{r}{3^3} + \cdots \qquad (p, q, r, \ldots = 0, 2),$$

and D is the set of those numbers x that admit of *at least* one such triadic development entirely in terms of zeros and twos without any ones. The qualification *at least* has reference to those numbers between zero and one (triadic rational numbers) that have two triadic developments; if one of them is free of ones, then the number is to belong to D. For example, the numbers

$$\frac{1}{3} = \frac{0}{3} + \frac{2}{3^2} + \frac{2}{3^3} + \cdots \quad \left(= \frac{1}{3} + \frac{0}{3^2} + \frac{0}{3^3} + \cdots\right)$$
$$\frac{2}{3} = \frac{2}{3} + \frac{0}{3^2} + \frac{0}{3^3} + \cdots \quad \left(= \frac{1}{3} + \frac{2}{3^2} + \frac{2}{3^3} + \cdots\right)$$

belong to D, but a number between these two does not, since its first triadic numeral will certainly be $p = 1$.

The open complement $E - D$ consists, apart from the half-lines $(-\infty, 0)$ and $(1, \infty)$, of the middle thirds of $V, V_p, V_{pq}, \ldots$, and so consists of the open intervals $\left(\frac{1}{3}, \frac{2}{3}\right), \left(\frac{1}{9}, \frac{2}{9}\right), \left(\frac{7}{9}, \frac{8}{9}\right), \ldots$. As is easily seen, this is dense in E, so that D contains no interval no matter how small (D is nowhere dense in E, § 27). The limiting value to which the lengths of the sums of the intervals $\Sigma V_p, \Sigma V_{pq}, \ldots$ converge is called the (Lebesgue, one-dimensional) *measure* of D. Here these lengths are $\frac{2}{3}, \frac{4}{9}, \ldots$, and so the measure is zero. It seems paradoxical that a set of measure zero should nonetheless have the cardinality $\aleph$ of the whole interval. We can, however, choose the lengths of the intervals differently: those of the open intervals of $E - D$ smaller and the sums of the lengths $\lambda_1, \lambda_2, \ldots$ of $\Sigma V_p, \Sigma V_{pq}, \ldots$ decreasing so slowly that the measure $\lambda = \lim \lambda_n$ of D becomes positive and even as close as we please to (although of course less than) 1. But then we have another paradox: namely, that a set of positive length contains no interval no matter how small.

How to carry over this simple construction to the case of the plane is obvious. For instance, we take a square V (a closed square area defined by, say, $0 \leqq x_1 \leqq 1$, $0 \leqq x_2 \leqq 1$; that is, the product of two intervals

[0, 1]) and divide it into nine sub-squares by dividing the sides into three equal pieces, V_1, V_2, V_3, V_4 being the small squares in the corners of V.

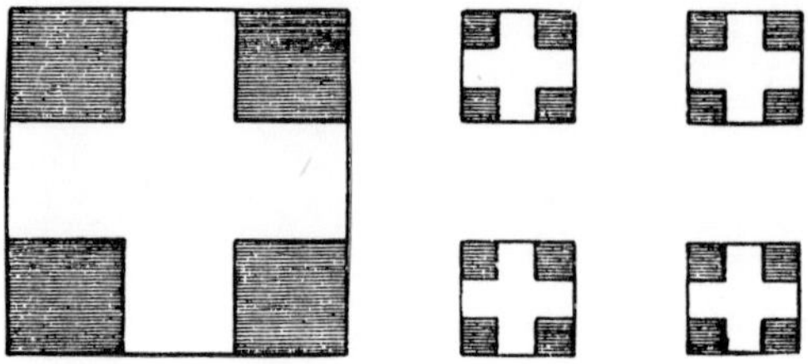

Fig. 5

$V - \Sigma V_p$ is a cross formed by the five remaining sub-squares with some of the edges missing. In the same way, we form the sub-squares $V_{p1}, V_{p2}, V_{p3}, V_{p4}$ from V_p. The polyadic discontinuum generated by the V,

$$D = \Sigma V_p \cdot \Sigma V_{pq} \cdot \Sigma V_{pqr} \cdots$$

is the product of two Cantor triadic sets. Its (Lebesgue, two-dimensional) measure — the limit of the areas of ΣV_p, $\Sigma V_{pq}, \ldots$ — is zero, but it can also be made positive < 1 by changing the construction slightly.

3. Theorems on Cardinality.

VI. (Cantor). *In a complete space, every non-empty perfect set has at least the cardinality* $\aleph$.

VII. (Cantor). *In a complete space, every closed set whose dense-in-itself kernel does not vanish has cardinality at least* $\aleph$.

VIII. (W. H. Young). *In a complete space, every set* $Y = G_\delta$ *(the intersection of a sequence of open sets) whose dense-in-itself kernel does not vanish has cardinality at least* $\aleph$.

We premise the proof with a few explanatory remarks. Each of these theorems is a special case of the one following (a closed set F is the intersection of a sequence of open sets G). On the other hand, VII also follows from VI; and later on (because of the homeomorphism of the G_δ in complete spaces with the complete spaces themselves, § 38, III), VIII will also be found to be a consequence of VII. The sets

$G_\delta =$ intersection of a sequence of open sets,
$F_\sigma =$ sum of a sequence of closed sets

form the next class of Borel sets (§ 32) following the open sets G and the closed sets F, and in the sequel we shall extend the theorems on cardinality to them. These attributes of sets are of course relative, being dependent on the space E, and actually we ought to write explicitly $F(E)$, and so on. If, however, we once more ignore the argument E, then we have, for $D \leqq E$,

$$F(D) = DF, \quad G(D) = DG, \quad F_\sigma(D) = D F_\sigma \quad G_\delta(D) = DG_\delta;$$

the sets with respect to D are the intersections with D of the corresponding sets referred to E. There also exist *absolute* F_σ and G_δ, sets that have this attribute in *every* space containing them. This is obvious for the F_σ; an absolute F_σ (considered, for example, as a subset of its complete hull) is the sum of a sequence of absolutely closed (complete) sets belonging to some metric space, and vice versa. At first glance, the non-existence of absolutely open sets appears to militate against the existence of absolute G_δ. But the truth is otherwise: the three statements

A is a G_δ in its complete hull;
A is a G_δ in a complete space;
A is a G_δ in every containing space, that is, an absolute G_δ;

are equivalent. For if A is a G_δ in E, then this is also the case in every smaller space D ($A \leqq D \leqq E$); if, on the other hand, A is a G_δ in its closed hull A_α, then $A = A_\alpha G_\delta$ is a G_δ even in the space E, because A_α is closed and is thus a G_δ, and the intersection of two G_δ is itself a G_δ. The equivalence of the three statements for a complete space E now follows. In consideration of Young's Theorem VIII, the absolute G_δ are often called *Young sets*.

We can now eliminate the reference to the containing space in the three cardinality theorems and say:

IX. *Every absolutely perfect set, every absolutely closed (complete) set, every absolute G_δ (Young set) has cardinality at least* $\aleph$ *provided that its dense-in-itself kernel is non-vanishing.*

Let us now turn to the proof; we need only prove the third theorem but, in the course of doing so, we shall come across the first two. We shall show that the sets in question contain a dyadic discontinuum D; as the generating closed (complete) sets V we shall choose closed spheres. We distinguish here between the

open sphere $U_x(\varrho)$ = set of points y for which $xy < \varrho$
closed sphere $V_x(\varrho)$ = set of points y for which $xy \leqq \varrho$

(the open spheres are our old neighborhoods); we speak of them as corresponding, or belonging, to each other whenever they have the same radius and center. Spheres U and V belonging to each other are labelled with the same subscripts. (In Euclidean space, U is then the open kernel of V, and V the closed hull of U.)

Now let $A > 0$ be a dense-in-itself set in the complete space E. We choose two points a_1, a_2 in A and make them the centers of disjoint closed spheres V_1, V_2, to which there belong the open spheres U_1, U_2. Each of the two sets AU_p is non-empty and dense-in-itself (§ 23, V); we can therefore repeat the construction and circumscribe disjoint closed spheres $V_{p1}, V_{p2} \leqq U_p$ about two of their points a_{p1}, a_{p2}. Each of the four sets AU_{pq} is non-empty and dense-in-itself; we circumscribe disjoint closed spheres $V_{pq1}, V_{pq2} \leqq U_{pq}$ about two of their points a_{pq1}, a_{pq2}, and continue in this way.

Nothing in all this prevents us from choosing the radii of these spheres as small as we please – say, choosing the radii of the $V_p, V_{pq}, V_{pqr}, \ldots$ smaller than 1, 1/2, 1/3, ... In this way we obtain a dyadic discontinuum D, and this is contained in A_α; for a point x of D that belongs to $V_p V_{pq} V_{pqr} \cdots$ is the limit of the centers $a_p, a_{pq}, a_{pqr}, \ldots$ of the spheres. Therefore:

X. *If A is a dense-in-itself non-empty set in the complete space E, then A_α contains a dyadic discontinuum D.*

This proves VI (if A is dense-in-itself then A_α is perfect, and vice versa), and even proves VII: If F is closed and contains A, then $F \geqq A_\alpha \geqq D$. In order to prove VIII, we assume

$$A \leqq y = G_1 G_2 G_3 \ldots \qquad (G_n \text{ open}),$$

and we are still free to take the radii of the spheres so small that $V_p \leqq G_1$ (since, after all, $a_p \varepsilon G_1$), $V_{pq} \leqq G_2$, $V_{pqr} \leqq G_3, \ldots$ and thus $D \leqq y$.

Our theorems are thus proved; we have even shown somewhat more, namely, that the sets in question contain a perfect subset D. Further – to stay with the most general case (VIII) of a Young set Y – since DV_1 has cardinality $\aleph$ and V_1 may be taken to refer to an arbitrarily small sphere about any point a_1 of A, it follows that every point of A is a point of condensation of Y, and since A was an arbitrary dense-in-itself subset of Y, this means: *Every point of the dense-in-itself kernel of Y is a point of condensation of Y,*

$$Y_k \leqq Y_c. \tag{5}$$

Let us finally combine all this with the facts valid in a separable space (§ 25) : in this case every point set has at most the cardinality $\aleph$; furthermore, we always had $A_c \leqq A_k$, so that for a Young set $Y_k = Y_c$, and

$A_j \geqq A_s$ is at most countable. Thus:

XI. *In a complete separable space every Young set* $Y = G_\delta$ *is either at most denumerable or of cardinal number* $\aleph$, *depending on whether its dense-in-itself kernel* $Y_k = Y_c$ *vanishes or not.*

For a closed set, $Y_k = Y_\gamma$; for a perfect set, $Y = Y_\gamma$. (That every set A_γ is perfect is valid, by p. 147, in every separable space; here we also find the converse, that every perfect set is an A_γ.)

In a separable space every closed set F can be split by virtue of $F = F_k + F_s$ into a *perfect part* F_k and an *at most countable part* F_s (the dense-in-itself kernel of a closed set is perfect (p. 141), a fact usually called the Theorem of Cantor-Bendixson. The decomposition $A = P + Q$ of a set into a perfect part P and an at most countable part Q, however, is not in general unique; if, for example, E is the space of rational numbers, and P the set of rational numbers $\geqq a$ (a arbitrary), then $E = P + (E - P)$ is such a decomposition, for P is perfect in E. But in a complete separable space this splitting, if possible at all, can be made in only one way; for we have $A_\gamma = P_\gamma \dotplus Q_\gamma = P + 0 = P$. The splitting, then, can only be performed if $A_\gamma \leqq A$ (and therefore, in particular, for closed sets), and then only as follows: $A = A_\gamma + (A - A_\gamma) = A_c + A_j$; for Young sets of this kind, this is identical with $A = A_k + A_s$.

A countable set of A of the complete space E whose dense-in-itself kernel does not vanish is certainly not a G_δ, for $A_k > 0$ and $A_c = 0$ contradicts the condition $Y_k \leqq Y_c$. But as a countable set it is an F_σ. *Example*: The set of rational points in Euclidean space. Its complement $E - A$ is a G_δ but not an F_σ.

§ 27. Sets of the First and Second Categories

We consider an arbitrary space E. *The closed set F will be said to be nowhere dense in E if its open complement G is dense in E.* This is equivalent with $G_\alpha = E$ and thus with $F_i = 0$: *closed nowhere dense sets are identical with closed border sets.* They are also identical with the *frontiers*, or boundaries,[1] *of open sets*; for if F is nowhere dense, then $F = F_b$ is the frontier of its complement G, and, on the other hand, if G is any open set and F its complement, then the frontier F_b of G is a border set, and furthermore, like every frontier set, it is closed.

An arbitrary set A will be said to be nowhere dense in E if its closed hull A_α is nowhere dense in E. It is both necessary and sufficient for this that the open kernel B_i of its complement $B = E - A$ be dense in E.

[1] We use the terms interchangeably; see the footnote on p. 130.

Ordinary curves in the Euclidean plane E_2, as well as ordinary curves and surfaces in the space E_3, etc. are nowhere-dense sets. More precisely: If $f(x_1, x_2)$ is a real continuous function that can never vanish inside an entire neighborhood of a point — for instance a polynomial whose coefficients do not all vanish — then $f = 0$ represents a nowhere-dense set in E_2, for it is closed and has no interior points.

A dyadic discontinuum D (§ 26, 2) is nowhere-dense in the complete space E if we require the more stringent inequalities

$$V_p > V_{p1} + V_{p2}, \quad V_{pq} > V_{pq1} + V_{pq2}, \ldots$$

to hold (where equality is excluded). For, arbitrarily close to every point $x \varepsilon D$ — which belongs, say, to the intersection $V_p V_{pq} \ldots$ — there are points of

$$(V_p - V_{p1} - V_{p2}) + (V_{pq} - V_{pq1} - V_{pq2}) + \cdots,$$

and these points do not belong to D: x is not an interior point of D. In the construction involving spheres on p. 158 this strengthening of the inequalities can clearly be brought about; therefore, in every complete space with a non-vanishing dense-in-itself kernel there are nowhere-dense perfect sets of cardinality $\aleph$. The simplest example is Cantor's triadic set (p. 154), together with the sets derived from it by alteration of the lengths of the intervals.

Let us return to the discussion of the nowhere-dense sets A of E. For brevity, we set

$$E = A_\alpha + A_e,$$

where $A_e = E - A_\alpha$ denotes the set of the *exterior points* of A (the interior points of the complement $E - A$). Then the statements

A is nowhere dense in E, $\quad A_e$ is dense in E

are identical. Let us now replace E by any subset M of the space; $A_\alpha(E) = A_\alpha$ then has to be replaced, of course, by $A_\alpha(M) = MA_\alpha$. It is not required that A be contained in M, but only that A and M be sets in the space E, so that we obtain the more general relation 'A nowhere dense *to* M' as counterpart to the already familiar relation 'A dense to M.' In short, using the notation

$$(\alpha) \qquad P = MA_\alpha, \quad Q = MA_e, \quad M = P + Q,$$

we define the statements

A is nowhere dense to M, $\quad Q$ is dense in M

to be identical; by the earlier definition ($M \leqq A_\alpha$), the statements

$$A \text{ dense to } M, \qquad Q = 0, \qquad P = M$$

were identical. (The complete counterpart to this would be $Q = M$, $P = 0$, $M \leqq A_e$, M lies completely outside A; but this is of no particular interest.) In the case $A \leqq M$, we choose the preposition 'in': A is nowhere dense *in* M, A is dense *in* M. Like – more generally – the sets P and Q, these relations depend only on the sets A and M and not on the containing space E. P is closed in M; Q is open in M.

If A is closed in M, then $P = A$, and we have the identity of the statements:

$$A \text{ is nowhere dense in } M, \qquad M - A \text{ is dense in } M;$$
$$A \text{ is dense in } M, \qquad A = M.$$

We next compile several formal properties of these concepts whose proofs, where nothing further is said, are trivial.

I. (TRANSITIVE LAW). *If A is dense to B and B dense to C, then A is dense to C.*

II. *If A is dense to M (nowhere dense), then A^* is dense to M^* (nowhere dense), provided A^* and M^* are sets of the same denseness classes as A and M.*[1]

As a matter of fact, P and Q depend only on A_α, not on A. As far as M is concerned, we know that for an open set G, $(MG)_\alpha \geqq M_\alpha G \geqq MG$, so that $(MG)_\alpha = (M_\alpha G)_\alpha$; if in this we set $G = A_e$, then it follows that $Q_\alpha = Q^*_\alpha$, provided $Q = MA_e$ and $Q^* = M^*A_e$ belong to M and M^* in conformity with the decomposition (α). The statements $Q = 0$ and $Q_\alpha = M_\alpha$ are thus equivalent with the same ones for Q^* and M^*, respectively.

III. *If A is dense to M, then every set $\geqq A$ is dense to every set $\leqq M$. If A is nowhere dense to M, then every set $\leqq A$ is nowhere dense to M; if A is nowhere dense in M, then A is nowhere dense in every set $\geqq M$.*

Of these statements only the last requires proof; here we can take the set $\geqq M$ as the space E. We have

$$A_\alpha \leqq M_\alpha = Q_\alpha \leqq A_{e\alpha}$$

and simultaneously $A_e \leqq A_{e\alpha}$, so that $E \leqq A_{e\alpha}$, and A_e is dense in E. In this last statement we cannot say "to" in place of "in" (although in place of auxiliary condition $A \leqq M$ the milder one $A_\alpha \leqq M_\alpha$ would suffice); this follows from the mere fact that, in our terminology, every set A is nowhere

[1] This means that $A^*_\alpha = A_\alpha$, $M^*_\alpha = M_\alpha$ (p. 144).

dense to the empty set $M = 0$ without being, however, nowhere dense to every set $\geqq 0$.

IV. *Let G be open. If A is dense to M, then AG is dense to MG. If A is nowhere dense to M, then A is nowhere dense to MG.*

The first part follows from $(AG)_\alpha \geqq A_\alpha G \geqq MG$. The second rests on the first and on (α): Q is dense in M and so $QG = MGA_e$ is dense in MG, and A nowhere dense to MG.

V. *If A_1 and A_2 are open and dense in M, then their intersection is also (open and) dense in M.*

For let $A_1 = MG_1$, $A_2 = MG_2$ (G_1 and G_2 open). Then the following are dense: A_1 in M; by IV, $A_1 G_2$ in MG_2, that is, $A_1 A_2$ in A_2; next, A_2 in M and thus (by the transitive law), $A_1 A_2$ in M.

VI. *If A_1 and A_2 are nowhere dense to M, then their sum is also nowhere dense to M.*

For A_1, A_2, and $A = A_1 \dotplus A_2$ we make the following decompositions (α): $M = P_1 + Q_1 = P_2 + Q_2 = P + Q$. Then $P = P_1 \dotplus P_2$, $Q = Q_1 Q_2$. Q_1 and Q_2 are open and dense in M and thus, by V, so is Q.

The last two theorems are also valid, of course, for any finite number of sets $A_1, A_2, \ldots, A_n$. In a *complete* space they can be extended, in modified form, to the case of a countable number.

VII. *In a complete space, let there be given a sequence of sets $A_n (n = 1, 2, 3, \ldots)$ for which $A_{1\alpha} \leqq A_{2\alpha} \leqq \cdots$ and a sequence of open sets $G_n \geqq A_n$. Then $Y = G_1 G_2 \ldots$ is dense to A_1.*

We enclose a point $a_1 \,\varepsilon\, A_1$ in a closed sphere V_1 (that is, let a_1 be the center of the sphere); in the open sphere U_1 belonging to it there lies, because $a_1 \,\varepsilon\, A_{2\alpha}$, a point $a_2 \,\varepsilon\, A_2$ which we enclose in a closed sphere $V_2 \leqq U_1$; in U_2 there lies a point $a_3 \,\varepsilon\, A_3$ which we enclose in a sphere $V_3 \leqq U_2$, and so on. In this construction we choose the spheres so as to make their radii converge to 0 and furthermore take $V_n \leqq G_n$, so that the point x of $V_1 V_2 \ldots$ belongs to Y. Since V_1 may be as small as we please, it follows that $a_1 \,\varepsilon\, Y_\alpha$, so that $A_1 \leqq Y_\alpha$.

VIII. *In a complete space let a sequence of Young sets $Y_1, Y_2, \ldots$ belonging to the same denseness class ($Y_{1\alpha} = Y_{2\alpha} = \cdots$) be given; then their intersection $Y = Y_1 Y_2 \ldots$ belongs to that same class.*

Let $Y_m = G_{m1} G_{m2} \cdots$ (G_{mn} open); if we set $Y_{mn} = Y_m \leqq G_{mn}$ and apply VII to the sequence $Y_{11}, Y_{12}, Y_{21}, \ldots$, so that $\mathfrak{D}_{mn}\, G_{mn} = \mathfrak{D}_m\, Y_m = Y$ is dense to $Y_{11} = Y_1$, that is, dense in Y_1: $Y_\alpha = Y_{1\alpha}$. In particular:

IX. *If* $A_1, A_2, \ldots$ *is a sequence of sets that are open and dense in the Young set* M, *then their intersection is also dense in* M.

For the sets A_n are (as sets MG) themselves Young sets, and belong to the same density class that M does; the same follows for their intersection.

X. *If* $A_1, A_2, \ldots$ *is a sequence of sets that are all nowhere dense to the Young set* M, *and if* A *is their sum, then* $M - MA$ *is dense in* M.

If for the A_n we make the decompositions (α), $M = P_n + Q_n$, and if we set $P_0 = P_1 + P_2 + \ldots$ and $Q_0 = Q_1 Q_2 \ldots$, then the Q_n are open and dense in M and thus, by IX, Q_0 is dense in M. Furthermore $MA_n \leqq P_n$, $MA \leqq P_0$, $M - MA \geqq Q_0$, so that $M - MA$ is, a fortiori, dense in M.

We cannot go on to assert, however, that A is nowhere dense to M; as regards the decomposition $M = P + Q$ belonging to A one could infer, after all, only that $P \geqq P_0$ and $Q \leqq Q_0$, so that Q need no longer be dense in M. If we arrange the rational numbers in a sequence $r_1, r_2, \ldots$ and let A_n consist of the single number r_n, then A_n is nowhere dense in the set M of real numbers, whereas A is actually dense; Theorem X nevertheless remains valid, for $M - A$ is dense in M. If, however, the set M is understood to be the set of rationals itself, which is not a Young set (it is not a G_δ in its complete hull, that is, in the set of real numbers, p. 159), then the theorem is not applicable: $M - A$ is then empty and not dense in M.

In a somewhat colorless nomenclature (Baire) we say that a set A *is of the first or second category to* M *according to whether it is or is not a sum of a sequence of sets nowhere dense to* M. If $A \leqq M$, then it is said to be of the first or second category *in* M; this most important case is indicated concisely by the notation

M_{I}, a set of first category in M,
M_{II}, a set of second category in M.

Then Theorem X applied to $A \leqq M$ reads as follows:

XI. *If* M *is a Young set, then* $M - M_{\mathrm{I}}$ *is dense in* M.

From the definition, as well as from II, III, and IV, it follows that:

XII. *If the finite or countable number of sets* A_n *is of the first category to* M, *then so is their sum.*

XIII. *If* A *is of the first category to* M, *then it is to* M^* *also, where* M^* *belongs to the same density class as* M.

XIV. *If* A *is of the first category to* M, *then so is every set* $\leqq A$; *if* A *is of the first category in* M, *then it is also of the first category in every set* $\geqq M$.

XV. *If A is of the first category to M, then it is also of the first category to MG (G open).*

These theorems can, of course, be transformed into theorems about sets of the second category; instead of XIV, for example: If A is of the second category to M, then so is every set $\geqq A$, etc.

It may happen that M itself is an M_{I}; there can then be no M_{II} at all, since by XIV all the subsets of M are also M_{I}. But if M itself is an M_{II}, then by XII it cannot be the sum of two M_{I}, and the complement $M - M_{\mathrm{I}}$ of an M_{I} is in any case an M_{II} (whereas the complement of an M_{II} can equally well be an M_{I} or an M_{II}). *A non-empty Young set M is certainly an M_{II}.* For by XI, $M - M_{\mathrm{I}}$ is dense in M and cannot be empty.

On the basis of the property that cancellation of an M_{I} from a set $M = M_{\mathrm{II}}$ always leaves us with an M_{II}, we can form a mental picture in which the subsets M_{I} are, so to speak, superfluous trimming, of sparse structure, while their complements $M - M_{\mathrm{I}}$ contain the essential substance of the set M. This conception may serve a useful purpose in that it lends some color to the meaningless phrases "first and second category"; but it may also happen to collide with similar imagery based on other premises. In the decomposition $M = M_s + M_k$ into a separated part and a dense-in-itself kernel we would consider the latter, similarly, as substance and the former as trimming, especially when M_k is of the cardinality of the continuum and M_s only countable; nevertheless M_k may be an M_{I} and M_s an M_{II}. If, as an example, J is an isolated set with a perfect derived set J_β – say, the set of points $(m/n, 1/n)$ of Fig. 2, p. 131 – then $M = J_\alpha = J + J_\beta$ is such a decomposition, in which J_β is an M_{I} and J an M_{II} (for $M - J_\beta$ is dense in M; and furthermore each individual point of J itself represents a set M_{II}). A single point of M represents a set M_{II} or M_{I} depending on whether it is an isolated point or a point of accumulation. Every set M_{I} is thus contained in the coherence M_a and every finite or countable subset of M_a is an M_{I}. For example, in the set E of the real numbers the set R of the rational numbers is an E_{I}, and even an R_{I}; the set J of the irrationals is an E_{II}, since E, as a Young set, is an E_{II}, and all the more is it a J_{II}.

If $M = M_s$ is separated, then M_a is an M_{I}, since $M - M_a = M_h$ is dense in $M_s = M$ (§ 23, (15)). If, therefore, we construct the sequence of coherences $M_0, M_1, M_2, \ldots, M_\omega \ldots$, which begins with $M, M_a, M_{aa}, \ldots$, then each of these sets is of the first category in the ones preceding it, but (as long as it is non-empty) of the second category in itself, because it has isolated points.

If the set E, which we now take as our space, is a Young set, then every closed set F (closed in E) and every open set G (and even every set G_δ) is a Young set, and is thus, if non-empty, of the second category in itself. On the basis of these two properties we now wish to define two classes of sets which frequently play a role as *generalizations of the Young sets.* We say:

E will be called an F_{I}-set if every non-empty closed set F is of the second category (an F_{II}) in itself.[1] *E will be called a G_{II} set if every non-empty open set G is of the second category (a G_{II}) in itself.*

The condition on the F_{II}-set can be confined to requiring that only *perfect* sets $P > 0$ need be sets P_{II}; for a set F with isolated points is an F_{II} in any event.

The condition on the G_{II}-set can be replaced by the condition that every non-empty open set G be an E_{II}. For, if G is a G_{I}, then it is also an E_{I} (by XIV); if G is an E_{I}, then it is also a G_{I} (by XV). That is, G is of the same category in itself and in E (whereas a closed set F can be an F_{II} and an E_{I} at the same time – every nowhere-dense, closed, non-empty subset of Euclidean space, for example.) In addition, the sets G_{II} can also be characterized by:

E is a G_{II}-set if and only if $E - E_{\mathrm{I}}$ is always dense in E.

For if $E - E_{\mathrm{I}}$ is always dense in E, then $G > 0$ is not an E_{I}, since $E - G = F$ is not dense in $E (F_\alpha = F < E)$. If, conversely, E is a G_{II}-set and A an E_{I}, $G > 0$, then the second summand in $G = (E - A)G + AG$ is an E_{I}; therefore the first summand is an E_{II} and in any case is > 0. From $G > 0$ it now follows that $(E - A)G > 0$; that is, $E - A$ is dense in E.

Whenever E is a G_{II}-set, so is $E - E_{\mathrm{I}}$. For if A and B are of the first category in E and in $D = E - A$ respectively, then B and $A + B$ are also of the first category in E, so that $E - (A + B) = D - B$ is dense in E and all the more is it in D; D is a set for which $D - D_{\mathrm{I}}$ is dense in D, that is, a G_{II}-set.

Every Young set is an F_{II}-set; but, as we shall see later on (§ 43, 2), there also exist F_{II}-sets that are not Young sets.

Every F_{II}-set is a G_{II}-set. Let E be an F_{II}-set, G non-empty and open, $F = G_\alpha$, and further, let $F - G = G_\alpha - G = H$ be the boundary of G. H is nowhere dense in F (because it is closed and its complement $F - H = G$ is dense in F) and thus is an F_{I}; hence G is an F_{II} and, a fortiori, a G_{II}.

[1] Compare Appendix A.

But there are also G_{II}-sets that are not F_{II}-sets. Let E be the Euclidean plane, and let A be the set of irrational points $(i, 0)$ on the x-axis X; then A is an E_{I} and $D = E - A$ is also a G_{II}-set. However, it is not an F_{II}-set, since the set DX which is closed in it, the set of rational points $(r, 0)$ on the x-axis, is of the first category in itself.

The sets F_σ, the sums of sequences of closed sets, also warrant a remark. Every set A nowhere dense in E is a subset of a set A_α closed and nowhere dense in E, and thus every set E_{I} is a subset of a set $F_\sigma = E_{\text{I}}$. The sets F_σ, which are of the first category in E, are therefore the greatest sets of the first category, in the sense that they and their subsets generate all the E_{I}. We also have that:

For $A = F_\sigma$ to be an E_{I} it is sufficient, and in the case of a G_{II}-set also necessary, that $E - A$ be dense in E.

For if $A = \mathfrak{S} F_n$ and $E - A$ is dense in E, then all the more must $E - F_n$ be dense in E, F_n nowhere dense in E, and A an E_{I}. The other half of the statement follows from the definition of the G_{II}-sets.

If the space E is an F_{II}-set then every $A = G_\delta > 0$ is of the second category in itself. For $F = A_\alpha$ is an F_{II}; $F - A$ is an F_σ and is therefore of the first category in F, since its complement A is dense in F; therefore A is of the second category in F and all the more, therefore, in itself. *In an F_{II}-set every G_δ, and in particular every closed or open set, is an F_{II}-set. Every set open in a G_{II}-set is a G_{II}-set.*

§ 28. Spaces of Sets

1. Distances between sets. We again consider points and subsets of a space E. The distance ab between pairs of points of two non-empty sets A and B always have a *greatest lower bound* $\delta(A, B) = \delta(B, A)$ and, in case both sets are bounded, a (finite) *least upper bound* $d(A, B) = d(B, A)$; we call these the *lower* and *upper distances* between A and B. In particular, $d(A, A) = d(A)$ is the *diameter* of A. If the point b is fixed, then $\delta(A, b) = \delta(b, A)$ is the lower distance, and $d(A, b) = d(b, A)$ the upper distance of the point b from the set A.

It follows from $xa \leqq ya + xy$, taking the least upper bound on both sides for $a \,\varepsilon\, A$ (A being bounded), that $d(x, A) \leqq d(y, A) + xy$ and, interchanging x and y, that

$$| \, d(x, A) - d(y, A) \, | \leqq xy;$$

for the lower distances the same result holds (p. 128). $\delta(x, A)$ and $d(x, A)$ are continuous functions of x. $\delta(x, A) = 0$ means the same as $x \,\varepsilon\, A_\alpha$. For $\varrho > 0$, $\delta(x, A) < \varrho$ means the same as (i) corresponding to x there exists some $a \varepsilon A$ for which $ax < \varrho$ or (ii) that x belongs to the neighborhood $U(A, \varrho)$ of A with radius ϱ (p. 135).

We shall now try to define a *distance* between two sets, one that will satisfy the distance axioms and thus enable us to treat the sets as elements of a new metric space. The upper and lower distances, as we might have suspected and as we can readily confirm by trial, are not suitable for this purpose.

We consider only *bounded* sets $A, B > 0$. The relation $(\varrho > 0)$

$$B \leqq U(A, \varrho),$$
$$\text{for every } b \varepsilon B, \delta(A, b) < \varrho,$$
$$\text{for every } b \varepsilon B, \text{there is an } a \varepsilon A \text{ for which } ab < \varrho,$$

the three forms of which are equivalent, certainly holds for $\varrho > d(A, B)$ (for in this case, all $ab < \varrho$) and does not hold for $\varrho \leqq \delta(A, B)$ (for in this case, all $ab \geqq \varrho$). The greatest lower bound of the numbers ϱ for which it holds is a number $\geqq 0$, which we denote by $\varrho(A, B)$ and which is to be distinguished from $\varrho(B, A)$; from the second form of the relation (ϱ) we get

$$(1) \qquad \varrho(A, B) = \sup_{b \varepsilon B} \delta(A, b),$$

and further

$$(2) \qquad \delta(A, B) \leqq \varrho(A, B) \leqq d(A, B).$$

The relation (ϱ) holds for $\varrho > \varrho(A, B)$; for $\varrho < \varrho(A, B)$, it does not (and for $\varrho = \varrho(A, B)$ it is valid if and only if the supremum in (1) is not attained for any b). $\varrho(A, B) = 0$ means the same as $B \leqq A_\alpha$, or, A is dense to B; in every other case, $\varrho(A, B) > 0$. In addition, we have

$$(3) \qquad \varrho(A, B) + \varrho(B, C) \geqq \varrho(A, C).$$

For if $B \leqq U(A, \varrho)$, $C \leqq U(B, \sigma)$, then $C \leqq U(A, \varrho + \sigma)$, from which the conclusion easily follows. If one of the sets consists of a single point, then by virtue of (1),

$$(4) \qquad \varrho(a, B) = \sup_{b \varepsilon B} ab = d(a, B), \quad \varrho(A, b) = \delta(A, b).$$

Because of its assymmetry, this $\varrho(A, B)$ is still not suitable as a distance; therefore we form

$$(5) \qquad \overline{AB} = \max\,[\varrho(A, B), \varrho(B, A)] = \overline{BA}$$

and conclude from (3) that this satisfies the triangle inequality $\overline{AB} + \overline{BC} \geqq \overline{AC}$. We have therefore defined a *distance*, and thus a metric space of sets, provided that, in analogy with earlier cases, we consider as identical two sets for which $\overline{AB} = 0$, that is, two sets of the *same denseness class*; for $\overline{AB} = 0$, we also have $\varrho(A, C) = \varrho(B, C)$ and $\varrho(C, A) = \varrho(C, B)$ and $\overline{AC} = \overline{BC}$ as well.

By virtue of (2), the distance $\overline{AB}$ lies between the lower and upper distances; when one of the sets contains only a single point, then from (4) we find that

$$\overline{Ab} = \max[\delta(A, b),\ d(A, b)] = d(A, b).$$

Hereafter, for the sake of precision of speech, we shall retain only the greatest (closed) set of each density class, thus restricting the domain of definition of $\varrho(A, B)$ and $\overline{AB}$ to the *closed bounded sets* > 0 of the space E. In this metric space convergence, $A = \lim A_n$ or $A_n \to A$, must of course be defined by means of $\overline{AA_n} \to 0$; the sequence is then called *metrically convergent*; A, its *metric limit*; and the limit of a metrically convergent subsequence of A_n, a *metric element of accumulation.*

2. Closed and open limit. Next we must take into account, at first for any sequence of sets A_n of the metric space E, the following limit sets, which are analogous to those for pure sets (upper and lower limit, § 3): the *upper* and *lower closed limits*

(6) $$\overline{F} = \overline{\mathrm{Fl}}\, A_n, \qquad \underline{F} = \underline{\mathrm{Fl}}\, A_n$$

and, in the case of equality, the *closed limit*

(7) $$F = \mathrm{Fl}\, A_n;$$

as well as the *upper* and *lower open* limits

(8) $$\overline{G} = \overline{\mathrm{Gl}}\, A_n, \qquad \underline{G} = \underline{\mathrm{Gl}}\, A_n$$

and, in the case of equality, the *open limit*

(9) $$G = \mathrm{Gl}\, A_n$$

(the abbreviations Fl and Gl may be read, say, as F-limit and G-limit). The points of these various sets are defined by the following properties:

$x \varepsilon \overline{F}$: every neighborhood U_x has points in common with infinitely many A_n.

$x \varepsilon \underline{F}$: every neighborhood U_x has points in common with almost all the A_n.

$x \varepsilon \overline{G}$: there exists a neighborhood U_x that belongs to infinitely many A_n.

$x \varepsilon \underline{G}$: there exists a neighborhood U_x that belongs to almost all the A_n.

We have: $\overline{F} \geqq F$, $\overline{G} \geqq \underline{G}$. If $B_n = E - A_n$ are the complements of the A_n, then, as a moment's reflection will show,

$$(10) \qquad E = \overline{\mathrm{Fl}}\, A_n + \underline{\mathrm{Gl}}\, B_n = \underline{\mathrm{Fl}}\, A_n + \overline{\mathrm{Gl}}\, B_n;$$

that $\overline{G}$ and $\underline{G}$ are open follows immediately from the definition: $\overline{G}$ and $\underline{G}$ are the sum of all the neighborhoods that belong respectively to infinitely many and almost all of the A_n; nearly as directly, or else from (10), it follows that $\overline{F}$, $\underline{F}$ are closed. The alteration, omission, or introduction of a finite number of sets has no influence on the limit sets; in passing to a subsequence we have, with the Greek letters relating to the latter,

$$(11) \qquad \underline{F} \leqq \underline{\Phi} \leqq \overline{\Phi} \leqq \overline{F}, \quad \underline{G} \leqq \underline{\Gamma} \leqq \overline{\Gamma} \leqq \overline{G},$$

so that whenever the whole sequence has a closed (open) limit, every subsequence has such a limit also.

Examples. For the sequence $A, B, A, B, \ldots$ we have

$$\overline{F} = A_\alpha \dot{+} B_\alpha, \quad \underline{F} = A_\alpha B_\alpha,$$
$$\overline{G} = A_i \dot{+} B_i, \quad \underline{G} = A_i B_i.$$

If the sequences A_n with the limit sets $\overline{F}, \underline{F}, \overline{G}, \underline{G}$, and the sequences B_n with the limit sets $\overline{\Phi}, \underline{\Phi}, \overline{\Gamma}, \underline{\Gamma}$ are combined into a sequence

$$A_1, B_1, A_2, B_2, \ldots,$$

then the latter has the limit sets

$$\overline{F} \dot{+} \overline{\Phi}, \quad \underline{F}\underline{\Phi}, \quad \overline{G} \dot{+} \overline{\Gamma}, \quad \underline{G}\underline{\Gamma}$$

If $A(t)$ is the ellipse in the Euclidean plane defined, for $t > 0$, by $x_1^2 + \left(\frac{x_2}{t}\right)^2 = 1$, with vertices $(\pm 1, 0)$ and $(0, \pm t)$, then the closed limit of the sequence $A(n)$ with $n = 1, 2, 3, \ldots$ is the pair of lines $x_1 = \pm 1$, of the sequence $A\left(\frac{1}{n}\right)$, the interval $-1 \leqq x_1 \leqq 1$, $x_2 = 0$.

I. (SELECTION THEOREM). *If the space is separable, then every sequence of sets contains a subsequence for which the closed limit exists (and one for which the open limit exists).*

Because of (10), it suffices to prove the theorem in the case of the open limit (besides, a two-fold application of the theorem produces a subsequence for which both the open and the closed limits exist). Instead of using the neighborhoods U, we make use once more of the countable special neighborhoods V (§ 25); the V — whose sum is $\overline{G}$ — contained in infinitely many A_n may be called *upper* V; those — whose sum is $\underline{G}$ — contained in almost all the A_n may be called *lower* V; and those among the upper V that are not lower V, may be called *discrepant* V. In the transition to a subsequence, the set of upper, lower, and discrepant V becomes, respectively, smaller, greater, and smaller (in the wider sense: that is, the possibility of their remaining the same is not excluded); but if the subsequence is chosen suitably, then a particular discrepant V can actually be eliminated. For if V belongs to all of the infinitely many A_p, but not to almost all the A_n, then the transition from the A_n to the subsequence A_p is sufficient to make V into a lower V and thus to eliminate it from the ranks of the discrepant V. Accordingly, in case $\overline{G} > \underline{G}$, that is, in case there are actually discrepant V present, we proceed as follows: We put the (at most countably many) discrepant V in the form of a sequence $V_1, V_2, \ldots$ and eliminate V_1 by passing from A_n to a subsequence A_p; in case there are discrepant V for this sequence also, say $V_m, \ldots$, then we eliminate the lowest V_m by passing from A_p to a subsequence A_q, and so on. Either a finite number of steps brings us to a subsequence for which there are no further discrepant V, and the open limit exists, or the process can be continued without limit. If that happens to be the case, we form the diagonal sequence t from the sequence of numbers $p, q, r, \ldots$ (arranged in ascending order); that is, from

$$\begin{aligned} p &= p_1, p_2, p_3, \ldots \\ q &= q_1, q_2, q_3, \ldots \\ r &= r_1, r_2, r_3, \ldots \\ &\ldots \end{aligned}$$

we form the sequence

$$t = p_1, q_2, r_3, \ldots .$$

Since, apart from a finite number of elements, this latter is a subsequence of every preceding one, it yields a sequence of sets A_t for which there are no longer any discrepant V, so that the open limit exists.

3. The relation between the closed and metric limits. Leaving the open-limit sets aside for the moment, we now ask whether any relations exist between the closed and the metric limits, $\mathrm{Fl}\, A_n$ and $\lim A_n$ or, more generally, between the two closed-limit sets and the metric elements of accumulation. We note that $\overline{F}$ and $\underline{F}$ remain unchanged if the A_n are replaced by their closed hulls, for $A\, U_x > 0$ is equivalent with $A_\alpha U_x > 0$. Therefore in future we suppose the A_n to be closed and, in addition, bounded and non-empty. If a_n denotes a point of A_n, then we can say, after a certain amount of reflection, that:

$x \varepsilon \overline{F}$ means: There exists a sequence a_n with the point of accumulation x (that is, with a subsequence convergent to x).

$x \varepsilon \underline{F}$ means: There exists a sequence $a_n \to x$.

We obtain, in addition, the following theorem, where X and Y denote non-empty closed, bounded sets.

II. *If* $\varrho(A_n, X) \to 0$, *then* $X \leqq \underline{F}$; *if* $\varrho(Y, A_n) \to 0$, *then* $Y \geqq \overline{F}$.

Proof: Let $\varrho_n = \varrho(A_n, X) \to 0$, $x \varepsilon X$; there exists (because the relation (ϱ) holds for $\varrho > \varrho(A, B)$), a point $a_n \varepsilon A_n$ for which $x a_n < \varrho_n + \frac{1}{n}$, so that $a_n \to x$, $x \varepsilon \underline{F}$.

Let $\varrho_n = \varrho(Y, A_n) \to 0$, $x \varepsilon \overline{F}$; there exists a sequence $a_n \varepsilon A_n$ with a convergent subsequence $a_p \to x$ and, for every a_n, a point $y_n \varepsilon Y$ for which $a_n y_n < \varrho_n + \frac{1}{n}$. Thus $y_p \to x$; x is an α-point of Y; $x \varepsilon Y_\alpha = Y$.

This proves II. From $X \leqq \underline{F} \leqq \overline{F} \leqq Y$ it now follows that, for $X = Y$, this set is also identical with the set $\underline{F} = \overline{F}$, that is:

III. *If the metric limit* $X = \lim A_n$ *exists, then* $X = \mathrm{Fl}\, A_n$ *is at the same time the closed limit of the sequence of sets.*

Even a trivial example makes it immediately apparent that the converse of this theorem cannot be obtained without further assumptions: If, in the space E of real numbers, we let A_n be the interval $[-n, n]$, then the closed limit of this sequence exists, namely E itself, but E is not bounded, and $\overline{A_n E}$ is meaningless. This sequence has no element of accumulation, since the distances $\overline{A_m A_n} = | n - m |$ between two distinct sets are $\geqq 1$.

Another example is obtained by taking

$$A_{2n} = \left\{0, \frac{1}{n}\right\}, \quad A_{2n-1} = \{0, n\} \quad (n = 1, 2, \ldots),$$

where each A_n thus consists of two numbers. Here the closed limit F exists and consists of the single number 0; it is at the same time the (only) metric element of accumulation $\lim A_{2n}$, but the sequence as a whole is not metrically convergent.

In general, we can only say: If X is a metric element of accumulation of A_n, that is, if a subsequence exists for which $\overline{A_p X} \to 0$ then, by III and (11), $\underline{F} \leqq X \leqq \overline{F}$; all the possible elements of accumulation lie between the lower and upper closed limits. If, in particular, $F = \mathrm{Fl}\, A_n$ exists, then the sequence has no element of accumulation different from F; it need not have any at all, however, as the examples have shown, or it may have the unique element of accumulation F without converging metrically at all.

If, however, the space E is *compact in itself*[1] then our theorems do have converses. First we have, as counterpart to II:

IV. *If E is compact in itself, then $\varrho(A_n, \underline{F}) \to 0$ (provided that $\underline{F}$ is non-empty) and $\varrho(\overline{F}, A_n) \to 0$.*

Proof. For every point $x \varepsilon \underline{F}$, which we know can be represented as $\lim a_n$, we have $\delta(A_n, x) \leqq a_n x \to 0$. If for $\underline{F} > 0$ we do not have $\varrho(A_n, \underline{F}) \to 0$, that is, if for a suitable subsequence $\varrho(A_p, \underline{F}) > \varrho > 0$, then according to definition (1) there must be a point $x_p \varepsilon \underline{F}$ for which $\delta(A_p, x_p) > \varrho$. Because of the compactness, the x_p have a convergent subsequence $x_q \to x$, where x belongs to the closed set $\underline{F}$ and $\delta(A_q, x) \to 0$. From $|\delta(A_q, x_q) - \delta(A_q, x)| \leqq x x_q$, it therefore follows that $\delta(A_q, x_q) \to 0$, contradicting $\delta(A_p, x_p) > \varrho$.

For the proof of the second part we first note that $\overline{F}$ is non-empty, since every sequence $a_n \varepsilon A_n$ has at least one point of accumulation $x \varepsilon \overline{F}$. If we did not have $\varrho(\overline{F}, A_n) \to 0$, that is, if $\varrho(\overline{F}, A_p) > \varrho > 0$ for a certain subsequence, then there would have to be a point $a_p \varepsilon A_p$ for which $\delta(\overline{F}, a_p) > \varrho$, and this contradicts the fact that the a_p must have a point of accumulation $x \varepsilon \overline{F}$.

From IV it follows, as a converse to III, that:

V. *If E is compact in itself and the closed limit $X = \mathrm{Fl}\, A_n$ of the sequence of sets A_n exists, then $X = \lim A_n$ is also the metric limit of the sequence.*

Since a compact space is at most separable (p. 146), the Selection Theorem gives, in conjunction with V:

VI. *If the space E is compact in itself, then every non-empty sequence of sets A_n has a metrically convergent subsequence. That is, the metric space of the closed sets F $(0 < F \leqq E)$ is also compact in itself.*

§ 29. Connectedness

1. Foundations. A decomposition

$$A = A_1 + A_2 = AF_1 + AF_2 \tag{1}$$

of the set A into two disjoint summands *closed in A* is called a *partition* of A, provided that both summands are non-empty. A set that can be thus decomposed is said to be disconnected; *a non-empty set that cannot be thus decomposed is called connected.* The summands A_1 and A_2 are

[1] It suffices to require that all the A_n belong to some set compact in E, or that $S = \mathfrak{S} A_n$ be compact in E; in that case, S_α may be taken as the space.

at the same time also *open in A*. In particular, therefore, every non-empty closed set is connected if it cannot be decomposed into two disjoint non-empty closed sets, and a non-empty open set is connected if it cannot be decomposed into two disjoint non-empty open sets. *A closed connected set is called a continuum; an open connected set is called a domain.* Whether a given set A is connected or not depends only on itself and not on the containing space E (whereas the concepts of continuum and domain are relative to E).

Examples. An hyperbola is disconnected; its division into two branches is a partition.[1] The set of the positive and negative real numbers exclusive of zero is disconnected. A set consisting of a single point counts as being connected (a continuum). An interval $[a, b]$ in the set of real numbers is connected; for suppose a division $A_1 + A_2$ into disjoint sets is given, with $a \in A_1$, and with c the greatest lower bound of the numbers of A_2. If A_2 is closed, then c is the smallest number of A_2, so that $c > a$; and A_1 is not closed, since the half-open interval $[a, c)$ belongs to A_1 while c itself does not.

In order to show that a set $A > 0$ is connected, it must be shown that, in every decomposition (1), one of the summands is the null set. It should be noted here that such a decomposition also induces a corresponding decomposition

$$B = B_1 + B_2 = BA_1 + BA_2 = BF_1 + BF_2$$

for any subset B of A.

I. *If every pair of points of A can be "joined to each other in A," that is, if they belong to a connected subset of A, then A is connected.*

For if a decomposition (1) exists, such that $x_1 \in A_1$, $x_2 \in A_2$, then we join x_1 and x_2 with a connected subset B; but then $B = B_1 + B_2$ is a partition.

II. *The sum of two connected sets whose intersection is non-empty is connected.*

Let $S = A \dot{+} B$, $D = AB > 0$. To a decomposition $S = S_1 + S_2$ there corresponds $A = A_1 + A_2$, $B = B_1 + B_2$, and $D = D_1 + D_2$. Since A is connected, one of the summands is 0, say $A_2 = 0$, and thus $D_2 = 0$, $D_1 > 0$, $B_1 > 0$; since B is connected, we have $B_2 = 0$, $S_2 = 0$: S is connected.

A sort of converse of II is the theorem:

[1] We are in the Euclidean plane E_2, remember, without infinitely distant or improper points.

III. *Two closed sets whose sum and intersection are connected are themselves connected.*

Again, we let $S = A \dot{+} B$, $D = AB$. To a decomposition $A = A_1 + A_2$ there corresponds $D = D_1 + D_2$, so that – say – $D_2 = 0$, $A_2 B = 0$. Then $S = (A_1 \dot{+} B) + A_2$. In order for this not to be a partition, we must have $A_2 = 0$: A is connected. The theorem is valid even if A and B are only assumed to be closed in S (which can be taken as the space).

Let us say of a finite number of sets $A, B, C, \ldots$, written in a particular order, that they constitute a *chain* if any two adjacent sets have points in common ($AB > 0$, $BC > 0$, ...). If these sets are connected, then $A \dot{+} B$, $(A \dot{+} B) \dot{+} C, \ldots$, because of II, are also connected. From I, it then follows that:

IV. *The sum of any number of sets any two of which belong to a chain is connected.*

This holds, in particular, if any two sets have points in common.

A *greatest connected subset* – that is, a connected subset not contained in any other – of A is called a *component* of A. A component is obtained by forming either the set $A(x)$ of all the points that can be joined to a point $x \varepsilon A$, or the sum of all the connected subsets of A that contain x (by IV, this sum is connected). It can happen that $A(x)$ reduces to the set $\{x\}$ consisting of a single point. Two components $A(x)$ and $A(y)$ are either disjoint or identical. We obtain in this way a decomposition of A into components

$$A = A(x) + A(y) + \ldots \tag{2}$$

of which there may be only one, as is the case when A is connected, or more than one (finitely or infinitely many). A set all of whose components consist of single points – a set, that is, containing *no connected subset of more than one point* – is called *totally disconnected*, while a set *not containing a continuum of more than a single point* is called *discontinuous*.[1] The first condition is thus more stringent, and a set may be discontinuous without being totally disconnected and may even be discontinuous and connected (examples are given in § 31, 2 and § 42, 5). Total disconnectedness is an absolute concept; discontinuity is relative. A is discontinuous in E means: A has no connected subset closed in E which has more than one point. A set discontinuous in itself is totally disconnected as well (by virtue of VI).

[1] Here also, there is no uniformity of terminology.

V. *If A is connected, then every set between A and A_α ($A \leqq B \leqq A_\alpha$) is connected.*

To a decomposition $B = B_1 + B_2$ into relatively closed sets, there corresponds the decomposition $A = A_1 + A_2$. Here we have say, $A_2 = 0$, $A_1 = A$, $A \leqq B_1 \leqq A_\alpha$, $B_{1\alpha} = A_\alpha$, and since B_1 is closed in B, it follows that $B_1 = BB_{1\alpha} = BA_\alpha = B$, $B_2 = 0$.

VI. *The components of A are closed in A.*

Let P be a component; AP_α (lying between P and P_α) is connected, by V, and thus, since P is a greatest connected subset $\leqq A$, we have $AP_\alpha = P$.

VII. *A connected set C that joins two points a and b of complementary sets A and B ($A + B = E$) intersects the boundary of these sets.*

A connected set of more than one point is dense-in-itself and has at least the cardinality of the continuum.

For if we had $CA_f = C(A_b + B_b) = 0$, we would have a partition $C = CA_i + CB_i$.

If A is taken specifically as the set of points x for which $ax \leqq \varrho$, and B as the set of points x for which $ax > \varrho$, where $0 < \varrho < ab$, then it follows that C must contain, for each of these ϱ, at least one point for which $ax = \varrho$, and this proves the second half of the theorem.

In particular, a continuum of more than one point is perfect. A finite or countable set is totally disconnected.

2. Linear and locally connected spaces. In linear spaces (§ 20, 2), where the distance $xy = |x - y|$ was derived from a norm $|x|$, which was a positive homogeneous function of degree 1 in the coordinates, the segments $[x, y]$ are isometric with the intervals $[a, b]$ of real numbers and are therefore connected. It follows from I that *convex* sets (sets that contain the segment $[x, y]$ joining any two of their points x, y), are connected, as are the whole space, an open sphere (neighborhood), a closed sphere, and the like. Furthermore, a *polygonal path*

$$(3)\quad [x_0, x_1, x_2, \ldots, x_{n-1}, x_n] = [x_0, x_1] \dotplus [x_1, x_2] \dotplus \cdots \dotplus [x_{n-1}, x_n]$$

as a special case of a chain (p. 174), is connected; hence so is any set in which two points can be joined by a polygonal path belonging to the set. Thus, in the Euclidean plane (or, for $m \geqq 2$, in E_m), the set J of irrational points is connected; for if x and y are two points of J and z a third point lying on one of the (countably many) lines joining x or y to a rational point, then x and y are joined by the polygonal path $[x, z, y]$.

For an *open* set in a linear space or a convex subspace, this condition of connectivity (joining by a polygonal path) is not only sufficient but also necessary. For if G is open and if $G(x)$ is the set of those points y that can be joined to $x \varepsilon G$ by a polygonal path $[x, \ldots, y]$, then $G(x)$ is open, because for $U_y \leqq G$, every point $z \varepsilon U_y$ is joined to y by $[y, z] \leqq U_y$, and thus to x by $[x, \ldots, y, z]$. Two sets $G(x)$, $G(y)$ are either disjoint or identical. Therefore, just as in the decomposition into components, we have

$$(4) \qquad G = G(x) + G(y) + G(z) + \ldots.$$

If there is only one summand, then $G = G(x)$ is connected; if there are two or more, then

$$G = G(x) + [G(y) + G(z) + \ldots]$$

yields a partition. If we form the intersection with a subset of G, then this, too, is partitioned, provided that it has points in common with at least two of the summands, say $G(x)$ and $G(y)$; a connected subset of G therefore lies completely inside one summand. This means that the $G(x)$ are components of G. We have therefore shown:

VIII. *If the space is convex, then the components of an open set are themselves open; an open set is connected (a domain) if and only if every pair of points can be joined by a polygonal path.*

In separable spaces of this kind – in Euclidean space, for example – the set of components of an open set is at most countable.

If E is the straight line or the set of real numbers then, according to VII, a connected set contains the intervals $[a, b]$ joining any two of its points a and b, whence it follows easily that E can have no connected sets other than single points, intervals, half-lines, and the whole line itself (the intervals may be open, half-open, or closed; the half-lines, open or closed). The domains are the open intervals (a, b), the open half-lines (a, ∞) and $(-\infty, b)$, as well as the whole line. The most general open set G is obtained by adding together a finite or countable number of disjoint domains. If there are abutting intervals, such as (a, b) and (b, c), then b becomes an isolated point of the closed complement $F = E - G$; if this does not happen at all, then F is perfect.

The property first named in VIII belongs to a more general class of spaces, as we shall now show.

Let us call a decomposition – in a, for the moment, arbitrary space – of the set A into the sum of disjoint non-empty sets

$$(5) \qquad A = P + Q + R + \ldots$$

a *natural decomposition* if it does not tear apart the connected subsets of A – if its summands, that is, are sums of components or, if connected, components. Natural decompositions thus comprise, among others, the decomposition into components and, further, into a finite number of relatively closed or into any number of relatively open sets (P and $A - P$ are then simultaneously closed or open in A, whence the statement follows easily). If, for example, an open set can be decomposed into open sets then, insofar as they are connected, they are components of G. A domain G with the boundary H is a component of $E - H$, for $G_\alpha = G + H$ is closed, $E - (G + H) = G_1$ is open, $E - H = G + G_1$ is a natural decomposition. A domain is uniquely determined by its boundary together with a single one of its points.

The space E will be called *locally connected*[1] if *every neighborhood* U_x *of an arbitrary point* x *contains a domain* G_x *containing the point* x. The space need not, therefore, be connected (as a whole).[2] A convex space is locally connected, since the neighborhoods themselves are connected. The simplest example of a space that is not locally connected is the set $E = \{1, \frac{1}{2}, \frac{1}{3}, \ldots, 0\}$; the only connected set containing the point 0 is the set $\{0\}$ consisting of this one point alone, and this set is not open in E. An example of a connected space that is not locally connected is given following Theorem XII. Now we have:

IX. *If the space is locally connected and* $A = P + Q + R + \ldots$ *is a natural decomposition of* A, *then*

$$(6) \qquad A_i = P_i + Q_i + \ldots, \qquad A_b = P_b + Q_b + \ldots,$$

$$(7) \qquad A_f = S_\alpha, \qquad S = P_f \dot{+} Q_f \dot{+} \ldots.$$

The open kernel, the border, and the frontier (boundary) of the whole set depend in this simple way on those of the summands. For the proof of (6) we recall that, in general,

$$A_i \geqq P_i + Q_i + \ldots, \qquad A_b \leqq P_b + Q_b + \ldots$$

On the other hand, if $x \,\varepsilon\, A_i$, $U_x \leqq A$, and G_x is a domain for which $x \,\varepsilon\, G_x \leqq U_x$, then G_x is contained in a single summand of the decomposition, say $G_x \leqq P$, $x \,\varepsilon\, P_i$, and so $A_i \leqq P_i + Q_i + \ldots$.

---

[1] Or connected *in the small* (Hahn).

[2] An isolated space is locally connected; every set $\{x\}$ consisting of only one point is a G_x.

In order to prove (7) let us consider the complement $B = E - A$; we have

$$\begin{aligned} E - P &= B + Q + R + \cdots \\ (E-P)_b &\leqq B_b + Q_b + R_b + \ldots \\ P_f = P_b + (E-P)_b &\leqq B_b + P_b + Q_b + R_b + \ldots = B_b + A_b = A_f, \end{aligned}$$

and thus $A_f \geqq P_f \dot{+} Q_f \dot{+} \cdots = S$ and $A_f \geqq S_\alpha$ since A_f is closed. On the other hand,

(8) $$A_f \leqq S_\alpha ,$$

and this half of the assertion is valid even for an arbitrary decomposition (in a locally connected space) $A = P \dot{+} Q \dot{+} R \dot{+} \ldots$ (which need be neither a natural decomposition nor even a decomposition into disjoint summands). For let $x \varepsilon A_f$, let U_x be arbitrary, and let $G_x \leqq U_x$; since x is an α-point of A and of B, the set G_x contains points of both sets; suppose it contains a point of, say, P and one of $B \leqq E - P$; then (by VII) it contains also a point of P_f or S, so that $x \varepsilon S_\alpha$.

In a natural decomposition into a finite number of summands, (7) simplifies to $A_f = S = P_f \dot{+} Q_f \dot{+} \ldots$.

X. *If the space is locally connected, then the components of open sets are always domains, and conversely.*

For if A is open, then, by (6), $P, Q, R, \ldots$ are also open, and this holds in particular for the components. If, conversely, the components of the open sets are domains, then the component of U_x containing x is a domain G_x, and the space is locally connected.

The following theorem is an application of (8):

A connected and locally connected space that is also an F_{II}-set cannot be decomposed into countably many disjoint non-empty closed sets.

Assuming that $E = F_1 + F_2 + \ldots$ (F_n closed and non-empty), then since E is connected, F_n has a boundary $H_n = F_{nb} > 0$; the sum $H = H_1 + H_2 \ldots$ (as the complement of ΣF_{ni}) is also closed. For the boundary of

$$E - F_1 = F_2 + F_3 + \ldots$$

it turns out, according to (8), that

$$H_1 \leqq (H_2 + H_3 + \cdots)_\alpha,$$

that is, $H_2 + H_3 + \ldots$ is dense in H; H_1 and each H_n are nowhere dense in H; and thus H is of the first category in itself, in contradiction to the hypothesis that E be an F_{II}-set.

This more stringent kind of connectedness, which excludes a partition not only into a finite number, but even into a countable number of closed summands, is a property of, amongst others, Euclidean spaces; later on we shall prove the result, by another method, for compact continua also (p. 185).

Thus far we have defined local connectedness simply for the whole space. It would seem reasonable to call E locally connected at the single point x if every U_x contained a G_x (a domain containing x); however, it is useful to relax the condition somewhat and make the following definition:

The space E is said to be *locally connected at the point x if every neighborhood U_x contains a connected set C of which x is an interior point* ($x \varepsilon C_i$); we may take C here as the component of U_x that contains x.

XI. *If the space E is locally connected at every point x, then it is* (simply) *locally connected; and conversely.*

For if C_x is the component of U_x that contains x, $y \varepsilon C_x$, $U_y \leqq U_x$ and C_y the component of U_y that contains y, then $C_y \leqq C_x$, because $C_x \dotplus C_y$ is connected, is properly contained in U_x, and thus is identical with C_x. Now y is an interior point of C_y and therefore also of C_x; C_x consists entirely of interior points and is a domain $\leqq U_x$ containing x. The converse is trivial.

It is possible to formulate local connectedness in x somewhat differently (Mazurkiewicz). Let $\widehat{xy}$ be the lower bound of the diameters $d(C)$ of all the *bounded connected sets* C that contain x and y; when none exist, we leave $\widehat{xy}$ undefined. We have $\widehat{xy} \geqq xy$; if, furthermore, $\widehat{xy}$ and $\widehat{yz}$ exist, then we also have $\widehat{xz} \leqq \widehat{xy} + \widehat{yz}$ as a consequence of the easily verifiable fact that $d(A \dotplus B) \leqq d(A) + d(B)$ whenever AB is non-empty. This $\widehat{xy}$ then, in so far as it exists, has the properties of a distance, so that we can say:

XII. *The space is locally connected at x if and only if $\widehat{xy}$ converges to zero whenever xy converges to zero.*

The condition is intended, of course, to mean: For any $\varrho > 0$ and a suitable $\sigma > 0$, $\widehat{xy}$ is defined and is $< \varrho$ whenever $xy < \sigma$.

If this condition is satisfied, then let U_x and V_x be the neighborhoods of x with the radii ϱ and σ. Every $y \varepsilon V_x$ may be joined to x by means of a connected set C_y for which $d(C_y) < \varrho$. The set $C = \mathfrak{S}_{y}^{V_x} C_y$ is connected, by IV, and is contained in U_x, since each of its points has a distance $< \varrho$ from x; it contains V_x and therefore has x as an interior point; E is locally connected at x.

If, conversely, E is locally connected at x, then let U_x have the arbitrarily chosen radius ϱ; the component C of U_x that contains x has x as an interior point and therefore contains some neighborhood V_x of radius σ. For $xy < \sigma$, we then have $\widehat{xy} \leqq d(C) \leqq 2\varrho$.

Example: In the Euclidean $\xi\eta$-plane, let r_n be the point $\xi = n^{-1}$, $\eta = (-1)^n$ for $n = 1, 2, 3, \ldots.$ The sum of the intervals $[r_1, r_2]$, $[r_2, r_3], \ldots$ is the infinite polygonal path

$$R = [r_1, r_2, r_3, \ldots]$$

which, as it gets closer and closer to the η-axis, travels back and forth infinitely often between the lines $\eta = 1$ and $\eta = -1$, so that every point of the segment

$$S: \qquad \xi = 0, \quad -1 \leqq \eta \leqq 1$$

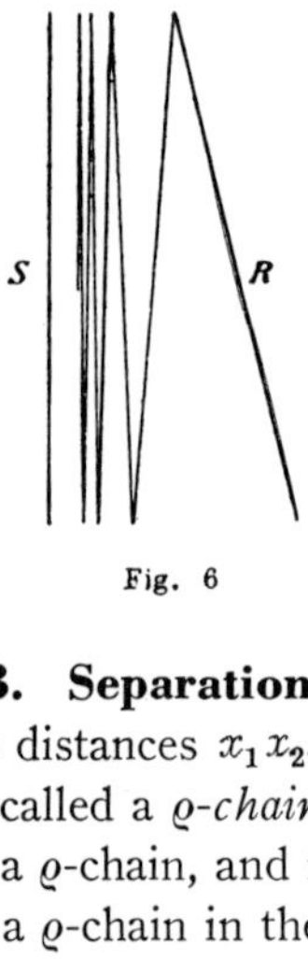

Fig. 6

is a point of accumulation of R. The set $E = R + S$, thought of as the space, is not locally connected at the points of S. For if we try to connect a point $s \varepsilon S$ to a point $r \varepsilon R$ by means of a connected set $C \subseteqq E$, then, no matter how close r may be to s, C must cut every line $\xi =$ const. lying between s and r in at least one point; but then C contains a residual portion $[r_n, r_{n+1}, \ldots]$ of the polygonal path and has a diameter > 2, so that $\widehat{sr}$ cannot converge to 0 with sr. R and E, however, are connected.

3. Separations. A finite complex of points $(x_1, x_2, \ldots, x_n)$ in which the distances $x_1x_2, \ldots, x_{n-1}x_n$ between neighboring points are $\leqq \varrho$ will be called a *ϱ-chain* ($\varrho > 0$); we say then that x_1 and x_n can be joined by a ϱ-chain, and in particular, if all the points of the chain belong to A, by a ϱ-chain in the set A. Let us look for all the ϱ-chains joining, in A, two points x and y of A; the greatest lower bound of the numbers ϱ occurring in this will be called the *separation* of the points x and y and will be denoted by $\overline{xy}$ (although it depends not only on the two points but also on A). For $\varrho > \overline{xy}$, it is therefore possible to join x to y by a ϱ-chain in A; for $\varrho < \overline{xy}$, it is not possible; for $\varrho = \overline{xy}$, it depends on the particular case. Clearly, $\overline{xy} \leqq xy$. The separations satisfy the triangle inequality in the more stringent form

$$\overline{xz} \leqq \max\,[\overline{xy}, \overline{yz}]\,; \tag{9}$$

for if x and y can be joined by a ϱ-chain, and y and z by a σ-chain, then x and z can be joined by a τ-chain, where $\tau = \max\,[\varrho, \sigma]$. If $x \to \xi$, $y \to \eta$, then $\overline{x\xi} \to 0$, $\overline{y\eta} \to 0$, $\overline{xy} \to \overline{\xi\eta}$; the separation $\overline{xy}$ is a *continuous function* of x and y. Of course, we set $\overline{xx}=0$; but $\overline{xy}=0$ does not mean that $x=y$ but, rather, that x and y can be joined by a ϱ-chain for *every* $\varrho>0$. In the set of the real or the rational numbers any two points have the separation 0.[1] Now we have (as regards the lower distances $\delta(P, Q)$, compare pp. 166-7):

XIII. *If* $A=P+Q$, *where* $\delta(P,Q)=\delta>0$, *then every point* $p \varepsilon P$ *has a separation* $\overline{pq} \geqq \delta$ *from every point* $q \varepsilon Q$. *If two points* p, q *of* A *have the separation* $\overline{pq}=\varrho>0$, *then a decomposition* $A=P+Q$ *for which* $p \varepsilon P$, $q \varepsilon Q$, *and* $\delta(P,Q) \geqq \varrho$ *is possible.*

The first is evident. The second is proved as follows: Let P be the set of points $x \varepsilon A$ for which $\overline{px}<\varrho$ and $Q=A-P$. Then $p \varepsilon P$ and $q \varepsilon Q$. If we now had $\delta(P,Q)<\varrho$, then there would be two points $x \varepsilon P$ and $y \varepsilon Q$ for which $xy<\varrho$; a fortiori, we would then have $\overline{xy}<\varrho$, and by (9), $\overline{py} \leqq \max[\overline{px}, \overline{xy}]<\varrho$; contrary to hypothesis, we would then have $y \varepsilon P$.

Since the decomposition $A=P+Q$ of Theorem XIII is clearly a partition (P and Q closed in A), it follows that: *In a connected set any two points have separation zero.* The converse[2] is not true, however, as is shown by the set of rational numbers, which is not connected, although every pair of its points has separation zero. The partition of A into two parts with positive lower distance happens to be a very coarse lack of connectedness, visible, so to speak, to the naked eye, while the set may happen to be disconnected in a subtler, microscopic manner that may allow, say, of a partition $A=P+Q$ with $\delta(P,Q)=0$ (as does the set of the rational numbers into those of the numbers that are $<\sqrt{2}$ and $>\sqrt{2}$).

There is, however, an important case in which the above result has a converse. If the set $A=P+Q$ *compact in itself* (consequently, compact and closed) is partitioned, that is, split into two closed non-empty sets, then their lower distance $\delta(P,Q)=\delta>0$. In fact, the greatest lower bound δ of the distances pq is actually attained here, the infimum becoming a minimum; for if $p_n q_n \rightarrow \delta$, then there exists a subsequence for which $p_n \rightarrow p$, a subsequence of this for which $q_n \rightarrow q$, and then we have $p \varepsilon P$, $q \varepsilon Q$, and $\delta=pq>0$. Thus every partition here is "visible to the naked eye," and if every two points in A have separation 0, then A is connected. Furthermore, if A is not connected, then the component P containing the point p is identical with the set $P(0)$ of the points $\overline{px}=0$.

[1] See Footnote 2 below.

[2] According to a definition of Cantor, from which we have deviated, a set is called connected merely if every two of its points have the separation zero. A set of this latter kind is now called well-chained.

For, on the one hand, we always have $P \leqq P(0)$; on the other hand, $P(0)$ is closed, because the separation $\overline{px}$ is a continuous function of x; and thus it is compact in itself and therefore connected, since after all any two of its points have[1] the separation 0, whence $P(0) \leqq P$. We have thus shown:

XIV. *A set compact in itself is connected if (and only if) any two of its points have the separation* 0. *The component containing the point* p *is the set of those points that have a separation* 0 *from* p.

In the proof of XIII, we showed that the set of the points x for which $\overline{px} < \varrho$, as well as its complement, it closed; the same holds also for the set $P(\varrho)$ of the points $\overline{px} \leqq \varrho$ and its complement $Q(\varrho) = A - P(\varrho)$ for $\varrho > 0$; we see, as we did there, that the lower distance between the two sets is $> \varrho$ (assuming $Q(\varrho) > 0$). For $\varrho = 0$, this no longer holds; it is still true that the component containing p

$$(10) \qquad P(0) = \mathfrak{D}_{\varrho > 0} P(\varrho) = P(1)\, P(\tfrac{1}{2})\, P(\tfrac{1}{3}) \ldots$$

is closed, but $Q(0)$ need not be, and the lower distance between the two of them may well be 0.

The following three theorems are applications of the separations to compact sets.

XV. *A set compact in itself remains compact in itself if separations replace distances as the metric, and the set becomes a totally disconnected set.*

Split into components, let the set be

$$A = P + Q + R + \ldots;$$

if we make it into a metric space by using the separation in A as distance, then all the points of a component of A coalesce into a single point. By choosing one point from each component it is possible to set[2]

$$\overline{A} = \{p, q, r, \ldots\}.$$

A sequence of points x_n has a point of accumulation x in A, that is, a subsequence for which $xx_\nu \to 0$, all the more then does $\overline{xx_\nu} \to 0$, so that x_n

[1] Compare Appendix B.

[2] Incidentally, $\overline{A}$ is a continuous map of A, and XV is therefore a consequence of § 35, III.

has the point of accumulation x in $\overline{A}$ as well. $\overline{A}$ is therefore compact in itself, and in the same way there corresponds to every subset B compact in itself of A, a subset $\overline{B}$ compact in itself of $\overline{A}$; if p and q are points of different components of A and if ϱ is positive and $< \overline{pq}$, then the set $P(\varrho)$ of the points $\overline{px} \leqq \varrho$, as well as its complement $Q(\varrho) = A - P(\varrho)$, is closed in A; the sets corresponding to them, of which one contains the point p and the other the point q, are in turn closed in $\overline{A}$, and consequently two different points of $\overline{A}$ never belong to a connected subset of $\overline{A}$; thus, $\overline{A}$ is totally disconnected (p. 174).

Since the set $\overline{A}$ is complete and at most separable, it follows that: *The set of components of a set A compact in itself is either at most countable or of the cardinality of the continuum.*

XVI. *The compact, perfect, totally disconnected sets are identical with the dyadic discontinua.*

Suppose, first, only that A is compact in itself. With $\varrho > 0$ we form a greatest set of points whose pairwise separations in A are $> \varrho$ (so that their distances are certainly $> \varrho$). This set is finite and consists of points that we may call $x_1, x_2, \ldots, x_n$. For each point $x \,\varepsilon\, A$ there exists at least one x_i $(i = 1, 2, \ldots, n)$ for which $\overline{xx_i} \leqq \varrho$ (otherwise these greatest sets could be extended) and also at most one (otherwise we should have $\overline{x_i x_k} \leqq \varrho$). If, therefore, A_i is the set of points $\overline{xx_i} \leqq \varrho$, then

$$(11) \qquad A = A_1 + A_2 + \cdots + A_n$$

is decomposed into disjoint, closed, compact sets each of which has a "separation diameter" $\leqq \varrho$ — that is, two points of A_i have a separation $\leqq \varrho$.

If, second, A is also totally disconnected, then the distance xy $(\geqq \overline{xy})$ converges to zero whenever the separation $\overline{xy}$ does and even converges uniformly, so that some $\varrho > 0$ corresponds to every $\sigma > 0$ in such a way as to make $xy < \sigma$ whenever $\overline{xy} < \varrho$. For otherwise there would have to be a sequence of pairs of points for which $\overline{x_n y_n} \to 0$, $x_n y_n \geqq \sigma$, where by restricting consideration to subsequences we may assume $x_n \to x$, $y_n \to y$, so that $\overline{xy} = 0$, $xy \geqq \sigma$; the distinct points x, y would belong to the same component. A can therefore be decomposed for every $\delta > 0$ into a finite number of disjoint sets compact in themselves and of diameter $\leqq \delta$.

If, third, A is perfect as well, then the summands of such a decomposition (11) are also perfect, since they are also open in A and hence dense-in-themselves. The A_i are therefore sets like A, and the process can be repeated:

$$A = \sum_i A_i, \quad A_i = \sum_k A_{ik}, \quad A_{ik} = \sum_l A_{ikl}, \ldots$$

in which the diameters of the sets with n subscripts can be taken smaller than $1/n$ or even so small that every sum has at least two summands. Then

$$A = \Sigma A_i \,.\, \Sigma A_{ik} \,.\, \Sigma A_{ikl} \cdots$$

is a polyadic discontinuum (p. 154) and can be transformed into a dyadic discontinuum.

Conversely, a dyadic discontinuum

$$A = \Sigma V_p \,.\, \Sigma V_{pq} \,.\, \Sigma V_{pqr} \cdots$$

is totally disconnected. For if $C \leqq A$ is connected then, in order that $C = CV_1 + CV_2$ not be a partition, C can have points in common with only one V_p, then with only one V_{pq}, then with only one V_{pqr}, and so on; that is, $C = V_p V_{pq} V_{pqr} \cdots$ contains only one point. The proof of XVI is thus complete.

XVII. (Janiszewski's Border Theorem). *Let F be closed; let $G = E - F$ be its open complement, $H = F_b$ the boundary of both sets, and C a compact continuum with $CH > 0$.*[1] *Then* (i) *every component of CF has points in common with H,* (ii) *for $CG > 0$ every component of CG has points of accumulation in H* (iii) *for $CF_i > 0$ every component of CF_i has points of accumulation in H.*

The figure illustrates the case in which F is a closed circular disc in the Euclidean plane E, G the exterior of the circle, and H its periphery.

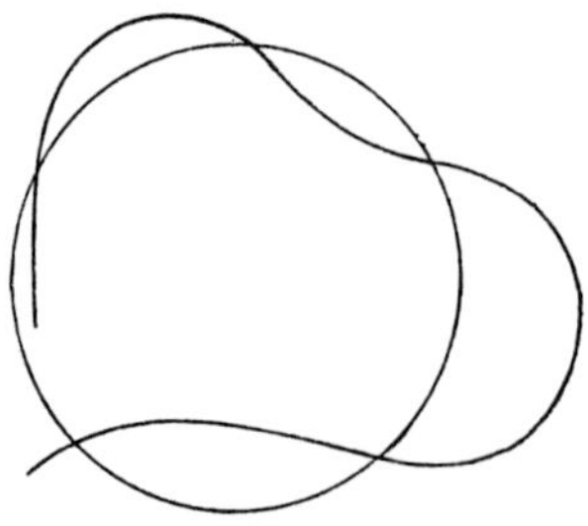
Fig. 7

Proof. (i) If $CF = P + Q$ is decomposed into two closed sets and $P > 0$, then PH is also > 0. For on account of $C = CF \dotplus CG_\alpha$ we have $C = P \dotplus (Q \dotplus CG_\alpha)$; in order that the latter not be a partition, the intersection of both summands $PCG_\alpha = PFG_\alpha = PH$ must be nonempty. If now $p \,\varepsilon\, CF$ and $P(\varrho)$ is the set of points x that have a separation $\overline{px} \leqq \varrho$ in the closed compact set CF, then for $\varrho > 0$, $P(\varrho)$ and the

[1] By virtue of VII, this hypothesis is satisfied, in particular, when $CF > 0$, $CG > 0$.

complement $Q(\varrho) = CF - P(\varrho)$ are, as we know, closed, and so $P(\varrho)H > 0$. By the First Intersection Theorem (§ 26, I), the intersection of the sets $P(\varrho)H$ for $\varrho = 1, \frac{1}{2}, \frac{1}{3}, \ldots$ is also non-empty, and therefore, by (10), $P(0)H$ is non-empty, where $P(0)$ can denote any component of CF.

(ii) Let F_n be the closed set of points $\delta(x, F) \geqq 1/n$ $(n = 1, 2, 3, \ldots)$; we have $G = F_1 \dotplus F_2 \dotplus \ldots$ and, for $p \,\varepsilon\, CG$, *ultimately* $p \,\varepsilon\, CF_n$. By what has been proved in (i), the component of CF_n containing p (C intersects F_n as well as $E - F_n \geqq F$ and therefore, by virtue of VII, also the border of F_n) and, a fortiori, that of CG, has a point x_n on the border of F_n, that is, one for which $\delta(x_n, F) = 1/n$; and these points have a point of accumulation x in C for which $\delta(x, F) = 0$, $x \,\varepsilon\, F G_\alpha = H$.

(iii) C intersects F_i as well as $E - F_i \geqq H$ and thus, by VII, also the boundary of F_i; by (ii), applied to F_i instead of G, every component of CF_i has points of accumulation in this boundary, which is the same as $F_{i\alpha} - F_i \leqq F - F_i = H$.

Applications: If C is a compact continuum and A a subcontinuum $< C$, then there exists a continuum B for which $A < B < C$. For proof, we choose a point $y \,\varepsilon\, C - A$ and a positive number $\varrho < \delta(y, A)$, and put for F the set of points $\delta(x, A) \leqq \varrho$ and for B the component of CF containing A. C intersects F as well as $E - F$ (at the point y) and thus intersects the border of F; consequently B contains a border point of F for which $\delta(x, A) = \varrho$, and therefore $B > A$; on the other hand, $y \,\bar{\varepsilon}\, B$, and therefore $B < C$.

A compact continuum cannot be decomposed into countably many disjoint, non-empty, closed sets[1] (Sierpiński).

Suppose the compact continuum A to be representable as a sum

$$A = A_1 + A_2 + \ldots$$

of disjoint non-empty closed sets A_n. We show that A contains a continuum B that has points in common with infinitely many A_n although not with A_1:

$$B = BA_{p_1} + BA_{p_2} + \cdots = B_{p_1} + B_{p_2} + \cdots$$

$(1 < p_1 < p_2 < \cdots,\ B_p > 0)$. Once we have this, everything is already proved; for the repetition of the process produces a continuum

$$C = CB_{q_1} + CB_{q_2} + \cdots = C_{q_1} + C_{q_2} + \cdots$$

with non-empty C_q, where the q form a subsequence of the p and $p_1 < q_1 < q_2 < \ldots$, etc. $ABC \ldots$ would therefore be the empty set, in contradiction to the First Intersection Theorem.

---

[1] Compare with the similar theorem on p. 178.

In order to prove the statement concerning B, let us understand by $2\varrho = \delta(A_1, A_2) > 0$ the lower distance between A_1 and A_2 and (say in the space A itself) by F the closed set of the points for which $\delta(x, A_1) \geqq \varrho$, so that $A_2 \leqq F \leqq A - A_1$. Let then B be the component of F containing any point whatever of A_2, so that $BA_1 = 0$, $BA_2 > 0$. But, according to XVII, B now contains a border point of F, that is, one for which $\delta(x, A_1) = \varrho$, and this point does not belong to A_2; B therefore has points in common with at least two A_n and therefore, as a continuum, with infinitely many A_n, as stated.

4. Sequences of connected sets.

XVIII. *The intersection of a decreasing sequence* $A_1 \geqq A_2 \geqq \cdots$ *of compact continua is a continuum.*

Let us remark first that two disjoint closed sets F_1 and F_2 can always be enclosed in disjoint open sets G_1 and G_2; all that is necessary is to enclose each point $x_1 \varepsilon F_1$ in a neighborhood of radius $\frac{1}{2}\delta(x_1, F_2)$ and similarly, every point $x_2 \varepsilon F_2$ in a neighborhood of radius $\frac{1}{2}\delta(x_2, F_1)$. If now $A = A_1 A_2 \ldots$ (a compact non-empty closed set) could be partitioned into two closed sets, we should enclose these in disjoint open sets G_1 and G_2, so that $A = AG_1 + AG_2$; setting $F = E - (G_1 + G_2)$, we have $AF = 0$. But because of the First Intersection Theorem, $A_n F$ would then have to be 0 for some n, and $A_n = A_n G_1 + A_n G_2$ could be partitioned.

XIX. (ZORETTI'S THEOREM). *If the space is compact in itself, then the upper closed limit of a sequence of connected sets is itself connected, provided that the lower closed limit is non-empty.*

Let the sets A_n be connected, and let $\underline{F} = \underline{\mathrm{Fl}}\, A_n$ be non-empty; it is to be shown that $\overline{F} = \overline{\mathrm{Fl}}\, A_n$ is connected. Let $x \varepsilon \underline{F}$, $y \varepsilon \overline{F}$; then (p. 171) there exists a sequence $a_n \to x$ with $a_n \varepsilon A_n$, a subsequence $b_p \to y$ with $b_p \varepsilon A_p$, and finally (§ 28, IV) $\varrho(\overline{F}, A_n) \to 0$, whence it follows that for any $\varrho > 0$ there exists a set $A_p = A$ and in it two points a and b such that

$$ax < \varrho, \quad by < \varrho, \quad \varrho(\overline{F}, A) < \varrho.$$

The last relation says that for each $c \varepsilon A$ there exists some $z \varepsilon F$ such that $cz < \varrho$. Now a and b can be joined in A by a ϱ-chain $(c_0, c_1, \ldots, c_n)$ with $c_0 = a$, $c_n = b$ and, for each c_i, some $z_i \varepsilon \overline{F}$ with $c_i z_i < \varrho$ can be specified where, in particular, we can set $z_0 = x$ and $z_n = y$. Then $(z_0, z_1, \ldots, z_n)$ is a 3ϱ-chain that joins x and y in $\overline{F}$. Since this is possible for every ϱ, x and y have the separation 0 in $\overline{F}$; since this holds for every $y \varepsilon \overline{F}$, any two points of $\overline{F}$ have separation 0; since $\overline{F}$ is closed, and therefore compact in itself, $\overline{F}$ is connected.

The example of the sequence $A, B, A, B, \ldots$ with

$$\overline{F} = A_\alpha \dot{+} B_\alpha, \ \underline{F} = A_\alpha B_\alpha$$

shows that the hypothesis $\underline{F} > 0$ is indispensable, and that $\underline{F}$ need not be connected. The compactness of the space is also essential: if in the Euclidean plane $A_n = [a, c_n, b]$ is the polygonal path connecting the points $a = (-1, 0)$, $c_n = (0, n)$, $b_n = (1, 0)$, then $\overline{F} = \underline{F}$ consists of the two half-lines $x = \pm 1$, $y \geqq 0$ and is not connected.

If the space is compact in itself and the sequence of the connected sets A_n has the closed limit A or – what, by § 28, III and V, is the same thing – the metric limit A, then A is a continuum. XVIII is a special case of this. If the space is compact in itself then, by § 28, VI, every sequence of connected sets has a metrically convergent subsequence whose limit is itself a continuum. (It is to be recalled that the metric limit was supposed to be closed.) The continua of a space compact in itself thus themselves constitute a space compact in itself.

CHAPTER VII

POINT SETS AND ORDINAL NUMBERS

§ 30. Hulls and Kernels

The theory of well-ordering, originally developed by Cantor precisely for the purpose of point-set theory was later somewhat kept back from playing this role — not always for praiseworthy motives — and we have seen for ourselves in the chapter just concluded how much can be done without it. Nevertheless, situations arise in which the ordinal numbers are occasionally indispensable, and others in which they are, at the very least, most welcome as tools in a more elegant exposition of a result that may have been found without them. In particular, they make their appearance, in one or the other of these roles, whenever we are concerned with the formation of sets or systems of sets which are in some way the *greatest* or *smallest* of their kind.

1. Schema for hulls and kernels. Suppose that in a space E (which may, for the moment, be taken to be a pure set) a set A_φ is made to correspond uniquely to every set A (both $\leqq E$; φ is a function symbol). Let this set function be *monotone*, that is.

$$\text{(1)} \qquad \text{for } A < B \text{ we have } A_\varphi \leqq B_\varphi .$$

If then

$$S = A \dot{+} B \dot{+} \ldots, \quad D = AB \ldots$$

are the sum and intersection of any number of sets, then

$$S_\varphi \geqq A_\varphi \dot{+} B_\varphi \dot{+} \cdots, \quad D_\varphi \leqq A_\varphi B_\varphi \ldots .$$

There exist sets A for which $A \leqq A_\varphi$, for example the null set $A = 0$; there also exist sets A for which $A \geqq A_\varphi$, for example the whole space $A = E$. We see at once:

I. *The sum of any number of sets for which* $A \leqq A_\varphi$ *is itself such a set; the intersection of any number of sets for which* $A \geqq A_\varphi$ *is itself such a set.*

Accordingly, for an arbitrary set M we can define:

The sum $\underline{M}$ of all the sets $A \leqq M$ for which $A \leqq A_\varphi$ (to which $A = 0$

certainly belongs) or the greatest set $A \leqq M$ for which $A \leqq A_\varphi$: *the φ-kernel of M*;

The intersection $\overline{M}$ of all the sets $A \geqq M$ for which $A \geqq A_\varphi$ (to which $A = E$ certainly belongs) or the smallest set $A \geqq M$ for which $A \geqq A_\varphi$: *the φ-hull of M.*

The typical example is given by $A_\varphi = A_\beta$, the set of points of accumulation of A in a (metric) space. Here

$$A \leqq A_\beta : \text{ means } A \text{ is dense-in-itself, and}$$
$$A \geqq A_\beta : \text{ means } A \text{ is closed,}$$

and we obtain the dense-in-itself kernel $\underline{M} = M_k$ as well as the closed hull $\overline{M} = M_\alpha$.

It can happen that $A \leqq A_\varphi$ always; in that case $\underline{M} = M$, and $\overline{M}$ is the smallest set $A \geqq M$ for which $A = A_\varphi$. *Example*: $A_\varphi = A_\alpha$, the set of α-points of A, and once more $\overline{M}$ turns out to be the closed hull of M.

It can happen that $A \geqq A_\varphi$ always; in that case $\overline{M} = M$, and $\underline{M}$ is the greatest set $A \leqq M$ with $A = A_\varphi$. *Example*: $A_\varphi = A_i$, the set of interior points of A, where $\underline{M}$ turns out to be the open kernel M_i.

It is possible to induce these special cases by considering the functions

$$A_s = A + A_\varphi, \quad A_d = A A_\varphi \tag{2}$$

which are monotone simultaneously with A_φ.[1] Here we always have $A \leqq A_s$ and $A = A_s$ is equivalent with $A \geqq A_\varphi$; furthermore, we always have $A \geqq A_d$, and $A = A_d$ is equivalent with $A \leqq A_\varphi$. Thus, in the formation of the kernel, A_φ can be replaced by A_d; in the formation of the hull, A_φ can be replaced by A_s; and we have:

The φ-kernel $\underline{M}$ is the greatest set $A \leqq M$ for which $A = A_d$; the φ-hull $\overline{M}$ is the smallest set $A \geqq M$ for which $A = A_s$.

Example: For $A_\varphi = A_\beta$ we find $A_s = A_\alpha$, and $A_d = A_a$ (coherence of A); the dense-in-itself kernel M_k is the greatest set $A \leqq M$ for which $A = A_a$; the closed hull M_α is the smallest set $A \geqq M$ for which $A = A_\alpha$.

2. Utilization of the ordinal numbers. Let us consider first $\underline{M}$, the greatest set $A \leqq M$ for which $A = A_d$. This set A. because of the monotonicity of the function A_d, satisfies the inequality $A = A_d \leqq M_d$ and is contained not only in M, but also in the (in general) smaller set M_d. It is consequently contained also in $M_{dd}, M_{ddd}, \ldots$, where we of course mean the repeated formation of the set function A_d: $M_{dd} = (M_d)_d$, etc.

[1] A_s does not here denote the separated part of A.

This set is contained also in the intersection $MM_dM_{dd}\ldots$ of the sets formed thus far and, even further than this, is contained in all the sets arising from the further application of the process d. This means that if we assign inductively to each ordinal number ξ a set M_ξ by the rule

$$(3) \qquad \begin{cases} M_0 = M \\ M_{\xi+1} = (M_\xi)_d \\ M_\eta = \mathfrak{D}_{\xi<\eta} M_\xi \quad (\eta \text{ a limit number}), \end{cases}$$

then our $A = \underline{M}$ is contained in all the M_ξ.

For every ordinal number $\eta > 0$ the decomposition[1]

$$(4) \qquad M = \sum_{\xi<\eta} (M_\xi - M_{\xi+1}) + M_\eta$$

holds.

For if $x \varepsilon M$ does not belong to M_η then let M_ζ $(0 < \zeta \leqq \eta)$ be the set of lowest index to which x does not belong; this ζ, because of the third requirement in (3), may not be a limit ordinal, and therefore we can set $\zeta = \xi + 1$ $(0 \leqq \xi < \eta)$ and $x \varepsilon M_\xi - M_{\xi+1}$.

The disjoint summands $M_\xi - M_{\xi+1}$ cannot, however, continue to be non-empty indefinitely, since their sum may not exceed the cardinality of M. Let η be the smallest ordinal number for which $M_\eta = M_{\eta+1} = M_{\eta d}$. Since this set M_η also satisfies the condition $A = A_d$, it must be contained in the greatest set $\underline{M}$ of this sort, and since, on the other hand, $\underline{M}$ was contained in every M_ξ, it follows that $\underline{M} = M_\eta$.

The φ-kernel of M is thus obtained in this way: We examine the system of decreasing sets

$$(5) \qquad M_0, M_1, M_2, \ldots, M_\omega, M_{\omega+1}, \ldots,$$

formed according to (3), which begins with M, M_d, M_{dd}, ..., and we look for the first set M_η that coincides with $M_{\eta+1}$. It coincides, also, with all the following sets and is the *smallest* set of the system. It is worth noting that the φ-kernel $\underline{M}$, originally defined as the greatest set $A \leqq MA_d$ or as the sum of all these sets, now appears as the smallest set of the system (5) or as the intersection of all the sets of this system, and is reached not from below, but from above. The "kernel" makes its appearance here as its "shell" is peeled off.

In the example $A_\varphi = A_\beta$, $A_d = A_a$, the sets (5) are the coherences M, M_a, M_{aa}, ... of M, in which the process $A_a = A - A_h$ consists in the splitting off of the isolated points; thus the summands $M_\xi - M_{\xi+1}$ of

[1] Even for $\eta = 0$, if we replace $\sum_{\xi<\eta}$ by the null set.

formula (4) are now isolated sets, and we obtain the *dense-in-itself kernel* or the *smallest coherence* by continuing the splitting off of the isolated points until the process comes to a standstill.

If, in particular, M is closed, then (5) is the sequence of derived sets $M, M_\beta, M_{\beta\beta}, \ldots$, and the *dense-in-itself* — and, in this case, *perfect* — *kernel* is the *smallest derived set*.

Before exhibiting a further example of the formation of a kernel, we still have to give an analogous discussion of the φ-hull $\overline{M}$, the smallest set $A \geqq M$ for which $A = A_s$ Because of the monotonicity of A_s, we then have $A = A_s \geqq M_s$; in containing M, A also contains the (in general) larger sets M_s, and thus M_{ss}, M_{sss}, etc. as well. If we define the sets M^ξ by the inductive rule

$$(6) \qquad \begin{cases} M^0 = M \\ M^{\xi+1} = (M^\xi)_s \\ M^\eta = \mathfrak{S}_{\xi<\eta} M^\xi \qquad (\eta \text{ a limit number}), \end{cases}$$

where the decomposition

$$(7) \qquad M^\eta = M^0 + \sum_{\xi<\eta} (M^{\xi+1} - M^\xi)$$

holds and where the summands $M^{\xi+1} - M^\xi$ must at some point become zero since their sum may not exceed the cardinality of the space, then we find the φ-hull of M as the greatest set of the increasing system

$$(8) \qquad M^0, M^1, M^2, \ldots, M^\omega, M^{\omega+1}, \ldots,$$

that is, as the first set that coincides with its successor (and with all the sets following).

In the example $A_\varphi = A_\beta, A_s = A_\alpha$, the system (8) begins with $M, M_\alpha, M_{\alpha\alpha}, \ldots$, and the second set is already the greatest; $M_\alpha = M_{\alpha\alpha} = \ldots$ is the closed hull of M.

If the elements of the space happen to be real functions $x = x(t)$ of a variable t which, in turn, ranges over the real numbers or over any set T whatever, and if A_φ is then taken to mean the set of the functions $y = y(t)$ that can be represented as the limit functions $y(t) = \lim x_n(t)$ of sequences of functions $x_n \varepsilon A$ convergent everywhere (in T), then $A_\varphi = A_s$. A set of functions or a system of functions $A = A_s$ which is thus not extended by the formation of limits is called a *Baire system of functions*.[1] The smallest Baire system $\overline{M}$ over a given system M appears

[1] More about these in § 43.

as greatest member of the sequence (8). Here this greatest member M^η surely has an index $\eta \leqq \Omega$, where $\Omega = \omega_1$ is the beginning number of $Z(\aleph_1)$; for if $x_1, x_2, \ldots$ are functions of $M^\Omega = \underset{\xi<\Omega}{\mathfrak{S}} M^\xi$ and, say, $x_n \varepsilon M^{\xi_n}$, then let ξ $(< \Omega)$ be the first ordinal exceeding all the ξ_n and then all the x_n belong to M^ξ, and thus $\lim x_n$ belongs to $M^{\xi+1} \leqq M^\Omega$; M^Ω is a Baire system.

The smallest Borel system (§ 18) over a given system of sets also comes under the schema of φ-hulls; we need merely replace our present sets A by the system of sets $\mathfrak{A}$ and choose, say, $\mathfrak{A}_\varphi = \mathfrak{A}_{\sigma\delta}$ (the smallest δ-system over the smallest σ-system over $\mathfrak{A}$), so that every two steps of our earlier construction are now coalesced into one.

3. Residues. A very remarkable example of the formation of kernels is obtained in the following way. Let

$$A_\varrho = A_\alpha - A \tag{9}$$

be the set of those points of accumulation of A that do not belong to A (the border of the complement $E - A$) and let

$$A_\psi = A_{\varrho\varrho} \tag{10}$$

be the set resulting from a two-fold application of this process. It follows that

$$A_\alpha \geqq A_{\varrho\alpha} \geqq A_{\psi\alpha}\,; \tag{11}$$

and comparison of the formulas

$$\begin{aligned} A_\alpha &= A_\varrho + A \\ A_{\varrho\alpha} &= A_\varrho + A_\psi \end{aligned}$$

shows that $A \geqq A_\psi$, that $A_\psi = A\,A_{\varrho\alpha}$ is closed in A, and that

$$A - A_\psi = A_\alpha - A_{\varrho\alpha} \tag{12}$$

is the difference of closed sets.

The function A_ψ is not monotone; for example, we have for the whole space $E_\varrho = 0$, $E_\psi = 0$, while for a set A, say, that is dense in E and has a complement dense in E (such as the set of the rational points in Euclidean space), $A_\varrho = E - A$ and $A_\psi = A$ If we consider, however, not the system of all point sets but only the *system $\mathfrak{P}$ of the sets closed in a fixed set P*, then whenever $A \varepsilon \mathfrak{P}$ we also have $A_\psi \varepsilon \mathfrak{P}$ and A_ψ is a monotone function in $\mathfrak{P}$. For let $E = P + Q$; then

$$A_\varphi = P(Q\,A_\alpha)_\alpha$$

is a monotone function (defined for all $A \leqq E$) of A; let us write

$$B = QA_\alpha, \quad A_\varphi = PB_\alpha.$$

Since B is closed in Q, we clearly have $A_\varphi = B_\alpha - QB_\alpha = B_\alpha - B = B_\varrho$, and if A is closed in P then, similarly, $B = A_\varrho$, $A_\varphi = A_\psi$; A_ψ is closed in A and thus also in P and $A_d = A_\varphi = A_\psi$. If we therefore form the sequence (5) for a set M closed in P, then it follows inductively that all the M_ξ are also closed in P and that $M_{\xi+1} = M_{\xi\psi}$; these sets M_ξ, the sequence of which begins with M, M_ψ, $M_{\psi\psi}$, . . . ,we call *residues* of M. The *smallest residue* is the φ-kernel $\underline{M}$ of M, that is (since it is possible to take $P = M$), *the greatest set A closed in M for which* $A = A_\psi$. A set whose smallest residue vanishes will be called *reducible*.

From § 17, 3, we find:

II. *The reducible sets are the (finite or infinite) chains of differences formed from closed sets.*

For, first, it follows from (12) that

$$(13) \qquad \begin{cases} M_\xi - M_{\xi+1} = F_\xi - F'_\xi, \\ \qquad F_\xi = M_{\xi\alpha}, \quad F'_\xi = M_{\xi\varrho\alpha}. \end{cases}$$

Because of (11), applied to $A = M_\xi$, we have $F_\xi \geqq F'_\xi \geqq F_{\xi+1}$ and from $\xi < \eta$, it follows that $\xi + 1 \leqq \eta$, $M_{\xi+1} \geqq M_\eta$, and $F_{\xi+1} \geqq F_\eta$. Consequently,

$$(14) \qquad F_0 \geqq F'_0 \geqq F_1 \geqq F'_1 \geqq \cdots \geqq F_\omega \geqq F'_\omega \geqq \cdots,$$

and for a reducible set M, where M_η and F_η ultimately vanish, (4) gives

$$(15) \qquad M = \sum_\xi (M_\xi - M_{\xi+1}) = \sum_\xi (F_\xi - F'_\xi),$$

and M is a chain of differences of closed sets.

We preface the converse of this with: If A is closed in $M = F - N$ (F closed), then A_ϱ is closed in N; for since $A_\alpha \leqq F$, we have

$$A_\alpha - A = (F - M)\, A_\alpha = NA_\alpha.$$

A two-fold application gives: If A is closed in $M = (F - F') + P$ (F and F' closed, $F \geqq F' \geqq P$), then A_ϱ is closed in $F' - P$, and $A_{\varrho\varrho} = A_\psi$ in P. Let us form next from the closed, ultimately vanishing, sets (14) a chain of differences

$$M = \sum_\xi (F_\xi - F'_\xi)$$

and set

$$P_\xi = \sum_{\eta \geqq \xi}(F_\eta - F'_\eta);$$

then

$$P_0 = M, \quad P_\xi = (F_\xi - F'_\xi) + P_{\xi+1},$$
$$P_\eta = \mathfrak{D}_{\xi<\eta} P_\xi \quad (\eta \text{ a limit number}).$$

With a set A closed in M we form the residues

$$A_\xi \ (A_0 = A, A_1 = A_\psi, A_2 = A_{\psi\psi}, \ldots).$$

Then A_0 is closed in P_0; if A_ξ is closed in P_ξ, then it follows from the prefaced remark that $A_{\xi+1}$ is closed in $P_{\xi+1}$; if η is a limit ordinal and if, for $\xi < \eta$, A_ξ is closed in P_ξ, then A_η is closed in P_η. We have thus shown that every A_ξ is closed in P_ξ and ultimately becomes zero together with P_ξ; A is reducible. Every set closed in the chain of differences M, and in particular M itself, is reducible.

III. *The reducible sets constitute a field.*

This follows from the closing remark of § 17, since the intersection of any number of closed sets is itself closed.

The reducible sets include, among many others, the *separated* sets. For from (9) and (10) it follows that $A_\varrho \leqq A_\beta$, and $A_{\varrho\varrho} \leqq A_{\varrho\beta} \leqq A_{\beta\beta}$, and in any case $A_\psi \leqq A_\beta$, from which it follows that the smallest residue of every set is dense-in-itself($A = A_\psi \leqq A_\beta$)and, in the case of a separated set, vanishes. If the M_ξ denote coherences, then from (4), also, we obtain a separated set (whose smallest coherence is 0) directly as a chain of differences of closed sets, since $A_\alpha \geqq A_\beta \geqq A_{\alpha\alpha}$ and $A - A_a = A_\alpha - A_\beta$, so that

$$M_\xi - M_{\xi+1} = F_\xi - F'_\xi, \quad F_\xi = M_{\xi\alpha}, \quad F'_\xi = M_{\xi\beta}.$$

4. The case of a separable space. Here we have the simplification that the smallest coherence or the smallest residue is always attained after at most a countable number of steps. Specifically:

IV. *If the space is separable, then an increasing or a decreasing well-ordered system of open (or closed) sets is at most countable.*

Let

$$\{G_0, G_1, \ldots, G_\xi, \ldots\} \qquad (\xi < \mu)$$

be an increasing system of open sets, $G_\xi < G_\eta$ for $\xi < \eta$; we may suppose its ordinal type μ to be a limit number. Among the special neighborhoods V (p. 146) contained in $G_{\xi+1}$ there surely is one, V_ξ, which is not contained in G_ξ. Then we have $V_\xi \neq V_\eta$ for $\xi < \eta$ (V_ξ is contained in G_η; V_η is not) and the set of the V_ξ, just like that of the G_ξ, is at most countable. The proof for a decreasing system takes a similar course; for closed sets, the theorem is obtained by taking complements.

It is applied, for example, to decreasing sequences of closed sets in the form: Let Ω be the beginning number of $Z(\aleph_1)$ and let a closed set F_ξ be assigned to each $\xi < \Omega$; for $\xi < \eta$ let $F_\xi \geqq F_\eta$. Then an at most countable number of these sets can be distinct, that is, there exists a (first) η such that $F_\eta = F_{\eta+1} = \cdots$ is identical with all the sets that follow.

Of course, all this holds also for the sets open and closed in a fixed set $M \leqq E$, since M is also an (at most) separable space.

In the system (5), therefore, if its sets are all closed in M (for example, if we are dealing with coherences or residues), then the smallest set – that is, the first M_η for which $M_\eta = M_{\eta+1}$ – is surely reached for $\eta < \Omega$.

The reducible sets are thus at most countable chains of differences (of type $< \Omega$) or sums of at most countably many sets of the form $F - F'$. Every such set, which can also be written in the form $F(E - F') = FG'$ as the intersection of a closed with an open set, is an F_σ – the sum of a sequence of closed sets (§ 23, III). Hence a reducible set is an $F_{\sigma\sigma} = F_\sigma$; since by virtue of the field property its complement is also reducible, it is at the same time a G_δ – the intersection of a sequence of open sets. Therefore:

V. *The reducible sets of a separable space are simultaneously sets F_σ and G_δ.*

We remark that, as a counterpart:

VI. *If the space is an F_{II}-set, then the sets that are simultaneously F_σ and G_δ are reducible.*

Let M be simultaneously an F_σ and a G_δ, and let A be its smallest residue, so that $A = A_{\varrho\varrho}$ or, with $B = A_\varrho$,

$$A_\alpha = A + B = B_\alpha = F.$$

A is closed in M and therefore is simultaneously an F_σ and a G_δ; therefore $E - A$ and $B = F(E - A)$ are simultaneously an F_σ and a G_δ. A and B are both dense in F and, as F_σ with dense complement, they are of the first category in F; therefore F is also of the first category in itself; consequently $F = 0$ ($F > 0$ would be an F_{II}). M is reducible.

In a separable F_{II}-space – for example, in a separable complete space – the reducible sets are identical with those that are simultaneously F_σ and G_δ. It is noteworthy that the question whether a set is both F_σ and G_δ

can here be decided by a well-defined (although infinite) procedure, namely, by the formation of residues, while for the sets F_σ, for instance, nothing comparable is known.

Theorem IV allows of the following generalization:

VII. *If the space is separable, then an increasing or a decreasing well-ordered system of reducible sets is at most countable.*

It suffices to consider an increasing system (formation of complements). To every ordinal number $\beta < \Omega$ let us assign a reducible set M_β and, for $\beta < \gamma$, let $M_\beta \leqq M_\gamma$; we must show that the M_β ultimately become equal ($M_\beta = M_{\beta+1} = \cdots$ for suitable β). Let $M_{\beta\xi}$ be the ξ-th residue of $M_\beta = M_{\beta 0}$ ($\xi < \Omega$, just as all the ordinals yet to appear are also $< \Omega$). Because of (13) and (15), we have

$$M_\beta = \sum_\xi (M_{\beta\xi} - M_{\beta\xi+1}) = \sum_\xi (F_{\beta\xi} - F'_{\beta\xi}),$$
$$F_{\beta\xi} = M_{\beta\xi\alpha}, \quad F'_{\beta\xi} = M_{\beta\xi\varrho\alpha}.$$

We now assert: There exists a fixed sequence, independent of β, of closed sets

(16) $$F_0 \geqq F'_0 \geqq \cdots \geqq F_\xi \geqq F'_\xi \geqq \cdots$$

such that ultimately $F_{\beta\xi} = F_\xi$ and $F'_{\beta\xi} = F'_\xi$ (for $\beta \geqq \beta_\xi$, where in addition the β_ξ may be assumed to increase with ξ). If this has already been shown for all $\xi < \eta$ and γ_η is the first ordinal number following all the β_ξ, then for $\beta \geqq \gamma_\eta$ we have

$$M_\beta = \sum_{\xi<\eta} (F_\xi - F'_\xi) + M_{\beta\eta};$$

the $M_{\beta\eta}$ then increase with increasing β, and their closed hulls $F_{\beta\eta}$, for which the same is true, ultimately become identical, by IV: $F_{\beta\eta} = F_\eta$ for $\beta \geqq \delta_\eta$. We have, however,

$$M_{\beta\eta\varrho} = F_\eta - M_{\beta\eta};$$

these sets and their closed hulls $F'_{\beta\eta}$ decrease with increasing β and, again because of IV, we have $F'_{\beta\eta} = F'_\eta$ for $\beta \geqq \beta_\eta (\geqq \delta_\eta \geqq \gamma_\eta)$. The assertion is thus proved for η (the start of the induction, $\eta = 0$, also is the same). Again, the sets (16) themselves ultimately become identical: let $F_\eta = F'_\eta = F_{\eta+1} = \cdots = F$. Then for $\beta \geqq \beta_\eta$, we find

$$M_{\beta\eta} - M_{\beta\eta+1} = F_\eta - F'_\eta = 0;$$

$M_{\beta\eta}$ is the smallest residue of M_β; thus $M_{\beta\eta} = 0$, and

$$M_\beta = \sum_{\xi<\eta} (F_\xi - F'_\xi) = M$$

is independent of β, so that VII is proved.

It is of interest to establish that it is possible to form sets having *arbitrarily large* index ($< \Omega$) for the smallest coherence or the smallest residue. Consider, for example, bounded closed sets of real numbers well-ordered according to size[1]

$$M = \{m_1, m_2, \ldots, m_\mu\},$$

where thus the index of m_α takes on the values $\alpha = 1, 2, \ldots, \mu$ $(1 \leqq \alpha \leqq \mu)$, $m_\alpha < m_\beta$ whenever $\alpha < \beta$, and m_β is the least upper bound of the numbers $m_\alpha (\alpha < \beta)$ for a limit ordinal β. Such sets, with prescribed $\mu < \Omega$, can be formed immediately — for instance (μ assumed infinite), by ordering a convergent sequence of positive numbers according to the type μ, denoting it by c_α $(0 \leqq \alpha < \mu)$, and setting

$$m_\beta = \sum_{\alpha<\beta} c_\alpha$$

for $1 \leqq \beta \leqq \mu$.

The reader will see without difficulty that the first derived set M_1 consists of those m_α whose indices $\alpha = \omega\,\alpha_1$ are limit ordinals, the second derived set M_2 of those of the m_α just named for which $\alpha_1 = \omega\alpha_2$ is a limit ordinal also, so that $\alpha = \omega^2\,\alpha_2$ is a multiple of ω^2, and continuing in this way by induction, that the ξ-th derived set M_ξ consists of those m_α whose index $\alpha = \omega^\xi\,\alpha_\xi$ is a multiple of ω^ξ. For sufficiently large ξ, such multiples of course no longer occur in the sequence $1, 2, \ldots, \mu$, and M_ξ vanishes. For example, for $\mu = \omega^\eta$ and $\xi \leqq \eta$, M_ξ consists of the m_α for which

$$\alpha = \omega^\xi \cdot 1,\ \omega^\xi \cdot 2, \ldots,\ \omega^\xi \cdot \omega^{-\xi+\eta};$$

M_η consists of the single m_α for which $\alpha = \omega^\eta$, and $M_{\eta+1} = 0$ is the smallest derived set.

In order also to demonstrate the existence of sets having arbitrarily large index for the smallest residue, we form the chain of differences

$$A = (M_0 - M_1) + (M_2 - M_3) + \cdots + (M_\omega - M_{\omega+1}) + \cdots$$

from a closed separated set M (for example, a set of the kind just discussed) and its derived sets M_ξ and set

$$A_\xi = \sum_{\eta \geqq \xi} (M_{2\eta} - M_{2\eta+1}) = (M_{2\xi} - M_{2\xi+1}) + (M_{2\xi+2} - M_{2\xi+3}) + \cdots.$$

[1] Well-ordered sets of real numbers m, because of Theorem IV, are at most countable, since the corresponding half-lines $(-\infty, m]$ constitute a well-ordered system of closed sets.

Then $A = (M_0 - M_1) + A_1$. Since $M_0 - M_1 = M_h$ is the isolated part of M and is dense in the separated part (§ 23, (15)), in this case M itself, it follows that A is dense in M, $A_\alpha = M_0$, and $A_\varrho = M_0 - A = M_1 - A_1$. Here $A_1 \leqq M_2$, $A_\varrho \geqq M_1 - M_2$ is dense in M_1, and the repetition of the conclusion gives $A_\psi = A_1$. The first residue of A is thus A_1, and the steps of the induction show that A_ξ is the ξ-th residue of A; it ultimately vanishes, but only when $M_{2\xi}$ is the smallest derived set $(=0)$ of M; and when this has arbitrarily large index, so does the smallest residue.

§ 31. Further Applications of Ordinal Numbers

1. Maximal and Minimal sets. In the cases considered thus far, ordinal numbers might if necessary have been dispensed with, since the existence of hulls and kernels was already established. Nevertheless they served for the exploration of subtler characteristics, for example, the index of the smallest coherence. In other cases, however, it is not even possible to give an existence proof for certain objects without them. If in a system of sets $\mathfrak{A}$ there exists no greatest set (the sum of all the sets of the system), there may nonetheless exist (several) *maximal sets A*, in the sense that no sets $> A$ occur in the system. Such maximal sets will be attained, in general, only in some such way as the following. We choose an arbitrary set A_0 in the system; next, if sets $> A_0$ exist, a set A_1 from among them; if then sets $> A_1$ exist, a set A_2; and so on. If, for some finite ν, we reach a set A_ν for which there exists no set $> A_\nu$, then we have a maximal set. Otherwise, we have a sequence $A_0 < A_1 < A_2 < \cdots$ of sets of type ω. It may now be that no set of the system contains all the A_ν; our enterprise has failed.[1] We therefore make the assumption that an increasing sequence of sets without a last element can always be continued; thus:

(α) If η is a limit ordinal and if

$$A_0 < A_1 < \cdots < A_\xi < A_{\xi+1} < \cdots \quad (\xi < \eta)$$

is a sequence of increasing sets of the system $\mathfrak{A}$ of type η, then there exists a set A_η in $\mathfrak{A}$ that contains all the A_ξ ($A_\xi < A_\eta$).

The above process can now be continued, and it must finally lead to a maximal set. Let us therefore define $A_\eta (\eta > 0)$ by induction as a set greater than all the A_ξ $(\xi > \eta)(A_\xi < A_\eta)$ in case all the A_ξ have already been defined and there is such a set A_η available, while otherwise we do

[1] In a countable space there is no maximal set in the system of finite subsets and no minimal set in the system of countable subsets.

not define A_η; the set of the A_η so defined then cannot exceed the cardinal number of the system $\mathfrak{A}$, and there exists a smallest ordinal number $\zeta > 0$ for which A_ζ is not defined. Because of (α), ζ cannot be a limit ordinal, so that $\zeta = \eta + 1$; A_η is still defined, and the sets $A_0, \ldots, A_\eta$ increase with increasing index. There is no set $> A_\eta$ in the system, since otherwise such a set could have been taken as $A_{\eta+1}$; A_η is a maximal set.

The process described here differs from those in § 30 mainly in that it lacks direction; in general, we have a choice from among several possible sets for each A_ξ, and this may lead, in turn, to different maximal sets. This element of arbitrariness cannot be eliminated but can only be shifted back: we well-order the original system $\mathfrak{A}$ to form a system $\mathfrak{A}^*$ and then for our A_ξ we always choose from the sets available the one that is the first in $\mathfrak{A}^*$. A particular well-ordering produces a particular maximal set; different well-orderings may give rise to different maximal sets. If Zermelo's well-ordering process is used in such a way that, *whenever possible*, a set containing $A, B, \ldots$ as proper subsets is taken as differential element (§ 12) of $\{A, B, \ldots\}$, then $\mathfrak{A}^*$ begins with increasing sets $A_0 < A_1 < \cdots < A_\eta$, the last of which will be maximal. But this does not differ essentially from our original method except that there $A_{\eta+1}$ was no longer defined, whereas here the well-ordering $\mathfrak{A}^*$ continues.

It will frequently be possible to form the increasing sets A_ξ in such a way that each goes over into its successor $A_{\xi+1}$ by the addition of a single point x_ξ. A simple example is given by the *nets* $E(\varrho)$ we had occasion to use earlier (p. 145): maximal sets in the system of those sets A in which any two points have a distance $\geqq \varrho > 0$. Choose any point x_0 in the space; if for $\eta > 0$ the points x_ξ (with $\xi < \eta$) have already been defined, then we call the set of all these points A_η and define x_η as any point whose distance is $\geqq \varrho$ from all the x_ξ, if such a point exists; otherwise we leave x_η undefined. The set of points so defined cannot exceed the cardinality of the space. If η is the first ordinal number for which x_η is not defined, then A_η is a net $E(\varrho)$.

Similarly, we can construct, following Hamel, a *basis* A for the set E of the real numbers.[1] If A is a set of real numbers we let $[A]$ be the set of those real numbers

$$(1) \qquad y = \sum_x^A r x$$

that can be represented as linear combinations of *finitely* many numbers $x \varepsilon A$ with *rational* coefficients r (so that only finitely many $r \neq 0$ are

[1] Or, more generally, for a linear space E.

allowed in the sum). If at least one equation

$$(2) \qquad 0 = \sum_{x}^{A} r\, x$$

holds in which not all the r vanish, then we say that A is rationally *dependent*, otherwise rationally *independent*, or a *basis* for $[A]$. If A is rationally independent, then every number y of $[A]$ can be represented in the form (1) in only one way. We obtain a basis A for E, which is to be conceived as a maximal set in the system of all bases (and incidentally also as a minimal set in the system of sets A for which $[A] = E$) as follows: We choose a real number $x_0 \neq 0$, then an x_1 that is not a rational multiple $r_0 x_0$ of x_0, then an x_2 that is not a rational combination $r_0 x_0 + r_1 x_1$ of x_0 and x_1; in general: if $\eta > 0$, if the numbers x_ξ, the set of which is called A_η, are already defined for $\xi < \eta$, and if, finally, $[A_\eta] < E$, then let x_η be a number of $E - [A_\eta]$, and otherwise leave x_η undefined. If η is the smallest ordinal number for which x_η is not defined, then A_η is a basis for E.

If A is a basis for E, and if the real function $f(x)$ is defined for $x \varepsilon A$ in any way whatever and is then extended to every real y in accordance with the unique representation (1) by the formula

$$f(y) = \sum_{x}^{A} r\, f(x),$$

then we always have $f(y + z) = f(y) + f(z)$. This functional equation thus has $\aleph^{\aleph}$ solutions (since the basis A is obviously of the cardinality of the continuum). If we require, in addition, that $f(y)$ be continuous (at a single point, and consequently everywhere) then, as is well known, it has only the solutions $f(y) = cy$, with constant c.

For *minimal sets* (sets A for which there are in the system $\mathfrak{A}$ no sets properly contained in A), the existence proof proceeds analogously, with an assumption (β) corresponding to (α) concerning the possibility of the continuation of decreasing sequences whose type is a limit number. As an example, we consider all the continua A (connected, closed sets) in the space E that contain the two fixed distinct points x and y. A minimal set — one, therefore, that contains as a subset no smaller continuum joining the points x and y — is called, following Zoretti, a *continuum irreducible between x and y.*[1] The periphery of a circle on which x and y lie is reducible, while each of the two circular arcs that have x and y as end points is irreducible.

---

[1] This concept has no relation to the reducibility defined in § 30, 3. Compare § 39.

The existence of such minimal sets is of course not assured in all cases. Nevertheless it is true (Janiszewski) that:

A compact continuum E containing the points x and y has (at least) *one subcontinuum irreducible between x and y.*

For $\xi < \Omega$ (Ω a beginning number of $Z(\aleph_1)$, as usual) we define the sets A_ξ as follows:

$A_0 = E$;
$A_{\xi+1}$ a continuum $< A_\xi$ containing x, y, if there are any such continua; otherwise $A_{\xi+1} = A_\xi$;
$A_\eta = \mathfrak{D}_\xi A_\xi$ ($\xi < \eta$, η a limit ordinal).

We see that the A_ξ decrease with increasing index (equality not excluded) and are continua containing x and y; for the A_η with limit index this follows from Theorem XVIII of § 29, by representing η as limit of a sequence $\xi_1 < \xi_2 < \ldots$ and taking $A_\eta = A_{\xi_1} A_{\xi_2} \ldots$ into account. Since E is separable, Theorem IV of § 30 applies, and at some time we must have $A_\eta = A_{\eta+1}$, and A_η irreducible between x and y.

It is possible, incidentally, to proceed in such a way that, at the very latest, A_ω is irreducible. We consider the open complements G (open in the space E) of the sets A and look for a maximal set in the collection of the G. Let $V_1, V_2, \ldots$ be the special neighborhoods (§ 25) in the space E. If E is reducible, so that some non-vanishing G_1 exists, then we choose the latter so that the index of the first $V_p \leqq G_1$ is as small as possible. If $A_1 = E - G_1$ is reducible, so that some $G_2 > G_1$ exists, then we choose G_2 so that the index of the first V_q ($q > p$) contained in it but not in G_1 is as small as possible, and we continue in this way. Either some G_n with finite index or, at the latest, $G_\omega = G_1 \dotplus G_2 \dotplus \ldots$ is a maximal G, and thus $A_n = E - G_n$ or $A_\omega = E - G_\omega$ is irreducible.

We give still another example of the utilization of the ordinal numbers, one which no longer concerns maximal or minimal sets.

2. Totally imperfect sets. Let E be a perfect, separable, complete space (for example, a Euclidean space). The system of (non-empty) perfect sets P has the cardinality $\aleph$ (§ 25, V) and every set P, as well as E itself, has the cardinality $\aleph$ (§ 26, XI). A set that contains no P as a subset will be called, following Bernstein, *totally imperfect* — as, for example, every at most denumerable set, or any set of cardinality $< \aleph$. But there also exist *totally imperfect sets of cardinality* $\aleph$, and this again seems not to be demonstrable without making use of the ordinal numbers. We let $\aleph = \aleph_\mu$, where μ is an undetermined ordinal number $\geqq 1$ and ω_μ

is the beginning number of the class $Z(\aleph_\mu)$. We can arrange all the (non-empty) perfect sets P in a sequence of type

$$P_0, P_1, \ldots, P_\omega, \ldots, P_\xi, \ldots \quad (\xi < \omega_\mu).$$

We choose two distinct points $x_0, y_0 \varepsilon P_0$. If, for $0 < \eta < \omega_\mu$, all the points x_ξ and y_ξ $(\xi < \eta)$ have already been defined and if we call the sets formed by them A_η and B_η, then $A_\eta \dotplus B_\eta$ is of some cardinality $< \aleph$, and thus there remain infinitely many $(\aleph)$ points of P_η that do not belong to the set $A_\eta \dotplus B_\eta$. We define x_η and y_η as two distinct such points. It follows from this definition that for $\xi < \eta$ the four points $x_\xi, y_\xi, x_\eta, y_\eta$ are all different. Let A be the set of all points x_ξ; its complement $B = E - A$ contains all the points y_ξ (where it is possible, incidentally, to arrange matters so as to make B into just the set of the points y_ξ). Both the sets A and B are of cardinality $\aleph$ and are totally imperfect, for since AP_ξ contains the point x_ξ and BP_ξ the point y_ξ, we never have $P_\xi \leqq B$ or $P_\xi \leqq A$.

We have thus decomposed E into two totally imperfect sets A and B. This is of interest for the theory of connectedness as well; for A and B are *discontinuous* (p. 174), and yet, if E is a Euclidean space of dimension at least two, they are *connected*. For we have: *In a Euclidean space of dimension at least two the complement of a totally imperfect set is connected* (Sierpiński).

If we take E to be, say, the Euclidean plane, then we must show the impossibility of a decomposition $E = A + B$ in which A is totally imperfect and B disconnected. Let $B = P + Q$ be a partition into two relatively closed sets $P = BP_\alpha$ and $Q = BQ_\alpha$; since $PQ = BP_\alpha Q_\alpha = 0$, the closed set $F = P_\alpha Q_\alpha$ is contained in A. We join two points $p \varepsilon P$ and $q \varepsilon Q$ by a polygonal path, say $C = [p, m, q]$, where m lies on the perpendicular bisector of p and q. Every (closed) sub-segment of C is perfect, is therefore not contained in A, and consequently contains points of B. CB is dense in C, $C \leqq B_\alpha$, $C = CB_\alpha = CP_\alpha \dotplus CQ_\alpha$, where now, in order that this not be a partition of the continuum C, both summands (which are non-empty) must have points in common:

$$CP_\alpha Q_\alpha = CF > 0.$$

The closed set F is therefore intersected by C, and moreover, intersected in points $\neq p, q$, since the latter belong to B and $F \leqq A$. If we let m range over the bisector and so vary C, then we find that F has the cardinality of the continuum and that its perfect kernel is contained in A, in contradiction to our assumption that A is totally imperfect.

§ 32. Borel and Suslin Sets

The Borel and Suslin sets generated by the *closed* sets F (§§ 18 and 19) are called the *Borel and Suslin sets of the space E*.[1]

Since the intersection F_δ of a sequence of closed sets (and even of arbitrarily many closed sets) is also closed, we shall begin the generation of the Borel sets with the F_σ, as was done in § 18, (3) or according to the rule ($\dot{\alpha}$) there given. We therefore have the following definition for the ordinal numbers $\xi < \Omega$:

(α) The sets F^0 are the sets F.
The sets F^η are, for odd η, the sums and for even $\eta > 0$, the intersections, of sequences of sets F^ξ $(\xi < \eta)$.

The sets $F^0, F^1, F^2, F^3, \ldots$ are the $F, F_\sigma, F_{\sigma\delta}, F_{\sigma\delta\sigma}, \ldots$, next come the F^ω as the intersections of sequences of the earlier sets, etc.

Let us consider, in addition, the Borel sets generated by the *open* sets G, beginning with the G_δ as in § 18, (4) or in accordance with the rule (β); then we have the following definition:

(β) The sets G^0 are the sets G.
The sets G^η are, for odd η, the intersections and for even $\eta > 0$ the sums, of sequences of sets G^ξ $(\xi < \eta)$.

The sets $G^0, G^1, G^2, G^3, \ldots$ are the $G, G_\delta, G_{\delta\sigma}, G_{\delta\sigma\delta}, \ldots$, next come the G^ω as sums of sequences of earlier sets, etc.

Obviously the F^ξ and G^ξ are complements of each other. But more than that, both Borel systems are identical, so that the G^ξ, too, constitute in their totality the Borel sets for the space:

Every F^ξ is some $G^{\xi+1}$, every G^ξ some $F^{\xi+1}$.

This holds for $\xi = 0$ (every F is a G_δ, every G an F_σ, (§ 23, III)) and can be applied inductively to $\eta > 0$ if it holds for $\xi < \eta$: if η is odd, then F^η is sum of a sequence of sets F^ξ, these are sets $G^{\xi+1}$ and therefore surely sets G^η as well, and the sum of a sequence of sets G^η is a $G^{\eta+1}$. Similarly for even η.

The following as well is easy to see inductively. The F^ξ form a ring,[2] and furthermore for odd ξ form a σ-system, for even ξ a δ-system. The G^ξ form a ring and for odd ξ form a δ-system, for even ξ a σ-system. If η is a limit ordinal, then the system of all the F^ξ $(\xi < \eta)$ is identical with that of all the G^ξ and is a field, but it is in general neither a σ-system nor

[1] The usual notation is: B-sets and A-sets (ensembles mesurables B, ensembles A).

[2] Concerning the concepts ring, field, σ-system, and δ-system, see §§ 17 and 18.

a δ-system. The sums of sequences of sets of this system are the G^η, the intersections are the F^η. The whole Borel system is a field and is simultaneously a σ-system and a δ-system. The sets that are at the same time F^ξ and G^ξ (*two-sided* Borel sets) also form a field, as do the sets that are both open and closed (this can hold only for the two sets E and 0 in a connected space), and as do the sets that are both F_σ and G_δ at the same time (in a separable complete space, they are the reducible sets). The difference of two F^ξ or of two G^ξ or the intersection $F^\xi G^\xi$ of an F^ξ with a G^ξ is at the same time an $F^{\xi+1}$ and a $G^{\xi+1}$.

The *Suslin sets* of the space are the sets

$$F_S = \mathfrak{S}\, F_{n_1} F_{n_1 n_2} F_{n_1 n_2 n_3} \cdots$$

generated by closed sets F_{n_1} and so forth, in the notation familiar from § 19. We recall that all the Borel sets are also Suslin sets and that the iteration of the Suslin process yields nothing new: every F_{SS} is an F_S. The Suslin sets generated by the open sets

$$G_S = \mathfrak{S}\, G_{n_1} G_{n_1 n_2} G_{n_1 n_2 n_3} \cdots$$

are in their totality identical with the F_S; for every G is an F_σ and thus an F_S, and G_S is an $F_{SS} = F_S$, while similarly F_S is a G_S. The G_S are not, however, the complements of the F_S, which rather look as follows:

$$E - F_S = \mathfrak{D}(G_{n_1} \dotplus G_{n_1 n_2} \dotplus G_{n_1 n_2 n_3} \dotplus \cdots),$$

and as we shall shortly see, the Suslin sets do not in general form a field.

The property of being a Borel or a Suslin set is relative and depends on the space E; we ought therefore to write, more explicitly, $F^\xi(E)$, and so forth. We have already spoken of this in the case of the F, G, F_σ, and G_δ (§ 26, 3); if $D \leq E$ and the argument E is again omitted, then

$$F^\xi(D) = D\, F^\xi, \quad G^\xi(D) = D\, G^\xi,$$

that is, the Borel sets of the space D are the intersections of D with the corresponding Borel sets of the space E. The proof, by induction, is immediate. The same holds for the Suslin sets:

$$F_S(D) = D\, F_S, \quad G_S(D) = D\, G_S.$$

There also exist *absolute* Borel and *absolute* Suslin sets — sets, that is, that have this character in every containing space — and there are even absolute F^ξ; furthermore, for $\xi \geq 1$ there are absolute G^ξ (but not for $\xi = 0$, since there are no absolutely open sets), and there are absolute F_S or G_S, and the reader will see easily (as on p. 157) that a set A possesses this character absolutely if it possesses it in any complete space and, specifically, in its complete hull $\overline{A}$. We have already satisfied ourselves, for the case $\xi = 1$, that the non-existence of absolute G does not contradict the existence of absolute G^{ξ} $(\xi \geqq 1)$; even in G_g only summands of the form $G_\delta = G^1$ appear.

We prove now the *Theorem on Cardinality*:

I. *In a complete separable space every Suslin set — and thus, in particular, every Borel set — is either at most countable or of cardinality* $\aleph$.

This is a generalization of § 26, XI; but it is no longer the case that, as happened there, the vanishing or non-vanishing of the dense-in-itself kernel is decisive for the cardinality. The set of rational numbers (an F_σ) is dense-in-itself and yet only countable. We shall show, as was done then, that an uncountable Suslin set contains a dyadic discontinuum D as a subset, but in the construction of the spheres we must now use points of condensation instead of points of accumulation. Let

$$A = \underset{ikl\ldots}{\mathfrak{S}} F(i)\, F(i,k)\, F(i,k,l) \ldots$$

be a Suslin set generated by closed sets F, where the sum is taken over all the sequences of natural numbers $(i, k, l, \ldots)$ while, as we wish to point out immediately, $(p, q, r, \ldots)$ is to denote a dyadic sequence of numbers formed from the numerals 1 and 2. For simplicity, we may assume that

$$F(i) \geqq F(i,k) \geqq F(i,k,l) \geqq \cdots$$

for every sequence of natural numbers (where we replace the original F by the intersections with the preceding ones). Keeping initial indices fixed, we obtain the sets

$$A(i) = \underset{kl\ldots}{\mathfrak{S}} F(i)\, F(i,k)\, F(i,k,l) \ldots,$$
$$A(i,k) = \underset{l\ldots}{\mathfrak{S}} F(i)\, F(i,k)\, F(i,k,l) \ldots$$

and so on, where we have

$$A = \underset{i}{\mathfrak{S}} A(i), \quad A(i) = \underset{k}{\mathfrak{S}} A(i,k), \quad A(i,k) = \underset{l}{\mathfrak{S}} A(i,k,l), \ldots .$$

Now suppose A, and consequently $A_c = AA_\gamma$ as well, to be uncountable; we choose two points a_1 and a_2 of this set (condensation points of, and in, A) and make them the centers of disjoint closed spheres V_1 and V_2; for the open spheres U_1 and U_2 belonging to them, each of the two sets AU_p is therefore uncountable. Then at least one summand of $AU_p =$

$\mathfrak{S}_i A(i)\, U_p$ is uncountable — say, $A(i_p)\, U_p$. We choose two condensation points a_{p1}, a_{p2} of, and in, this set and enclose them in disjoint closed spheres $V_{p1}, V_{p2} \leqq U_p$; for the open spheres U_{p1}, U_{p2} belonging to them, each of the four sets $A(i_p)\, U_{pq}$ is uncountable. Then at least one summand of $A(i_p)\, U_{pq} = \mathfrak{S}_k A(i_p, k)\, U_{pq}$ is uncountable — say, $A(i_p, k_{pq})\, U_{pq}$. We continue in this way, and thus there corresponds to each dyadic sequence of numbers $(p, q, r, \ldots)$ a sequence of natural numbers $(i_p, k_{pq}, l_{pqr}, \ldots)$ such that the sets

$$A(i_p)\, U_p, \quad A(i_p, k_{pq})\, U_{pq}, \quad A(i_p, k_{pq}, l_{pqr})\, U_{pqr}, \ldots$$

are uncountable and therefore all the more so are the closed sets

$$F(i_p)\, V_p, \quad F(i_p, k_{pq})\, V_{pq}, \quad F(i_p, k_{pq}, l_{pqr})\, V_{pqr}, \ldots,$$

since $A(i) \leqq F(i)$, and so forth. If, now, we had taken the radii of the spheres $V_p, V_{pq}, V_{pqr}, \ldots$ to be $< 1, 1/2, 1/3, \ldots$ — and there was nothing to prevent our doing so — then the closed sets just referred to constitute a decreasing sequence whose diameters $\to 0$. Therefore they have a single point of intersection x which belongs to the dyadic discontinuum

$$D = \Sigma V_p \,.\, \Sigma V_{pq} \,.\, \Sigma V_{pqr} \ldots$$

as well as to the set A. This holds for every dyadic sequence, and thus for every point $x \,\varepsilon\, D$, and D is a subset of A.

Theorem I is the most comprehensive theorem on cardinality that we know. But nevertheless it applies only to a vanishingly small subsystem of the system of all point sets. In a separable space there are $\aleph$ closed sets (§ 25, IV) and therefore $\aleph^{\aleph_0} = \aleph$ sequences of closed sets or complexes $(F_1, F_2, F_{11}, F_3, F_{12}, F_{21}, F_{111}, \ldots)$ such as are needed to define a Suslin set, and therefore $\aleph$ Suslin sets (and also $\aleph$ Borel sets). The separable complete space is of cardinality $\aleph$, provided that its perfect kernel does not vanish,[1] and has $2^{\aleph} > \aleph$ subsets. For by far the greatest number of point sets, the question as to their cardinality, and with it the problem of the continuum, remain unelucidated.

§ 33. Existence Proofs

In the definition of the Borel set B in the form F^{ξ} or G^{ξ}, the question arises whether all the indices $\xi < \Omega$ are really necessary in order to obtain the whole Borel system $\mathfrak{B}$. This will, of course, depend on the

[1] Otherwise it is countable, and all its point sets are sets F_{σ}.

space E. If E consists entirely of isolated points, then every point set is closed and open at the same time, and even the very first step of the process is superfluous. If the space is countable, then every point set is an F_σ and a G_δ at the same time, and the $F_{\sigma\delta}$, and so forth, give us nothing new. If, therefore, we say that a set G^η is *exactly* a G^η or belongs *exactly* to the Borel class $\mathfrak{G}^\eta$ if it is not already a G^ξ $(\xi < \eta)$, then there remains the question, under what circumstances does there exist for each index $\eta < \Omega$ sets that are exactly sets G^η. As regards this, it is to be noted that in

$$\mathfrak{G}^0 \leqq \mathfrak{G}^1 \leqq \cdots \leqq \mathfrak{G}^\omega \leqq \mathfrak{G}^{\omega+1} \leqq \cdots$$

there are either only strict inequalities or, from some index on, nothing but equalities, for if $\mathfrak{G}^\eta = \mathfrak{G}^{\eta+1}$, then $\mathfrak{G}^\eta$ is already the whole Borel system (p. 101).

Furthermore, every Borel set B has already been shown to be a Suslin set S, and we may ask whether sets S exist that are not sets B. In the above trivial spaces all the point sets were indeed Borel sets, and so every S was also a B. In order that an S be a B it is in any event necessary that its complement $E - S$ also be (a B, and so) an S, inasmuch as the B form a field; and therefore an S whose complement is not an S is certainly not a B.

Both these questions can be discussed together, and their answer is given in the existence theorem:

I. *In a complete space whose dense-in-itself kernel does not vanish, there exist Suslin sets that are not Borel sets, and for every ordinal number $\xi < \Omega$ there exist Borel sets that are exactly sets G^ξ (or F^ξ) and not of lower class.*

For the proof, we construct, in the complete space E with non-vanishing E_k, a dyadic discontinuum

$$D = \Sigma V_{p_1} \cdot \Sigma V_{p_1 p_2} \cdot \Sigma V_{p_1 p_2 p_3} \cdots$$

in the usual way (p. 151); the dyadic sequences $(p_1, p_2, \ldots)$ are formed from the numerals 1 and 2, and to every such sequence there corresponds bi-uniquely (that is, one-to-one) a point x of D, namely the point of intersection of the sets

$$V_{p_1} > V_{p_1 p_2} > \cdots,$$

whose diameters converge to 0.

There exist countably many sequences of numerals containing only a finite number of ones; if we eliminate the corresponding points, there remains the set C of those x that have infinitely many $p_n = 1$, and this set is a G_δ, since it is obtained from the perfect set D by the removal of a set F_σ (which is countable). We should like to represent the points $x \varepsilon G$ somewhat differently — by means of sequences of natural numbers $(x_1, x_2, \ldots)$ rather than by dyadic sequences. For a natural number x let $[x]$ denote a dyadic complex consisting of a sequence of $x - 1$ 2's followed by the numeral 1, for example

$$[1] = (1), \quad [2] = (2, 1), \quad [3] = (2, 2, 1), \ldots,$$

and further, let $[x_1, x_2, \ldots, x_k]$ denote the dyadic complex resulting from adjoining $[x_1], [x_2], \ldots, [x_k]$ in this order — for example, $[2, 3, 1] = (2, 1, 2, 2, 1, 1)$ — and similarly, denote by $[x_1, x_2, \ldots]$ the sequence of numerals, formed in a similar way, that has infinitely many ones (namely, $p_{x_1} = p_{x_1+x_2} = p_{x_1+x_2+x_3} = \cdots = 1$, with the remaining $p_n = 2$). If we then set

$$F_{x_1 x_2 \ldots x_k} = V_{[x_1, x_2 \ldots, x_k]},$$

then for every sequence of natural numbers

$$F_{x_1} > F_{x_1 x_2} > F_{x_1 x_2 x_3} > \cdots$$

with diameters $\to 0$, the sets F with k indices are disjoint (e.g., $F_2 = V_{21}$, and $F_3 = V_{221} < V_{22}$), and we have

$$(1) \qquad C = \Sigma F_{x_1} \cdot \Sigma F_{x_1 x_2} \cdot \Sigma F_{x_1 x_2 x_3} \cdots,$$

where every point x corresponds bi-uniquely to a sequence $(x_1, x_2, \ldots)$ of natural numbers (such that x is the only point of the intersection $F_{x_1} F_{x_1 x_2} \cdots$).

It will now suffice to prove Theorem I for the (not complete) space C. For, Suslin sets in C and Borel sets G^ξ in C $(\xi \geqq 1)$ are Suŝlin and Borel sets in E as well, because C is a $G_\delta = G^1$ in E, and conversely; sets having this character in E have it in C as well, if they are subsets of C.

The sets D and C are separable (the countable set $D - C$, for instance, is dense in D). In the separable space C we consider the special neighborhoods already found useful so often (denoted, on p. 146 by V). Here we shall call them $U_1, U_2, \ldots$ and shall use them to form the system of sets

$$(2) \qquad \mathfrak{M} = \{U_1, U_2, \ldots\}.$$

The Borel sets B^ξ $(B^0 = M,\ B^1 = M_\delta,\ B^2 = M_{\delta\sigma}, \ldots)$ and the Suslin sets S generated by $\mathfrak{M}$ are identical with those of the space C, since even the sets M_σ (and thus surely the B^2) include all the open sets G of this space. Every B^ξ is a G^ξ and every G^ξ at least a $B^{2+\xi}$ (for $\xi \geqq \omega$, a B^ξ).

Now let $\nu = (n_1, n_2, \ldots)$ be an increasing sequence of natural numbers, N a collection of such sequences, and

$$(3) \qquad X = \underset{\nu}{\overset{N}{\mathfrak{S}}} M_{n_1} M_{n_2} \ldots = \Phi(M_1, M_2, \ldots) \quad (M_n \, \varepsilon \, \mathfrak{M}),$$

where the δs-function Φ of its arguments (which are arbitrary sets of $\mathfrak{M}$), is determined by the set N. From Theorem II of § 18 and Theorem II of § 19, we know that for suitable N or Φ the set X represents exactly the sets S or even the sets B^ξ $(1 \leqq \xi < \Omega)$. We choose and hold fixed any particular function Φ whatever; then all the sets representable in the form (3) by means of this function we call *the sets* Φ.

By means of the sequence of natural numbers $x_1, x_2, \ldots$ determined by x, we can now assign uniquely to each point $x \, \varepsilon \, C$ the set

$$(4) \qquad \Phi(x) = \Phi(U_{x_1}, U_{x_2}, \ldots)$$

determined by x. This is therefore a set Φ, and *every* set Φ can be so represented, for $M_n \, \varepsilon \, \mathfrak{M}$ means precisely that $M_n = U_{x_n}$ is to be one of the U. (The natural numbers $x_1, x_2, \ldots$ are quite arbitrary and not, say, increasing or pairwise distinct.) Every Φ is therefore some $\Phi(x)$ where, incidentally, it may very well happen that $\Phi(x) = \Phi(y)$ even though $x \neq y$.

The point x can now either belong to the set $\Phi(x)$ assigned to it, or not. Let A be the set of $x \, \varepsilon \, \Phi(x)$, B the set of $x \, \bar{\varepsilon} \, \Phi(x)$; $A + B = C$. Then B is different from all the $\Phi(x)$ since, of the two sets B and $\Phi(x)$, one and only one contains the point x. *B is therefore not among the sets Φ.*

For a natural number n let A_n be the set of x for which $x \, \varepsilon \, U_{x_n}$. Then

$$(5) \qquad A = \Phi(A_1, A_2, \ldots)$$

with the same function Φ as before. For, $x \, \varepsilon \, A$ or $x \, \varepsilon \, \Phi(x)$ means: For a sequence $\nu = (n_1, n_2, \ldots)$ occurring in N, x belongs to the summand $M_{n_1} M_{n_2} \ldots = U_{x_{n_1}} U_{x_{n_2}} \ldots$ of $\Phi(M_1, M_2, \ldots) = \Phi(U_{x_1}, U_{x_2}, \ldots)$, but then $x \, \varepsilon \, A_{n_1} A_{n_2} \ldots$ and x belongs to the corresponding summand of $\Phi(A_1, A_2, \ldots)$. And conversely.

Finally, we have still to show that the A_n are Borel sets. If k is a natural number, let A_{nk} be the set of x for which $x_n = k$. That is equivalent to saying that x belongs to one of the closed sets (closed in C)

$$C \, F_{x_1 \ldots x_{n-1} k}$$

(for $n = 1$, to the set CF_k), with arbitrary natural numbers $x_1, \ldots, x_{n-1}$; A_{nk} is the sum of these sets over the $x_1, \ldots, x_{n-1}$, and is thus an F_σ (in C). Finally,

$$A_n = \sum_k A_{nk} U_k$$

is thus also a Borel set; for $x \varepsilon U_{x_n}$ means, after all, that there exists a natural number k for which $x \varepsilon U_k$, $x_n = k$, that is, $x \varepsilon A_{nk} U_k$.

With this we have reached our goal, which is the following:

If Φ represents exactly the Suslin sets S, then by (5), A_n is a Suslin set generated by Suslin sets (and even Borel sets) A_n, and so is itself a set S. But its complement B is not an S, and therefore A is not a Borel set.

If Φ represents exactly the Borel set B^ξ, then, by (5), A is a Borel set generated by the Borel sets A_n, and so is itself a Borel set of the space C. Its complement B is then also a Borel set, although not a B^ξ, rather it is exactly some B^η with *arbitrarily* high index, and the same, then, holds for G^η. But then for *every index* η there are sets that are exactly G^η. This holds, first, for indices $\xi + 1$: if every $G^{\xi+1}$ were a G^ξ, then $\mathfrak{G}^\xi = \mathfrak{G}^{\xi+1}$ would be the whole Borel system, and all the G^η would already be sets G^ξ. But this holds also for the limit number η: if every G^η were a G^ξ ($\xi < \eta$), and thus an $F^{\xi+1}$, then every $G^{\eta+1}$ would have to be an F^η, every $F^{\eta+1}$ a G^η and every $G^{\eta+2}$ a G^η. This concludes the proof of the existence theorem.

§ 34. Criteria for Borel sets

1. Necessary conditions. The existence theorem has taught us that in a suitable space there may be Suslin sets S that are not Borel sets B. We therefore must now seek criteria that an S be a B. Two conditions for this have been set up; the first by Suslin, that the complement $E - S$ also be an S, the second by Lusin, that S be *representable by means of disjoint summands,* that is, that there be a representation (that is, among the various possible representations there be at least one)

$$S = \Sigma F_{n_1} F_{n_1 n_2} \ldots$$

in which the summands $F_{n_1} F_{n_1 n_2} \ldots$ and $F_{\nu_1} F_{\nu_1 \nu_2} \ldots$ belonging to different number sequences $(n_1, n_2, \ldots)$ and $(\nu_1, \nu_2, \ldots)$ are always disjoint (for which reason we use the summation sign Σ rather than $\mathfrak{S}$). We show first that both conditions are *necessary,* no matter what the nature of the space.

I. *If the Suslin set S is a Borel set, then its complement $E - S$ is also a Suslin set.*

For $E - S$ is even a Borel set. We have already used this obvious fact in the existence proof.

II. *If the Suslin set S is a Borel set, then it can be represented by means of disjoint summands.*

The proof rests on the following conclusions, in which, for the sake of brevity, a Suslin set representable by means of disjoint summands will be called an L-set, and an L-set A whose complement $E - A$ is also an L-set will be called a B-set.

(A). *The sum of a sequence of disjoint L-sets is an L-set.*

These L-sets can be represented in the form

$$A_{n_1} = \sum_{n_2 n_3 \ldots} F_{n_1 n_2} F_{n_1 n_2 n_3} \cdots;$$

if, in addition, we set $F_{n_1} = E$ (the whole space), then

$$\sum_{n_1} A_{n_1} = \sum_{n_1 n_2 n_3 \ldots} F_{n_1} F_{n_1 n_2} F_{n_1 n_2 n_3} \cdots$$

is an L-set.

(B). *The intersection of a sequence of L-sets is an L-set.*

Let

$$\begin{aligned} A &= \Sigma A_{a_1} A_{a_1 a_2} A_{a_1 a_2 a_3} \cdots \\ B &= \Sigma B_{b_1} B_{b_1 b_2} B_{b_1 b_2 b_3} \cdots \\ C &= \Sigma C_{c_1} C_{c_1 c_2} C_{c_1 c_2 c_3} \cdots \\ &\cdots \end{aligned}$$

be countably many L-sets (A_{a_1} etc. closed). We combine all the sequences of indices into a single sequence, say by means of the diagonal process:

$$\begin{aligned} &n_1\ n_2\ n_3\ n_4\ n_5\ n_6\ \ldots \\ = &a_1\ a_2\ b_1\ a_3\ b_2\ c_1\ \ldots . \end{aligned}$$

Then we find that

$$\begin{aligned} A\,B\,C \ldots &= \Sigma A_{n_1} A_{n_1 n_2} B_{n_3} A_{n_1 n_2 n_4} B_{n_3 n_5} C_{n_6} \cdots \\ &= \Sigma F_{n_1} F_{n_1 n_2} F_{n_1 n_2 n_3} \cdots, \end{aligned}$$

where $F_{n_1 \ldots n_k}$ denotes that one among the sets written above it whose highest index is n_k (so that $F_{n_1 \ldots n_k}$ depends only on $n_1, \ldots, n_k$, although not, perhaps, on all of them; for instance, $F_{n_1 n_2 n_3} = B_{n_3}$). $ABC \ldots$ has thus been represented as an L-set. Of course, the intersection of a finite number of L-sets is also an L-set.

(C). *The sum and the intersection of a sequence of B-sets are B-sets.*

Let the sets A_1, A_2, ... and their complements B_1, B_2, ... be L-sets. As a consequence of (B), the intersection $A_1 A_2$ ... and – bringing in (A) – the sum

$$A_1 \dot{+} A_2 \dot{+} A_3 \dot{+} \cdots = A_1 + B_1 A_2 + B_1 B_2 A_3 + \cdots$$

as well, are L-sets – and even B-sets, since the same is true of the B_n.

(D). *The sets F_σ are L-sets.*

A set F_σ

$$A = F_1 \dot{+} F_2 \dot{+} F_3 \dot{+} \cdots$$

can be supposed to be made up of increasing closed summands, so that

$$A = F_1 + (F_2 - F_1) + (F_3 - F_2) + \cdots$$

with disjoint summands which, as differences of closed sets, are (special) sets F_σ. In this way we find

$$A = \underset{n_1}{\mathfrak{S}} F_{n_1} = \sum_{n_1} A_{n_1}, \quad A_{n_1} = F_{n_1} - F_{n_1 - 1},$$
$$A_{n_1} = \underset{n_2}{\mathfrak{S}} F_{n_1 n_2} = \sum_{n_2} A_{n_1 n_2}, \quad A_{n_1 n_2} = F_{n_1 n_2} - F_{n_1\, n_2 - 1},$$

and so forth ($F_0 = F_{n_1 0} = \cdots = 0$). Because of

$$F_{n_1} \geqq A_{n_1} \geqq F_{n_1 n_2} \geqq A_{n_1 n_2} \geqq \cdots$$

we have a representation of A

$$A = \Sigma A_{n_1} A_{n_1 n_2} \ldots = \Sigma F_{n_1} F_{n_1 n_2} \ldots$$

as an L-set.

To this we add a comment which, although superfluous at the moment, will be used later: If the space is separable, then the representation of A by disjoint summands can be so arranged that the diameters of the sets $F_{n_1 \ldots n_k}$ converge to 0 as $k \to \infty$. For E can be represented as sum of a sequence of closed sets with arbitrarily small diameters $\leqq \delta$ (for example, by closed spheres of radii $\delta/2$ whose centers form a set dense in E); the same is true for every closed set and for every set F_σ. If, therefore, we write

$$A = V_1 \dot{+} V_2 \dot{+} \cdots, \quad F_n = V_1 \dot{+} \cdots \dot{+} V_n,$$

where the V_n are closed and have diameters $\leqq \delta$, then $A_n = F_n - F_{n-1} \leqq V_n$ has diameter $\leqq \delta$. If this is continued, we can thus arrange that the sets $A_{n_1 \ldots n_k}$ have diameters $< 1/k$. The diameter of any null sets that may occur is of course to be set equal to 0.

As a result of (D), the closed sets and the open sets, in particular, are L-sets, that is, B-sets; and since (C) shows that the B-sets form a Borel system, the Borel sets of the space are surely B-sets, thus proving II.

The proof that under certain conditions the two conditions are also *sufficient* is essentially deeper. We must preface it by a remarkable representation of the Suslin sets as sums and intersections of $\aleph_1$ Borel sets.

2. The indices. Let

$$A = \mathfrak{S}\, F(n_1)\, F(n_1, n_2)\, F(n_1, n_2, n_3) \ldots \tag{1}$$

be a Suslin set of the space E, and $B = E - A$ its complement. We have thus assigned here to every finite complex of natural numbers, which we denote for brevity by

$$r = (n_1, n_2, \ldots, n_k) \tag{2}$$

a closed set

$$F(r) = F(n_1, n_2, \ldots, n_k), \tag{3}$$

and the sum in (1) extends over all sequences $(n_1, n_2, \ldots)$ of natural numbers. We may suppose here, as we did earlier, that

$$F(n_1) \geqq F(n_1, n_2) \geqq F(n_1, n_2, n_3) \geqq \cdots. \tag{4}$$

If we adjoin one more natural number to the complex (2), we obtain a complex

$$(r, n) = (n_1, \ldots, n_k, n),$$

which we call *a successor* of r; r is called *the predecessor* of (r, n).

Let R_0 be any set of complexes r. If r, but no successor of r, belongs to R_0, we call r a *final element* of R_0. By leaving off the final elements of R_0, we obtain a new set R_1 of complexes, and if we continue to eliminate the final elements, we get a decreasing sequence

$$R_0, R_1, R_2, \ldots, R_\omega, R_{\omega+1}, \ldots$$

of sets of complexes, defined inductively by the requirement that $R_{\xi+1}$ are obtained from R_ξ by elimination of the final elements, and that for a limit ordinal η

$$R_\eta = \mathfrak{D}_{\xi<\eta} R_\xi.$$

Since R_0 is at most countable, at most countably many of the disjoint sets $R_\xi - R_{\xi+1}$ (the set of final elements of R_ξ) can be non-empty, and for some *first* index η $(0 \leqq \eta < \Omega)$ we reach a set $R_\eta = R_{\eta+1}$, which thus can no longer contain final elements, although it may, of course, be empty. Let us call this η the *index* of the set R_0; then for $\xi < \eta$, we still have $R_\xi > R_{\xi+1}$. The set $R = R_\eta = R_{\eta+1} = \cdots$ will be called, say, the *kernel* of R_0 (it is the greatest set $\leqq R_0$ that has no final elements). Processes of this kind are familiar to us from § 30; the present one greatly resembles the splitting off of the isolated points and the formation of the smallest coherence.

Every point x of the space now determines the set $R_0(x)$ of those r for which $x \varepsilon F(r)$, and if we perform on this set the process just described, then we reach the sets $R_\xi(x)$, ending with the kernel $R(x) = R_\eta(x) = R_{\eta+1}(x) = \ldots$; the index $\eta = \eta(x)$ of the set $R_0(x)$, which depends on x, is also called the *index of the point* x. We therefore have for the sets A and B a splitting according to the indices of their points:

$$(5) \qquad A = \sum_\eta A_\eta, \quad B = \sum_\eta B_\eta \quad (\eta < \Omega),$$

where A_η and B_η are the sets of those points of A and B whose index is $\eta(x) = \eta$. We shall now see that these sets are Borel sets.

Every set $R_\xi(x)$ contains the predecessors of its elements, or

$$(6) \qquad \text{for} \quad (r, n) \varepsilon R_\xi(x), \quad \text{we have} \quad r \varepsilon R_\xi(x);$$

for this holds for $\xi = 0$, as another form of the assertion $F(r, n) \leqq F(r)$ or (4). But if (6) holds for ξ, then it holds for $\xi + 1$ also; for if (r, n) occurs in $R_{\xi+1}(x)$, and so, a fortiori in $R_\xi(x)$, then r is an element, though not a final element, of $R_\xi(x)$, and hence remains as an element of $R_{\xi+1}(x)$. Finally, by the definition of $R_\eta(x)$ for a limit ordinal η, (6) holds for η if it holds for all $\xi < \eta$; (6) is thus proved by induction for all ξ.

We defined the $R_\xi(x)$ by beginning with $F(r)$ and defining $R_0(x)$ and then splitting off the final elements; we now turn about and call $F_\xi(r)$ the set of x for which $r \varepsilon R_\xi(x)$, so that the relations

$$(7) \qquad r \varepsilon R_\xi(x), \quad x \varepsilon F_\xi(r)$$

are equivalent. Just as the R_ξ decrease with increasing index, so do the F_ξ, for this means that (7) holds for ξ if it holds for $\eta > \xi$. Incidentally, the decreasing sets

$$F_0(r) \geqq F_1(r) \geqq \cdots \quad \geqq F_\omega(r) \geqq \cdots$$

do not, in general, ultimately become identical – since $R_\eta(x) = R_{\eta+1}(x)$ does not after all hold "uniformly" for some fixed η, but holds, rather, for an $\eta = \eta(x)$ or an $\eta \geqq \eta(x)$ that depends on x. From (6) there follows, furthermore,

(8) $$F_\xi(r, n) \leqq F_\xi(r) .$$

The sets F_ξ are now represented as follows:

(9) $$\begin{cases} F_0(r) = F(r) \\ F_{\xi+1}(r) = \mathfrak{S}_n F_\xi(r, n) \\ F_\eta(r) = \mathfrak{D}_{\xi<\eta} F_\xi(r) \quad (\eta \text{ a limit number}). \end{cases}$$

The first of these equations arises from the definition of $R_0(x)$ and the third from that of $R_\eta(x)$, so that (7) holds for η if and only if it holds for all $\xi < \eta$. The middle equation in (9) follows thus: $x \varepsilon F_{\xi+1}(r)$ or $r \varepsilon R_{\xi+1}(x)$ means that r is an element, though not a final element, of $R_\xi(x)$ and therefore has a successor $(r, n) \varepsilon R_\xi(x)$; or, that some (r, n) occurs in $R_\xi(x)$ (so that, by (6), the assertion $r \varepsilon R_\xi(x)$ becomes superfluous); or, that x belongs to one of the sets $F_\xi(r, n)$.

Furthermore,

(10) $$S_\xi = \mathfrak{S}_r F_\xi(r)$$

is the set of points x for which $R_\xi(x) > 0$; for this means just that there exists some r for which (7) holds. And

(11) $$T_\xi = \mathfrak{S}_r [F_\xi(r) - F_{\xi+1}(r)]$$

is the set of the points x for which $R_\xi(x) > R_{\xi+1}(x)$; for this means that there is some r which is a final element of $R_\xi(x)$, for which, therefore,

$$r \varepsilon R_\xi(x), \quad r \bar{\varepsilon} R_{\xi+1}(x),$$
$$\text{i.e.} \quad x \varepsilon F_\xi(r), \quad x \bar{\varepsilon} F_{\xi+1}(r)$$

or $x \varepsilon F_\xi(r) - F_{\xi+1}(r)$.

Now for these sets, we have

(12) $$\begin{cases} S_\xi = A \qquad\quad + \sum_{\eta>\xi} B_\eta \\ T_\xi = \sum_{\eta>\xi} A_\eta + \sum_{\eta>\xi} B_\eta . \end{cases}$$

For, first of all, the kernel $R(x)$ of $R_0(x)$ is non-empty if and only if $x \varepsilon A$. If $x \varepsilon A$ – say, $x \varepsilon F(n_1)\, F(n_1, n_2) \ldots .$ – then all the complexes (n_1), (n_1, n_2), (n_1, n_2, n_3), ... belong to $R_0(x)$; they are not final elements, and so belong to $R_1(x)$; continuing in this way, we find that they belong to every $R_\xi(x)$ and thus to the kernel $R(x)$, which is therefore non-empty. If, conversely, the kernel $R(x)$ is non-empty and therefore, by (6), contains a one-term complex (n_1); then, as a set without final element, it also contains a two-term complex (n_1, n_2), then a three-term one (n_1, n_2, n_3), and so forth; all these complexes also belong to $R_0(x)$; that is,

$$x \varepsilon F(n_1)\, F(n_1, n_2)\, F(n_1, n_2, n_3) \ldots \leqq A.$$

For $x \varepsilon B$, and in this case only, $R(x) = 0$.

Now, because of the definition of the indices $\eta(x)$, we have the equivalences of

$$R_\xi(x) > R_{\xi+1}(x) \text{ with } \xi < \eta(x),$$
$$R_\xi(x) = R_{\xi+1}(x) = R(x) \text{ with } \xi \geqq \eta(x).$$

Hence T_ξ is the set of points whose index is $> \xi$, while S_ξ (defined by $R_\xi(x) > 0$) contains all the points of A as well as those of B whose index is $> \xi$, and no others. (12) has thus been proved. From it we obtain further

(13)
$$\begin{cases} S_\xi - T_\xi = A_0 + A_1 + \cdots + A_\xi \\ E - S_\xi = B_0 + B_1 + \cdots + B_\xi. \end{cases}$$

Starting from the closed sets $F_0(r)$, it now follows from (9), using induction, that all the sets $F_\xi(r)$ are Borel sets of the space and from (10) and (11) that the S_ξ and T_ξ are Borel sets; the same follows for the A_ξ and B_ξ, say from (13) by induction. By (5), therefore, *the Suslin set A and its complement B are represented as sums of $\aleph_1$ Borel sets*;[1] both sets are then also intersections of $\aleph_1$ Borel sets, and in particular, from (12) we have simply

(14)
$$A = \mathfrak{D}_{\xi}\, S_\xi.$$

The sets S_ξ and T_ξ decrease with increasing index; the sets (13) increase. The intersection of all the T_ξ is 0. We remark also that on the basis of (8) we can write

(15)
$$S_\xi = \mathfrak{S}_{n}\, F_\xi(n)$$

in place of (10) and so can replace all the complexes r by one-term complexes only. For T_ξ this is not admissible. In addition

(16)
$$T_{\xi+\omega} \leqq \mathfrak{S}_{r\varrho}\, F_\xi(r)\, F_\xi(\varrho),$$

where $\xi + \omega$ is the first ordinal number following ξ, $\xi + 1$, $\xi + 2, \ldots$ and the sum on the right is to be taken with respect to all pairs of *different* complexes with the *same* number of numerals

[1] In the separable complete spaces we infer from this that the sets B, the complements of Suslin sets, are either at most countable, or have one of the two cardinalities $\aleph_1$ and $\aleph$. Because of the unsolved problem of the continuum, this is a less precise result than that of Theorem I of § 32, valid for the Suslin sets themselves.

(17) $r = (n_1, \ldots, n_k), \quad \varrho = (\nu_1, \ldots, \nu_k) \quad (r \neq \varrho).$

Suppose that $x \varepsilon T_{\xi+\omega}$, so that

(18) $$x \varepsilon F_{\xi+\omega}(r) - F_{\xi+\omega+1}(r)$$

for a certain r. Then on account of (9), we have

$$x \varepsilon F_{\xi+m+1}(r)\,, \quad x \varepsilon F_{\xi+m}(r, n_m)$$

for $m = 0, 1, 2, \ldots$, with suitable n_m. But these numbers $n_0, n_1, \ldots$ cannot all be equal, for from $x \varepsilon F_{\xi+m}(r, n)$ with n fixed it would follow that $x \varepsilon F_{\xi+\omega}(r, n) \leqq F_{\xi+\omega+1}(r)$, in contradiction to (18). Therefore there are at least two numbers m and μ for which $n_m \neq n_\mu$, and we have

$$x \varepsilon F_{\xi+m}(r, n_m)\, F_{\xi+\mu}(r, n_\mu) \leqq F_\xi(r, n_m)\, F_\xi(r, n_\mu)\,,$$

so that x thus belongs to the set on the right-hand side of (16).

3. Sufficient conditions.[1] Let us begin with two auxiliary considerations.

(α) If to every $\xi < \Omega$ there are assigned countably many sets D_ξ^n (say, for $n = 1, 2, \ldots$) which decrease as ξ increases ($D_\xi^n \geqq D_\eta^n$ for $\xi < \eta$), and if for each ξ

$$\mathfrak{S}_n\, D_\xi^n > 0\,,$$

then there exists an n such that for every ξ we also have that $D_\xi^n > 0$.

For, there exists for each ξ first some $n(\xi)$ for which $D_\xi^{n(\xi)} > 0$. The function $n(\xi)$, which can only take on a countable number of values, must take on at least one value n uncountably often. But then $D_\xi^n > 0$ for uncountably many ξ, and thus (because of the property of monotone decrease with increasing ξ) for all ξ.

(β) If the space is separable, then in the representation (1) of the Suslin sets we may assume that the diameters of the sets $F(n_1, \ldots, n_k)$ converge to 0 as $k \to \infty$. (The diameter of the null set must of course be put equal to 0.)

We remarked above (p. 212), under (D), that the sets F_σ and so, in particular, the space itself, are capable of such a representation, and moreover of one with disjoint summands. If, in accordance with this, we set

$$E = \Sigma\, E(m_1)\, E(m_1, m_2) \ldots,$$

[1] Compare this with § 46, I.

where the $E(m_1, \ldots, m_k)$ are closed and have diameters converging to 0 as $k \to \infty$,[1] if we then form the intersection of this with the set (1), assign the natural numbers p_k bi-uniquely to the number pairs (m_k, n_k), and set

$$F_{p_1 \ldots p_k} = E(m_1, \ldots, m_k)\, F(n_1, \ldots, n_k),$$

then

$$A = \mathfrak{S}\, F_{p_1} F_{p_1 p_2} \cdots$$

becomes a representation of the form desired; furthermore, as we should like to point out, it has disjoint summands whenever this is true for (1). The subsidiary condition $F_{p_1} \geqq F_{p_1 p_2} \geqq \cdots$ too can be maintained, if we assume $E(m_1) \geqq E(m_1, m_2) \geqq \cdots$.

These considerations out of the way, we shall next invert Theorems I and II.

III. *If the space is complete and separable, then a Suslin set whose complement is a Suslin set is a Borel set. Two disjoint Suslin sets are Borel sets considered as subsets of their sum.*

For the proof, we consider two Suslin sets A, $\bar{A}$ with the corresponding Borel sets $F_\xi(r)$, $\bar{F}_\xi(r)$ and S_ξ, $\bar{S}_\xi$. Let the representations (1) of A and $\bar{A}$ satisfy condition (β) on diameters. Then we show that *if $S_\xi \bar{S}_\xi$ is non-empty for every ξ, then $A\bar{A}$ is non-empty.*

In fact, we have by (15), *for every* ξ (and in what follows, as well)

$$\mathfrak{S}_{n\nu}\, F_\xi(n)\, \bar{F}_\xi(\nu) > 0\,,$$

where the sum extends over all pairs n and ν of natural numbers. As a consequence of the auxiliary consideration (α), there exists a summand

$$F_\xi(n_1)\, \bar{F}_\xi(\nu_1) > 0\,.$$

If we replace ξ by $\xi + 1$ in this, then

$$\mathfrak{S}_{n\nu}\, F_\xi(n_1, n)\, \bar{F}_\xi(\nu_1, \nu) > 0\,,$$

and there exists a summand

$$F_\xi(n_1, n_2)\, \bar{F}_\xi(\nu_1, \nu_2) > 0$$

etc. We obtain in this way two sequences of numbers

$$(n_1, n_2, \ldots) \text{ and } (\nu_1, \nu_2, \ldots)$$

such that, for every k (setting $\xi = 0$), we have

[1] Conversely, such a space is at most separable; for if we choose a point from each set $E(m_1, \ldots, m_k) > 0$, then the set of these points is dense in E.

$$F(n_1, \ldots, n_k)\,\bar{F}(\nu_1, \ldots, \nu_k) > 0\,.$$

These closed sets, decreasing for increasing k, and with diameters that approach zero, have by the Second Intersection Theorem, a (unique) common point of intersection x which belongs to A as well as to $\bar{A}$; therefore $A\bar{A}$ is non-empty.

If, for every ξ, $S_\xi \bar{A}$ is non-empty then, by (12) or (14), $S_\xi \bar{S}_\xi$ is a fortiori non-empty; and consequently so is $A\bar{A}$. Therefore, conversely:

If $A\bar{A} = 0$, then at some time for some ξ (and for all the ones following) we must have $S_\xi \bar{A} = 0$, so that

$$A = A\,S_\xi = (A + \bar{A})\,S_\xi\,,$$

and A is the intersection of $A + \bar{A}$ with a Borel set. Two disjoint Suslin sets are thus Borel sets in their sum. If, in particular, the complement $B = E - A$ of a Suslin set is also a Suslin set, then both are Borel sets (in $A + B = E$), and from a certain index on, we even have $A = S_\xi$.

III has now been proved; the Suslin condition is sufficient provided the space is complete and separable. The second half of III shows, incidentally, that the theorem also holds if the space is a Suslin set M in a complete separable space E.

Similarly, the Lusin criterion can be shown to be sufficient:

IV. *If the space is complete and separable, then every Suslin set representable by means of disjoint summands is a Borel set.*

From (12) and (13) we have $S_\xi - T_\xi \leqq A \leqq S_\xi$; if $T_\xi = 0$, then $A = S_\xi$ is a Borel set. If, therefore, A is not a Borel set, then $T_\xi > 0$ *for every* ξ (in what follows as well), so that from (16),

$$\mathfrak{S}_{r\varrho}\, F_\xi(r)\, F_\xi(\varrho) > 0\,,$$

where the sum extends over the (countably many) pairs of different complexes having the same number of numerals. The same method used to prove (α) shows that there exists a summand

$$F_\xi(r)\, F_\xi(\varrho) > 0$$

with a pair of complexes (17). If ξ is replaced by $\xi + 1$, then

$$\mathfrak{S}_{n\nu}\, F_\xi(r, n)\, F_\xi(\varrho, \nu) > 0\,,$$

and there exists a summand

$$F_\xi(r, n_{k+1})\, F_\xi(\varrho, \nu_{k+1}) > 0\,.$$

Continuing in this way, we obtain two (because $r \neq \varrho$) different sequences $(n_1, n_2, \ldots)$ and $(\nu_1, \nu_2, \ldots)$ of numbers such that $(\xi = 0)$

$$F(n_1, \ldots, n_h)\, F(\nu_1, \ldots, \nu_h) > 0$$

for every h; an application of the Second Intersection Theorem shows that the two different summands $F(n_1)\; F(n_1, n_2) \ldots$ and $F(\nu_1)\, F(\nu_1, \nu_2) \ldots$ yield the same point. Therefore if A is not a Borel set, then it surely can not be represented with disjoint summands (either with or without the condition on diameters, as we remarked under (β)), and IV is proved.

CHAPTER VIII

MAPPINGS OF TWO SPACES

§ 35. Continuous Mappings

1. Foundations. As in § 2, we begin with an already given set of ordered pairs (x, y); let the sets consisting of the elements x and y that enter into these pairs be called respectively A and B. Thus there correspond to each $x \in A$ one or more *images* (or image points, transforms, or maps) $y = \varphi(x)$, namely those y that in combination with x form a pair (x, y) of the set of pairs; similarly, there correspond to each y one or more *inverse images* (or pre-images) $x = \psi(y)$. What we have here are two functions φ and ψ inverse to each other — in general, many-valued — and a mapping between the spaces A and B, where the assymmetry induced by the ordered pairs and fixed in the terminology (image, inverse image) is, at this point, immaterial. From the point functions φ and ψ it is a natural step to set functions Φ and Ψ. A set $P \leqq A$ determines its *image* (or image set) $\Phi(P)$, the set of all the images of the points of P, where $\Phi(0) = 0$ and $\Phi(A) = B$; and in the same way, a set $Q \leqq B$ determines its *inverse image* $\Psi(Q)$. If every x has only one image $y = \varphi(x)$, then we say this function is *single-valued* and that B is a *single-valued image of* A. If both the functions $y = \varphi(x)$ and $x = \psi(y)$ are single-valued, then they are said to be *single-valued each way,* or *one-to-one,* or *schlicht,* and B is said to be a *one-to-one* image of A.

It is easy to see that

$$(1) \qquad \begin{cases} \Psi(\Phi(P)) \geqq P \\ \Phi(P_1 \dotplus P_2 \dotplus \cdots) = \Phi(P_1) \dotplus \Phi(P_2) \dotplus \cdots \\ \Phi(P_1\, P_2 \cdots) \leqq \Phi(P_1)\, \Phi(P_2) \ldots \end{cases}$$

as well as the corresponding relations obtained by interchanging the two functions; the sums and intersections in (1) refer to any number of sets. The signs of inequality are in general indispensable, because — to interpret just the first formula — although the inverse images of the images of P certainly include the points P themselves, they may in general include other points as well. If, however, the function $y = \varphi(x)$ is single-valued then, in the formulas obtained from (1) by interchange of the functions, only the equality signs apply:

$$(2) \qquad \begin{cases} \Phi(\Psi(Q)) = Q \\ \Psi(Q_1 \dot{+} Q_2 \dot{+} \cdots) = \Psi(Q_1) \dot{+} \Psi(Q_2) \dot{+} \cdots \\ \Psi(Q_1 Q_2 \ldots) = \Psi(Q_1)\, \Psi(Q_2) \ldots ; \end{cases}$$

this is most easily understood by noting that the set A now decomposes into disjoint subsets $\Psi(y)$, the inverse images of the individual points y of B. (It would be more accurate to write $\Psi(\{y\})$, the inverse image of the set $\{y\}$ consisting of only one point.) *In future we consider only the case in which $\varphi(x)$ is single-valued* without, however, assuming this to be the case for the inverse function; a genuine assymmetry between A and B has thus entered.

Now let A and B be metric spaces. *The function $\varphi(x)$ is said to be continuous at the point x if, for every sequence $x_n \rightarrow x$, $\varphi(x_n) \rightarrow \varphi(x)$.*

At the isolated points of A, every function is continuous. A continuous function of a continuous function is itself continuous. In more detail: Let $y = \varphi(x)$ and $z = \chi(y)$ be single-valued functions, where x, y, and z range over the sets A, B, and C, and suppose that $\varphi(x)$ is continuous at $x_0 = \varphi(x_0)$ and $\chi(y)$ continuous at $y_0 = \varphi(x_0)$; then $\chi(\varphi(x))$ is continuous at x_0. The proof is obvious: for, from $x_n \rightarrow x_0$ it follows that $y_n \rightarrow y_0$ and from this, that $z_n \rightarrow z_0$.

A function continuous at every point of A is said to be continuous on A or – simply – *continuous.* In that case B is called a *continuous image* of A.

A function continuous on A is known if its images at a set R dense in A are known. For each $x \varepsilon A$ can be represented as $x = \lim r_n$ $(r_n \varepsilon R)$, so that $\varphi(x) = \lim \varphi(r_n)$. In an easily understandable nomenclature, we say that the total function $\varphi(x) = \varphi(x \mid A)$ is determined by the *partial function* $\varphi(x \mid R)$. That this may have the effect of decreasing the cardinality of the system of the continuous functions as compared with that of all functions, is a fact we already know (p. 47).

Continuity at the point a means that when the distance ax converges to 0 so does the distance by, where $b = \varphi(a)$, $y = \varphi(x)$. In language familiar from our elementary work, this can also be expressed as follows: For every $\sigma > 0$, no matter how small, it is possible to find some $\varrho > 0$ sufficiently small that $by < \sigma$ whenever $ax < \varrho$. Or, *to every neighborhood V_b there corresponds a neighborhood U_a whose image lies in V_b.*[1] Now, as in the sequel (unless explicitly stated to the contrary), the U_a refer to the space A and[1] the V_b to the space B. Finally, we can also say that the *inverse image of every neighborhood V_b has a as an interior point.*

[1] The subscripts a and b of course do not indicate here points of accumulation or border points.

From this it follows that:

I. *B is a continuous image of A if and only if the inverse image of every set open (closed) in B is open (closed) in A.*

The corollary expressed by the words written in parentheses is proved by taking complements, since $\Psi(B - Q) = A\Psi(Q)$.

We already know a special case of the theorem: Theorem I of § 22. If $\varphi(x)$ is a real continuous function, so that B is a set of real numbers, then the set denoted in § 22 by $[\varphi > 0]$ is nothing but the inverse image of the set Q consisting of the intersection of B with the half-line $y > 0$ and which is thus a set open in B.

Because of the formulas (2), even more follows from I:

II. *If B is a continuous image of A, then the inverse images of the Borel and Suslin sets of the space B are Borel and Suslin sets of the space A, and in fact, the sets $F^\xi(B)$ and $G^\xi(B)$ have sets $F^\xi(A)$ and $G^\xi(A)$ as their inverse images.*

This actually follows from the very fact that the inverse images of sums and intersections are the sums and intersections of the inverse images. If, for example, it has already been proved that for $\xi < \eta$ every $F^\xi(B)$ has an $F^\xi(A)$ as its inverse image, then $F^\eta(B)$ is the sum or intersection (depending on whether η is odd or even) of countably many $F^\xi(B)$, and its inverse image is the sum or intersection of countably many $F^\xi(A)$; that is, its inverse image is an $F^\eta(A)$. G^ξ and the Suslin sets are handled in the same way.

If B is a continuous image of A, so that the function $\varphi(x)$ is (single-valued and) continuous, the inverse function $\psi(y)$ may still be many-valued. If it is single-valued, then B will be called a *one-to-one continuous image* of A. The simplest examples show that $\psi(y)$ need not therefore be continuous. If the set B of rational numbers is mapped one-to-one onto the set A of the natural numbers, then B is a continuous image of A (because every point of A is isolated) while the inverse function $x = \psi(y)$ is not continuous at any point. *In general, any set B whatever can be thought of as the one-to-one continuous image of an isolated, and even of an absolutely closed, set A*; all that is needed is to take a set A equivalent to B and to assign the distance 1 to any pair of distinct points of A. But the function $x = \psi(y)$ is then continuous only at the isolated points of B and thus continuous nowhere if B is dense-in-itself. Still another example. In the Euclidean plane, with points denoted by $x = (x_1, x_2)$, let A be a set which is cut by every line $x_1 =$ const. in exactly one point; that is, let A be the "curve" represented by $x_2 = f(x_1)$, where f is a single-valued but otherwise completely arbitrary function f. Let B be the orthogonal projection of A on the line $x_2 = 0$; that is, to each $x = (x_1, x_2)$ let there correspond $y = (x_1, 0) = \varphi(x)$. Then B is a one-to-one continuous image of A; the converse holds only if $f(x_1)$ is continuous.

If, however, both functions $y = \varphi(x)$ and $x = \psi(y)$ are single-valued and continuous, then each of them is called *bi-continuous* or *continuous both ways* (fonction bicontinue). B is also called a ***homeomorphic image*** of A (and A a homeomorphic image of B), and the one-to-one mapping between the two sets is called a *homeomorphism* (or *topological mapping*); furthermore, we say that A and B are homeomorphic to one another, which we shall express by the notation

$$B \approx A \qquad \text{or} \qquad A \approx B.$$

Once more — to summarize these concepts — we have the following cases depending on the nature of the function $x = \psi(y)$ ($y = \varphi(x)$ is assumed continuous):

B a continuous image of A : $\psi(y)$ may be many-valued.

B a one-to-one continuous image of A : $\psi(y)$ single-valued.

B homeomorphic image of A : $\psi(y)$ continuous.

The third case is to be regarded as a special case of the second, and the latter as a special case of the first. In the third case, the assymmetry between A and B has again disappeared.

2. Sets compact in themselves. Theorems I and II hold only for the inverse images, not for the images. If B is a continuous image of A, then the image of a set closed in A need not be closed in B; if A is isolated, so that every set B equivalent with A can be considered a one-to-one continuous image of A, then every subset of A is closed in A and *every* subset of B is thus the image of a set closed in A. We have seen that even the one-to-one continuous image of an *absolutely closed* (complete) set A can be quite arbitrary, up to the equivalence with A. However, if A is compact in itself (that is, compact and absolutely closed), then a simple and precise result holds:

III. *The continuous image B of a set A compact in itself is also compact in itself; if the mapping is one-to-one, then it is a homeomorphism.*

The hypothesis states that every sequence of points of A contains a convergent subsequence whose limit belongs to A. The same is to be shown for B. If $y_n \,\varepsilon\, B$ and $x_n = \psi(y_n)$ is an inverse image of y_n, then there exists a convergent subsequence $x_p \to x \,\varepsilon\, A$ and therefore $\varphi(x_p) \to \varphi(x)$

or $y_p \to y \, \varepsilon \, B : B$ is compact in itself. The second part of the theorem now follows most easily in this way: Every set P closed in A is compact in itself; its image $Q = \Phi(P)$ is compact in itself and is thus absolutely closed and therefore also closed in B; but by I this means that the function $x = \psi(y)$, single-valued by assumption, is continuous as well.

In a Euclidean space a set A is compact in itself if and only if it is bounded and closed; its continuous image B – also taken to be in a Euclidean space – is itself bounded and closed. In particular, a real function continuous in A ranges over a closed and bounded set of numbers and therefore has a greatest and smallest value (that is, the least upper bound is an actually attained maximum, the greatest lower bound an actually attained minimum).

If we denote by K a set compact in itself, and by K_σ the sum of a sequence of such sets, then the continuous image of a K is itself a K, that of a K_σ a K_σ. (Compare the middle formula in (1)). Euclidean space is a K_σ (it is, for example, the sum of concentric closed spheres with radii $n = 1, 2, 3, \ldots$), and so also is every set closed in it; the continuous image of such a set is thus a K_σ although, if it lies in a Euclidean space, it need not be closed. Every one-dimensional set F_σ, $B = B_1 \dotplus B_2 \dotplus \ldots$, is a projection of a closed planar set $A = A_1 \dotplus A_2 \dotplus \ldots$; we simply let the points (x_1, n) of A_n correspond to the points $(x_1, 0)$ of B_n; that is, we shift the set B_n from the line $x_2 = 0$ to the line $x_2 = n$. The continuous image of a Euclidean F_σ – and, in particular, that of an open set – is also a K_σ. It is to be noted, however, that Hilbert space is not a K_σ but that, rather, every K_σ in it is of the first category while the Hilbert space itself, as a complete space, is of the second category in itself. For every neighborhood of the origin $(0, 0, 0 \ldots)$ contains a set of points $(\varrho, 0, 0, \ldots)$, $(0, \varrho, 0, \ldots)$, $\ldots$, any two of which have a distance $\sqrt{2}\varrho$ between them and which therefore do not belong to any K; the same holds true of every point, and the complement of a K is therefore dense in Hilbert space and K nowhere dense.

The concept of uniform continuity should be mentioned at this point. The single-valued function $y = \varphi(x)$ is said to be *uniformly continuous* on A if for every sequence of pairs of points, $y_n \eta_n \to 0$ whenever $x_n \xi_n \to 0$. (For fixed $\xi_n = \xi$ this is the condition for continuity at the point ξ). As can be seen in the usual way, this condition is equivalent with: To every $\sigma > 0$ there corresponds some $\varrho > 0$ (depending only on σ) such that $y\eta < \sigma$ whenever $x\xi < \varrho$. Then we have:

IV. *If A is compact in itself, then every function continuous on A is uniformly continuous.*

Let $x_n \xi_n \to 0$; x_n has a convergent subsequence $x_p \to x$, so that $\xi_p \to x$ also; for the images we then have that $y_p \to y$, $\eta_p \to y$, $y_p \eta_p \to 0$. That is, $y_n \eta_n$ has a subsequence convergent to 0. The same is true for every subsequence $y_i \eta_i$, so that the whole sequence $y_n \eta_n$ must converge to 0 (otherwise it would have a subsequence $y_i \eta_i \geqq \sigma > 0$).

V. *Every set compact in itself is the continuous image of a compact, perfect, totally disconnected set. Two compact, perfect, totally disconnected sets are always homeomorphic.*

A compact, perfect, totally disconnected set can be represented, by § 29, XVI, as a dyadic discontinuum

$$A = \Sigma V_p V_{pq} V_{pqr} \cdots$$

(§ 26, 2), where the sets V may be assumed closed in A and therefore compact in themselves (by replacing V by AV). For fixed n, any pair of disjoint sets V with n indices have a positive lower distance between them, the smallest of which let us denote by ε_n. If x and ξ are distinct points of A, and if the corresponding dyadic sequences of numerals differ in their n-th numeral, then $x\xi \geqq \varepsilon_n$. From this it follows that for $x\xi \to 0$ the two corresponding sequences agree in a number of initial numerals that increases without limit. A set B compact in itself may be represented (p. 154) as a dyadic set

$$B = \mathfrak{S} W_p W_{pq} W_{pqr} \cdots$$

We assign to the single point x of the intersection $V_p V_{pq} V_{pqr} \cdots$ the single point y of the intersection $W_p W_{pq} W_{pqr} \cdots$ (belonging to the same dyadic sequence). By means of this correspondence $y = \varphi(x)$, B becomes a continuous image of A. For if δ_n is the greatest diameter of the sets W with n indices, then $y\eta \leqq \delta_n$ when y and η belong to two dyadic sequences of numerals whose n initial numerals coincide; from $\delta_n \to 0$ and from what we have already said, it then follows that when $x\xi \to 0$, $y\eta \to 0$ as well. If, finally, B is also compact, perfect, and totally disconnected, and thus representable as a dyadic discontinuum, then the mapping under discussion is one-to-one and consequently is a homeomorphism.

If, therefore, we choose any dyadic discontinuum A whatever — for example, the Cantor set, or even the set of dyadic sequences of numerals $(p, q, r, \ldots)$ itself with distance as defined in § 20, 4 (the dyadic Baire space) — then we obtain all the sets compact in themselves as the continuous images of A and all the compact, perfect, totally disconnected sets as homeomorphs of A. Conversely, every continuous image of A is compact in itself, and every homeomorphic image is even dense-in-itself (perfect) and, as we shall see in a moment, totally disconnected as well.

3. The conservation of connectivity.

VI. *The continuous image of a connected set is itself connected. The continuous image of an arbitrary set has no greater number of components than the set has.*

If B is a continuous image of A and $B = B_1 + B_2$ a partition of B into two closed sets (closed in B), then there corresponds to this partition a partition of $A = \boldsymbol{\Psi}(B_1) + \boldsymbol{\Psi}(B_2) = A_1 + A_2$ into two closed sets (closed in A). The disconnectedness of B implies that of A; the connectedness of A implies that of B. Since every partial function $\varphi(x \mid P)$ is continuous whenever the function $\varphi(x) = \varphi(x \mid A)$ is continuous, there corresponds to every connected subset of A a connected subset of B; the image of a component of A falls completely inside a component of B, and the system of components of B has at most the same cardinality as that of the components of A. If A and B are homeomorphic, then the components of the two sets correspond to each other; if one of the sets is totally disconnected, then so is the other.

In particular, a *real* function continuous on the connected set A (for instance on a real interval) has a connected set of values B and therefore takes on every intermediate value between any two of its values y_1 and y_2 $(y_1 < y < y_2)$. This "mean value property," by the way, is by no means characteristic only of continuous functions, since it can belong to discontinuous functions as well; it belongs, for example, to the derivatives $f'(x)$ of the differentiable functions $f(x)$ which may well be discontinuous (although, as we shall see, in a restricted sense). For if, say, $x_1 < x_2$, $f'(x_1) < 0$, $f'(x_2) > 0$, then in the closed interval $[x_1\, x_2]$ $f(x)$ has a minimum, which certainly cannot occur at the end points of the interval, and at this minimum, $f(x) = 0$; the general case is easily derived from this special one. Lebesgue gives a more extreme example: Let $x = 0.x_1x_2 \ldots$ be the decimal representation (where there is more than one, the representation having infinitely many zeros) of a number x with $0 \leqq x < 1$; if the sequence of digits $x_1, x_3, x_5, \ldots$ is ultimately periodic and the (shortest) period consists of n digits, we let

$$f(x) = 0.\, x_{2n}\, x_{2n+2}\, x_{2n+4} \cdots$$

and, say, $f(x) = x$ otherwise. The reader may convince himself that $f(x)$ is discontinuous everywhere but that nevertheless, in every interval no matter how small it takes on all the values $0 \leqq y \leqq 1$.

Local connectedness (§ 29, 2) is not, in general, conserved under continuous mappings; we refer as usual to the trivial example that every set is the continuous image of an isolated, and thus locally connected, set. Nevertheless, we have:

VII. *If the set A is compact in itself and is locally connected at every inverse image point $x = \psi(y)$ of y, then its continuous image B is locally connected at y.*

B, like A, is compact in itself and so at any rate is bounded. Let $y_n \to y$; in accordance with § 29, XII we have to prove that the numbers $\widehat{yy_n}$ there defined converge to 0. Suppose that $x_n = \psi(y_n)$ are any of the inverse images of the y_n; the x_n have a convergent subsequence $x_p \to x$, whence $y_p = \varphi(x_p) \to \varphi(x)$, so that $y = \varphi(x)$, and therefore $x = \psi(y)$ is an inverse image of y. A is locally connected at $x, \widehat{xx_p} \to 0$; this means that, except for a finite number of p, x and x_p are joined by a connected set $A_p \leqq A$ whose diameter converges to 0 as $p \to \infty$. Then y and y_p are joined by the connected image $B_p = \Phi(A_p)$, the diameter of which also converges to 0 because of the *uniform* continuity (Theorem IV), so that $\widehat{yy_p} \to 0$. Therefore the $\widehat{yy_n}$ (although some of them may not be defined) have a subsequence convergent to 0. The same is true for any subsequence $\widehat{yy_m}$, and so the whole sequence must converge to 0, since otherwise there would exist a subsequence $\widehat{yy_\nu}$ whose terms are either undefined or else are $\geqq \sigma > 0$.

From III and VII there follows:

VIII. *The continuous image of a set compact in itself and locally connected* (at all its points) *is itself a set of the same kind.*

§ 36. Interval-Images

1. Dyadic continua. The continuous image of a closed linear segment — say, of the interval $T = [0, 1]$ of the real number system $0 \leqq t \leqq 1$ — is called a *continuous curve*; a one-to-one continuous, and therefore, by § 35, III, homeomorphic image is called a *simple curve.* But we shall prefer to refer to continuous curves as *interval-images* since, as we shall see, they need have little resemblance to our intuitive notion of a curve. T is compact in itself, connected, and locally connected; because of Theorems VI and VIII of the preceding paragraph these properties must carry over to every interval-image, and we shall show that having these properties is also sufficient.

Let us first acquaint ourselves with a simple method of producing interval-images. As we have often done, we construct a dyadic set by letting closed, bounded, non-empty sets

$$V_p \geqq V_{pq} \geqq V_{pqr} \geqq \cdots \tag{1}$$

of a complete space E, with diameters converging to 0, correspond to every dyadic sequence $(p, q, r, \ldots)$ formed from the numerals 1 and 2.

As we know (p. 151), the convergence is uniform, that is, the greatest diameter δ_n of the sets V with n indices converges to 0 for $n \to \infty$. When we assumed the sets with n indices to be disjoint we obtained a dyadic discontinuum. Now we shall assume the other extreme: the sets to be discussed are to constitute a chain when arranged in lexicographic order; that is, in

(2) $\quad \mathfrak{S} V_p = V_1 \dotplus V_2, \quad \mathfrak{S} V_{pq} = V_{11} \dotplus V_{12} \dotplus V_{21} \dotplus V_{22}, \ldots$

neighboring sets are to have points in common. The dyadic set

(3) $$C = \mathfrak{S} V_p V_{pq} V_{pqr} \cdots,$$

generated by the V, for which, as we know, we might also write

(4) $$C = \mathfrak{S} V_p \cdot \mathfrak{S} V_{pq} \cdot \mathfrak{S} V_{pqr} \cdot \cdots$$

will then be called a *dyadic continuum*; justification for the name will appear at once.

I. *Interval-images and dyadic continua are identical.*

Let $T_1 = [0, 1/2]$ and $T_2 = [1/2, 1]$ be the left-hand and right-hand halves of the interval T; similarly, T_{p1} and T_{p2} the left-hand and right-hand halves of T_p; T_{pq1} and T_{pq2} the left-hand and right-hand halves of T_{pq}; and so on. If C is a continuous image of T in which the images $C_p, C_{pq}, \ldots$ correspond to the subintervals $T_p, T_{pq}, \ldots$, then the $C_p, \ldots$ are compact closed sets (and, moreover, continua) whose diameters, because of the uniform continuity of the mapping function, converge to 0 as the number of indices increases, and the sums

$$C = \mathfrak{S} C_p = \mathfrak{S} C_{pq} = \cdots$$

arranged lexicographically, constitute chains. An interval-image is therefore a dyadic continuum.

Conversely, let C be a dyadic continuum (3). For every dyadic sequence of numerals we let the single point x of $V_p V_{pq} V_{pqr} \cdots$ correspond to the single point t of $T_p T_{pq} T_{pqr} \cdots$. This function $x = \varphi(t)$ is *single-valued*, even though certain of the t (the points of subdivision in the halving of the intervals) belong to two dyadic sequences. Thus $t = 1/2$ is a point of the two intersections $T_1 T_{12} T_{122} \ldots$ and $T_2 T_{21} T_{211} \ldots$ (and of these two only). But the corresponding intersections $V_1 V_{12} V_{122} \ldots$ and $V_2 V_{21} V_{211} \ldots$ are identical as well; for since $V_1 V_2, V_{12} V_{21}, \ldots$ are all non-empty, the sets $V_1 \dotplus V_2$, $V_{12} \dotplus V_{21}, \ldots$ have diameters $\leqq 2\delta_1, 2\delta_2, \ldots$, and their intersection consists of a single point. The function $x = \varphi(t)$, furthermore, is *continuous*: $x\xi$ converges to 0 whenever $t-\tau$ does. For as soon as $|t-\tau| < 1/2^n$, t and τ belong either to one T^n (subintervals with n indices) or to two neighboring T^n; so that x and ξ belong to one V^n (sets V with n indices) or to two lexicographically neighboring V^n, and so $x\xi \leqq 2\delta_n$. A dyadic continuum is therefore an interval-image.

Let us take note of the following *corollary* to I. If in all the chains (2) the intersections of lexicographically neighboring V *and these only* are non-empty, then C is a *one-to-one and thus homeomorphic image* of T. A point x can then belong to two dyadic sequences of numerals only if they are lexicographical neighbors, and so in that case as well it has only a single inverse image $t = \psi(x)$. If, for example, x belongs to the sequences of numerals $(1, q_1, r_1, \ldots)$ and $(2, q_2, r_2, \ldots)$, then $x \varepsilon V_{1q_1} V_{2q_2}$ and this is possible only for $q_1 = 2$, $q_2 = 1$; and then $x \varepsilon V_{12r_1} V_{21r_2}$, which is possible only for $r_1 = 2$, $r_2 = 1$, etc.; x belongs to $(1, 2, 2, \ldots)$ and $(2, 1, 1, \ldots)$; its only inverse image is $t = 1/2$.

It is possible to modify the dyadic construction so that each of the numerals $p, q, r, \ldots$ ranges not over two, but over any finite number $(\geqq 2)$ of values and perhaps even a number $(\geqq 2)$ that depends on the preceding numerals; by means of the corresponding division of T, the "polyadic" continuum (3) as well proves to be an interval-image.

Several among the examples of Theorem I are quite surprising: the closed triangular, square, and circular *areas* are interval-images, and so are the three-dimensional tetrahedral, cubic, and spherical *solids*. That is, there exist continuous *curves* lying in a Euclidean space E_n $(n \geqq 2)$ and having interior points, so that they are in this sense n-dimensional structures. They are called, after their discoverer, *Peano curves*. We should like, using a method due to Knopp, to represent, say, a triangle V as interval-image — we mean here the closed triangular *area* — and suppose it, for the sake of definiteness, to be an isosceles right triangle; we drop a perpendicular from the vertex to the base and so obtain two

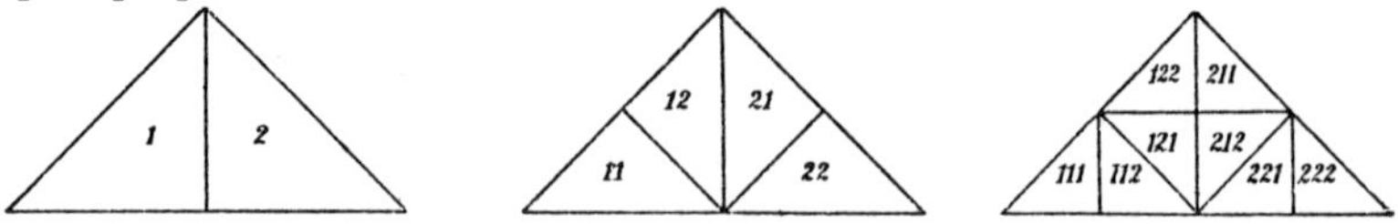

Fig. 8

isosceles right triangles V_1 and V_2. Each V_p is decomposed in the same way into V_{p1} and V_{p2}, etc., where the numbering is determined by the lexicographic chain condition.

We have

$$C = V = \mathfrak{S}\, V_p = \mathfrak{S}\, V_{pq} = \mathfrak{S}\, V_{pqr} = \cdots,$$

and since the diameters are decreased in each operation in the ratio $\sqrt{2}:1$, C is a dyadic continuum.

A square V can be decomposed (Hilbert) into four squares V_1, V_2, V_3, and V_4, by dividing the sides in half; each of the V_p into V_{p1}, V_{p2}, V_{p3}, and V_{p4} in the same way; the numbering can be so arranged as to satisfy the lexicographic condition. The arithmetical representation first given by Peano means the same geometrically as division of the sides into thirds and of the area into nine smaller squares.

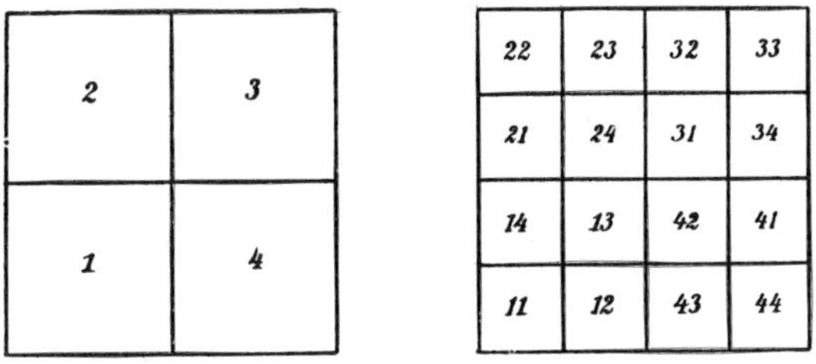

Fig. 9

An arithmetically very transparent mapping

$$x_1 = \varphi_1(t), \qquad x_2 = \varphi_2(t)$$

of the segment T onto the square $(0 \leqq x_1 \leqq 1,\ 0 \leqq x_2 \leqq 1)$ is due to Lebesgue. Let P be the Cantor triadic set consisting of the numbers $t \varepsilon T$ representable by the triadic fractions that involve only zeros and twos:

$$t = 2\left(\frac{t_1}{3} + \frac{t_2}{3^2} + \frac{t_3}{3^3} + \cdots\right) \quad (t_n = 0, 1).$$

This representation is unique: if two such numbers t and τ first differ in their n-th numerals, then $|t - \tau| \geqq \frac{1}{3^n}$, and thus if t converges to τ, then t coincides with τ in its first k numerals, where k increases without bound. From this it can be seen that

$$x_1 = \frac{t_1}{2} + \frac{t_3}{2^2} + \cdots = \varphi_1(t), \qquad x_2 = \frac{t_2}{2} + \frac{t_4}{2^2} + \cdots = \varphi_2(t)$$

are continuous functions of t in P; at this stage, $x = (x_1, x_2)$ already ranges over the whole square. Finally, we extend these functions to the whole interval T by continuing them linearly in the open intervals (α, β) (the components) of $T - P = Q$, that is, we set

$$\varphi_1(t) = \frac{\beta - t}{\beta - \alpha}\varphi_1(\alpha) + \frac{t - \alpha}{\beta - \alpha}\varphi_1(\beta)$$

and define $\varphi_2(t)$ similarly (α and β belong to P). The functions as thus extended are still continuous, since linear interpolation introduces only intermediate values between those we already have. If $t \varepsilon Q$ converges monotonically to $\tau \varepsilon P$ (the only case that needs consideration) and if (α, β) is the interval containing t, then α and β also converge to τ and $\varphi_1(\alpha), \varphi_1(\beta), \varphi_1(t)$ all converge to $\varphi_1(\tau)$; t can ultimately remain in a fixed interval (α, β). and converge to one of the endpoints, in which case $\varphi_1(t) \to \varphi_1(\tau)$ is trivial.

It is possible, by splitting the sequence of the t_n into three or more subsequences, to obtain also the three-dimensional or higher-dimensional cube as interval-image, and even to go as far as $\aleph_0$ dimensions. If we split the sequence in accordance, say, with the dyadic scheme of p. 34, then the functions $x_n = \varphi_n(t)$ defined in P by the dyadic fractions

$$x_1 = 0.\, t_1 t_3 t_5 \ldots, \quad x_2 = 0.\, t_2 t_6 t_{10} \ldots, \quad x_3 = 0.\, t_4 t_{12} t_{20} \ldots, \ldots$$

and extended as above to the interval T are, all of them, continuous and range independently of each other over all the values of the interval $0 \leqq x_n \leqq 1$; the sequence $x = (x_1, x_2, x_3, \ldots)$ ranges over the whole $\aleph_0$-dimensional cube W defined by these inequalities $0 \leqq x_n \leqq 1$. The function $x = \varphi(t)$ so defined becomes continuous, and W thus becomes an interval-image, provided that a suitable distance is adopted in the space of bounded sequences of numbers, say the one corresponding to the norm

$$| x - \xi | = \Sigma c_n | x_n - \xi_n |,$$

(where Σc_n is a fixed convergent series with positive terms). For the series $\Sigma c_n | x_n - \xi_n |$ converges uniformly for $x = \varphi(t)$, $\xi = \varphi(\tau)$ and is a continuous function of t, so that for $t \to \tau$ we have $| x - \xi | \to 0$.

With the existence of the Peano curves, the concept of *dimension* is dealt a second blow. The square has already proved to be a *one-to-one* map of the interval (by virtue of the equivalence of the two); it now develops that it can even be its *continuous* image. Only the requirement of *homeomorphism* will restore the concept of dimension to its rightful position; for we have the Theorem of the *Invariance of Dimensionality* (first proved in complete generality by Brouwer):

Provided that $n > m$ and that B has interior points, a set A in the Euclidean space E_m and a set B in the Euclidean space E_n are never homeomorphic.

Since we cannot present the general proof in this book, let us discuss at least the quite simple case $m = 1$: Let us assume, by replacing B by a subset, that B is a (closed) cube in E_n; then B remains connected after deletion of one of its points, while if any point of A lying between two other points is deleted, A becomes disconnected. Therefore A cannot be a one-to-one continuous image of B. (But B may well be such an image of A! For B is an interval-image, the continuous image of T;

if only a single one of the inverse images of every point of B is retained, then we obtain a set $A < T$ of which B is a one-to-one continuous image.)

In particular, a *simple curve* lying in E_n with $n > 1$ can have no interior points; this, at any rate, comes closer to the intuitive conception of a "curve" than did the continuous curve.

Simple curves of a most remarkable kind can easily be generated as dyadic continua. We return to Knopp's triangle construction. Let V be an isosceles triangle with base angles $\pi/5$ and a vertex angle of $3\pi/5$. By dividing the latter in three, we obtain three triangles, the middle one of which we ignore and the two outer (closed) ones of which we call V_1 and V_2; they are similar to V and have only one point in common.

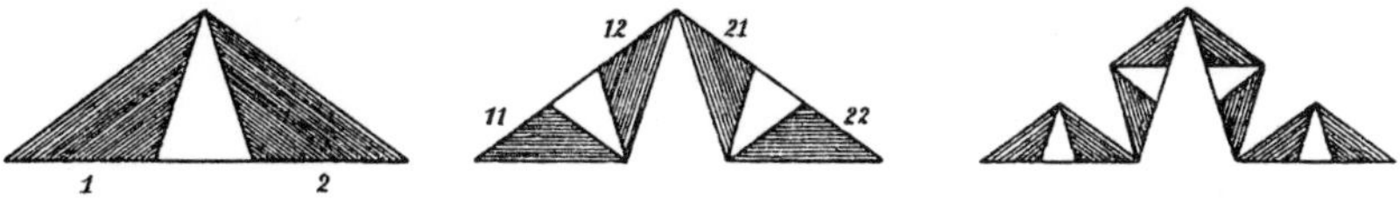

Fig. 10

We proceed with V_p as we did with V and obtain two new triangles V_{p1} and V_{p2}, etc. If the triangles are suitably labelled, the additional conditions that make the dyadic continuum C a *homeomorphic* interval-image will be satisfied. This simple curve C has a tangent nowhere, since in an arbitrary vicinity of a point $x \varepsilon V_p V_{pq}, \ldots$, there are triangles with fixed angles $(V_p, V_{pq}, \ldots)$ in which x lies, and whose corners belong to C; if there were a tangent at x, then the angles of these triangles would have to converge to 0 or to π.

If we change this construction by dispensing with fixed angles and isosceles triangles but retaining the principle that, starting from some suitable corner, every triangle is to be divided into three and that the middle one of the three is to be discarded, then it is possible to have the areas of the sums of the triangles $\mathfrak{S}V_p, \mathfrak{S}V_{pq}, \ldots$ decrease as slowly as we please and to have their limit, the (Lebesgue) area of C, become positive. Thus, there exist *simple curves having positive (Lebesgue) area,* a result which ought no longer to surprise us inasmuch as we already know of *totally disconnected* (point-like) plane sets of positive (Lebesgue) area (pp. 155-6).

2. Conditions for interval-images.

II. (SIERPIŃSKI'S THEOREM). *The set A is an interval-image if and only if it is a compact continuum and can be represented as the sum of a finite number of compact continua with diameters $\leqq \delta$ for every $\delta > 0$.*

Incidentally, the expression compact continuum could be replaced at both its occurrences in the theorem by complete or absolute continuum (a connected set which is complete or absolutely closed), since A is required to be totally bounded (p. 125).

That the condition is necessary is evident (decomposition of T into n equal intervals; the diameters of their images converge to 0 as $n \to \infty$). We are to show that it is sufficient.

For brevity, let us call a set A satisfying the condition of the theorem an S-continuum. The main point is to show that in a decomposition[1]

$$A = \underset{p}{\mathfrak{S}} A_p \tag{5}$$

of A into continua A_p with diameters $\leqq \delta$ these continua may themselves be taken as S-continua. And for this, in turn, we must prove that:

If C is a continuum $< A$, then C can be enclosed in an S-continuum $\leqq A$ whose diameter exceeds that of C by as little as we please.

Let $d(C) = \delta$ be the diameter of C and let $\delta_1 + \delta_2 + \ldots$ be a convergent series of positive numbers. We can enclose C in continua C_p of diameters $\leqq \delta_1$ all of which have points in common with C; to do so we need only choose a representation (5) with $d(A_p) \leqq \delta_1$ and take C_p to mean those of the A_p for which CA_p is non-empty. In the same way we can enclose every C_p in continua C_{pq} with diameters $\leqq \delta_2$, every C_{pq} in continua C_{pqr} with diameters $\leqq \delta_3$, etc. Therefore

$$C \leqq \underset{p}{\mathfrak{S}} C_p, \quad C_p \leqq \underset{q}{\mathfrak{S}} C_{pq}, \quad C_{pq} \leqq \underset{r}{\mathfrak{S}} C_{pqr}, \ldots \tag{6}$$

$$CC_p > 0, \quad C_p C_{pq} > 0, \quad C_{pq} C_{pqr} > 0, \ldots . \tag{7}$$

Every set C with n indices has diameter $\leqq \delta_n$. The set

$$B = C \dotplus \underset{p}{\mathfrak{S}} C_p \dotplus \underset{pq}{\mathfrak{S}} C_{pq} \dotplus \cdots$$

is connected and has a diameter $d(B) \leqq \delta + 2\delta_1 + 2\delta_2 + \ldots$. In fact, two points of B, say $x \in C_{pqr}$ and $\xi \in C_{\pi\chi}$, are joined by the set

$$C_{\pi\chi} \dotplus C_\pi \dotplus C \dotplus C_p \dotplus C_{pq} \dotplus C_{pqr}$$

which being, by (7), a chain of connected sets, is connected, and whose diameter, being at most equal to the sum of the diameters of the members of the chain, is thus

$$\leqq \delta_2 + \delta_1 + \delta + \delta_1 + \delta_2 + \delta_3 < \delta + 2\,\delta_1 + 2\,\delta_2 + \cdots.$$

Therefore, B_α is a continuum whose diameter $d(B_\alpha) = d(B)$ exceeds the diameter $d(C) = \delta$ by as little as we please when $\delta_1 + \delta_2 + \ldots$ is sufficiently small. But B_α is an S-continuum. For if, continuing, we set

[1] All the sums occurring here are to have only a finite number of summands.

$$B_p = C_p \dotplus \underset{q}{\mathfrak{S}} C_{pq} \dotplus \underset{qr}{\mathfrak{S}} C_{pqr} \dotplus \cdots,$$
$$B_{pq} = C_{pq} \dotplus \underset{r}{\mathfrak{S}} C_{pqr} \dotplus \cdots,$$

and so forth, then again these sets, formed just like B, are connected, their diameters $d(B_p)$ are $\leqq \delta_1 + 2\,\delta_2 + 2\,\delta_3 + \cdots, d(B_{pq}) \leqq \delta_2 + 2\,\delta_3 + \cdots$, and so forth. By (6) we then have

$$B = \underset{p}{\mathfrak{S}} B_p = \underset{pq}{\mathfrak{S}} B_{pq} = \cdots$$
$$B_\alpha = \underset{p}{\mathfrak{S}} B_{p\alpha} = \underset{pq}{\mathfrak{S}} B_{pq\alpha} = \cdots,$$

and this gives decompositions of B_α into a finite number of continua whose diameters, in the case of n indices, are $\leqq \delta_n + 2\,\delta_{n+1} + \cdots$.

We have thus proved our statement concerning the enclosing of C in an S-continuum, and we have shown that A can be decomposed into a finite number of S-continua of diameter as small as we please and that it is then possible to continue the process with the latter:

$$\text{(8)} \qquad A = \underset{p}{\mathfrak{S}} A_p, \quad A_p = \underset{q}{\mathfrak{S}} A_{pq}, \quad A_{pq} = \underset{r}{\mathfrak{S}} A_{pqr}, \ldots,$$

where all these sets are S-continua and the diameters of the A^n with n indices are $\leqq \delta_n$ (with $\delta_n \to 0$). We show, in addition, that the sets A^n, suitably numbered and arranged lexicographically, form a chain. In the first decomposition (5) we consider all the chains that can be formed from the A_p, repeated use of the same set being allowed; for example,

$$A_1, A_2, A_1, A_3, A_3, A_1, A_2, A_4$$

(provided $A_1 A_2 > 0$, $A_1 A_3 > 0$, $A_2 A_4 > 0$). If A_i can be joined to A_k by such a chain, and A_k to A_l, then A_i can also be joined to A_l. Because of this transitivity, every A_p can be joined to every other by some chain. We prove this as follows. If it were possible, say, to join A_1 to the A_i by means of a chain, but not to the A_k, then no A_i could be joined to any A_k and therefore, in particular, $A_i A_k = 0$; then $A = \mathfrak{S} A_i + \mathfrak{S} A_k$ would be a partition. Now, if x and y are any two points of A, $x \,\varepsilon\, A_i$, $y \,\varepsilon\, A_k$ (where it may happen that $i = k$), then it is possible, by joining, say, A_i to A_1, A_1 to A_2, A_2 to A_3, etc., and finally joining the last A_p to A_k, to form a chain $A_i \dotplus \ldots \dotplus A_k$ which will contain all the A_p at least once and is therefore $= A$; its first term contains x while its last term contains y; such a chain (that is, the sum of its members) we shall call $K(x, y)$. Incidentally, we remark that the number of members of the chain can be increased arbitrarily by repeating any term, and therefore we may assume in (8) that p goes from 1 to P, q from 1 to Q (independent of p), r from 1 to R (independent of p and q), and so on. We can then assume

$$A = A_1 \dot{+} \cdots \dot{+} A_P = K(x, y)$$

(x, y any points of A; $x \varepsilon A_1$, $y \varepsilon A_P$) ; next,

$$A_p = A_{p1} \dot{+} \cdots \dot{+} A_{pQ} = K(x_p, y_p)$$

(x_p, y_p any points of A_p; $x_p \varepsilon A_{p1}, y_p \varepsilon A_{pQ}$) ; and so forth. If we choose here

$$x_1 = x \varepsilon A_1, \ \ y_1 = x_2 \varepsilon A_1 A_2, \ \ y_2 = x_3 \varepsilon A_2 A_3, \ldots, \ \ y_{P-1} = x_P \varepsilon A_{P-1} A_P,$$
$$y_P = y \varepsilon A_P,$$

then the sets A_{pq}, in lexicographical order, form a chain, since, to take one example, $A_{1Q}A_{12}$ contains the point $y_1 = x_2$, and since it is evident that the procedure can be continued without limit. A is therefore a polyadic continuum (p. 230) and thus an interval-image, and II has been proved.

III. (HAHN-MAZURKIEWICZ THEOREM). *The set A is an interval-image if and only if it is a compact, locally connected continuum.*

To prove the condition sufficient, we show that a compact, locally connected continuum satisfies Sierpiński's condition of Theorem II (that of being an S-continuum). If we enclose every point $x \varepsilon A$ in a closed sphere V_x (with respect to A as the space) of radius ϱ, then the component A_x of V_x that contains x is a compact continuum with x as an interior point (because of the local connectedness) and so contains a neighborhood U_x. By the Borel Theorem (§ 26, II), A is contained in a sum of merely a finite number of U_x, so that for a suitable subset B of A

$$A = \mathfrak{S}_x^B U_x = \mathfrak{S}_x^B A_x,$$

and A can be represented as the sum of a finite number of continua with diameters $\leqq 2\varrho$.

The necessity of the condition in III follows from § 35, VI and VIII; but the local connectedness of an S-continuum also admits of direct proof. For if (5) is a decomposition of A into a finite number of continua with diameters $\leqq \delta$, and if x is contained in the continua A_i and not in the A_k, then $C = \mathfrak{S}A_i$ is a continuum containing x, of diameter $\leqq 2\delta$, that has x as an interior point because x is not contained in the closed set $\mathfrak{S}A_k$; A is locally connected at x.

§ 37. Images of Suslin Sets

In our attempt to infer from the nature of a set something of the nature of its continuous image, we have, thus far, found only one actual result: the continuous image of a set K *compact in itself* is itself a K — apart from the corollaries referring to the preservation of connectivity and local connectivity. For the moment, there seems to be even no prospect of improving on this one result, since we have already found that even an *absolutely closed set* F can have any set whatever (though of course one of the same cardinality as F) as its continuous image. If, however, we consider sets in *separable, complete spaces,* then we can still prove a relatively strong result: *The continuous images of Suslin sets are Suslin sets, and the one-to-one continuous images of Borel sets are Borel sets.* The Suslin and Borel sets of a complete space are of this character in every space — they are *absolute* Suslin and Borel sets — so that we may here speak of *separable absolute* S and B.

Before giving a precise statement of the theorem and proving it, we should like to make a few preliminary remarks about products of spaces, as well as about projections (p. 119), which we have already used frequently as an example of a continuous mapping and shall have occasion so to use again. The product $Z = (X, Y)$ of two metric spaces — that is, the set of pairs $z = (x, y)$ with $x \varepsilon X$, $y \varepsilon Y$ — was made into a metric space by setting up a definition such as (18) or (19) of § 20; it hardly matters what choice we make, since all these spaces Z are homeomorphic. Every pair $z = (x, y)$ determines its first element $x = \varphi(z)$, the projection of z on X; this is a continuous and even a uniformly continuous function. The image $A = \Phi(C)$ of a subset of Z is the projection of C on X. Among the subsets of the product there are, in particular, the products of subsets $C = (A, B)$, with $A \leqq X$, $B \leqq Y$; A and B may reduce to single points; and we let (A, y), for instance, be the set (isometric with A) of the points (x, y) for which y is fixed and $x \varepsilon A$. The product $C = (A, B)$ is distributive with respect to sum and intersection. We have

$$(\mathfrak{S}\, A_m, B) = \mathfrak{S}(A_m, B), \quad (\mathfrak{D}\, A_m, B) = \mathfrak{D}(A_m, B),$$

and the same, of course, for the second factor. If X and Y are complete, then Z is complete, and conversely. If A is closed in X, then (A, Y) is closed in (X, Y), and conversely. By taking complements and using the distributive law, we see that if A is open in X, or is a Borel set F^ξ or G^ξ, or a Suslin set S, then (A, Y) is open in (X, Y), or is an F^ξ, G^ξ, or S, and conversely. If A and B are sets F^ξ in X and Y respectively, then both (A, Y) and (X, B) as well as their intersection (A, B) are sets F^ξ in Z and conversely: if (A, B) is an F^ξ in $Z = (X, Y)$, then it is an F^ξ in (X, B), also, and A is an F^ξ in X; this holds for the G^ξ and the S as well.

Now let B be a continuous image of A, where A lies in a space X and B in a space Y. By means of the mapping function $y = \varphi(x)$ we can assign to every set $P \leqq X$ a set

(1) $$Q = (\Phi(AP))_\alpha$$

closed in Y; (1) means that we look for the image of AP and extend it in Y to its closed hull. Let us express this relation by $Q = \Delta(P)$. Then we have:

I. *If the sets $P_1 \geqq P_2 \geqq \cdots$ form a decreasing sequence with diameters converging to zero and have a (unique) point of intersection x belonging to A, then the sets $Q_n = \Delta(P_n)$ have a unique point of intersection $y = \varphi(x)$, the image of x.*

Since $x \,\varepsilon\, AP_n$, $y \,\varepsilon\, \Phi(AP_n) \leqq Q_n$ for every n, so that $y \,\varepsilon\, Q = Q_1 Q_2 \ldots$. It only remains to show that Q has no point other than y. Let $z \,\varepsilon\, Q$, $z \,\varepsilon\, Q_n$, so that z is an α-point of $\Phi(AP_n)$. Then there exists a point $y_n \,\varepsilon\, \Phi(AP_n)$ for which $zy_n < 1/n$. This in turn indicates that there is a point $x_n \,\varepsilon\, AP_n$ for which $y_n = \varphi(x_n)$. Since x_n and x belong to P_n, we have $xx_n \leqq d(P_n)$, and thus $x_n \to x$, $\varphi(x_n) \to \varphi(x)$, $y_n \to y$. Since at the same time $y_n \to z$, we have $z = y$.

Now we can show:

II. *The continuous image of a separable, absolute Suslin set is itself such a set (if it is not finite).*[1] *The one-to-one continuous image of a separable, absolute Borel set is itself such a set.*

We put the statement in this form: Let A lie in the separable, complete space X, which may be thought of as, say, the complete hull of A, let B lie in an arbitrary space y, and let B be a continuous (or a one-to-one continuous) image of A; then if A is a Suslin (or a Borel) set in X, so also is B in Y.

Let
$$A = \mathfrak{S}\, P_{n_1} P_{n_1 n_2} \cdots$$
be a Suslin set; the sets $P_{n_1 \ldots n_k}$ closed in X may be taken so as to have diameters going to 0 as $k \to \infty$, and furthermore, let $P_{n_1} \geqq P_{n_1 n_2} \geqq \cdots$. By means of the mapping $y = \varphi(x)$ we assign to each of these sets, in accordance with (1), the set
$$Q_{n_1 \ldots n_k} = \Delta(P_{n_1 \ldots n_k}),$$
closed in Y. Then we have
$$Q_{n_1} Q_{n_1 n_2} \cdots = \Phi(P_{n_1} P_{n_1 n_2} \cdots).$$

For if P and Q are these intersections, then *either* (i) P consists of a single point $x \,\varepsilon\, A$ and, by I, Q then consists of the single point $y = \varphi(x)$;

[1] The continuous image B of a separable set A is at most separable, since the image of a set dense in A is dense in B.

or (ii)$P = 0$; but then, because of the properties of a complete space (Second Intersection Theorem) $P_{n_1 \ldots n_k}$ must ultimately become 0, so that $Q_{n_1 \ldots n_k} = 0$ as well, and $Q = 0$. Therefore

$$B = \mathfrak{S}\, Q_{n_1} Q_{n_1 n_2} \cdots$$

is a Suslin set.

If A is a Borel set, so that (§ 34, II) it can be represented with disjoint summands

$$A = \Sigma P_{n_1} P_{n_1 n_2} \cdots$$

and if B is a *one-to-one* continuous image of A, then

$$B = \Sigma Q_{n_1} Q_{n_1 n_2} \cdots$$

can also be represented with disjoint summands. Since B as well as A is separable, and the space Y can therefore be taken as complete and separable, it follows that B is a Borel set.

The differences between Theorem II above and Theorem II of § 35 should be considered carefully. There it was a question of relative Borel and Suslin sts (in A and in B), inferences were drawn from sets $\leqq B$ to their inverse images $\leqq A$, and the Borel-class attributes F^ξ and G^ξ were conserved. Here we are concerned with absolute Borel and Suslin sets, our inferences proceed from the set A to its image B, and the Borel class attributes need not be conserved. In this respect it is rather the extreme opposite that holds: all separable, absolute Suslin sets are continuous images of separable, *absolutely closed* sets, and even of one particular such set, the *Baire null space.* We recall that by this was meant the space A of sequences of natural numbers

$$x = (n_1, n_2, \ldots)$$

with the definition of distance given in § 20, 4. That A is complete or absolutely closed has already been remarked on p. 122; and A is separable since, for example, the countable set of those x in which all the coordinates ultimately are 1 is dense in A. *The Baire null space is homeomorphic with the set of irrational numbers* (which is an absolute G_δ). For if we assign one-to-one to the sequence x the irrational number

$$i = \frac{1|}{|n_1} + \frac{1|}{|n_2} + \cdots$$

between 0 and 1, then the set of these numbers becomes a continuous image of A, and conversely: for, convergence $x_m \to x$ means that x_m agrees with x in a number of initial numerals that tends to ∞ with m; from this it follows that $i_m \to i$, and the converse follows in the same way. The open interval $(0, 1)$ can now be mapped homeomorphically, and with conservation of the attributes of rationality and irrationality, onto the set of all the real numbers by means of, say,

$$v = \frac{2u-1}{1-|2u-1|}, \quad 2u-1 = \frac{v}{1+|v|} \quad (0 < u < 1),$$

which maps the set of irrational numbers between 0 and 1 homeomorphically onto the set of all the irrational numbers. Having made these preliminary remarks, we now prove the theorem:

III. *Every separable, absolute Suslin set is the continuous image of the Baire null space A (or the set I of the irrationals). Every separable, absolute Borel set is the one-to-one continuous image of a set closed in A (or in I).*

As above, we let A be the Baire space of the sequences $x = (n_1, n_2, \ldots)$ and let

$$B = \mathfrak{S}\, F_{n_1} F_{n_1 n_2} \cdots$$

be a Suslin set in a separable complete space. For every sequence x we let the closed sets $F_{n_1} \geqq F_{n_1 n_2} \geqq \cdots$ form a decreasing sequence with diameters $\to 0$; the intersection

$$F(x) = F_{n_1} F_{n_1 n_2} \cdots$$

either contains a single point or is empty. In the first case, we let that one point $y = \varphi(x)$ correspond to x as its image, and thus we already have all the points of B. In order to define such a point $\varphi(x)$ in the second case as well (where the sets $F_{n_1}, \ldots$ ultimately vanish), we choose a fixed point y_0 from B and a fixed point $y_{n_1 \ldots n_k}$ from every set $BF_{n_1 \ldots n_k} > 0$; if then the very first set in the sequence of sets

$$B\,F_{n_1}, \quad B\,F_{n_1 n_2}, \cdots$$

vanishes, we let $\varphi(x) = y_0$; if $BF_{n_1} > 0$ and $BF_{n_1 \ldots n_k}$ is the last non-vanishing set, we let $\varphi(x) = y_{n_1 \ldots n_k}$. $\varphi(x)$ has thus been uniquely defined in A, and B is the image of A; we assert that this $\varphi(x)$ is continuous. Let $\xi \to x$, $\eta = \varphi(\xi)$, $y = \varphi(x)$. The number k of initial numerals in which $\xi = (\nu_1, \nu_2, \ldots)$ agrees with $x = (n_1, n_2, \ldots)$ tends to $+\infty$. If $F(x) > 0$, then η and y belong to the same set $F_{n_1 \ldots n_k}$ and its diameter converges to 0 as $k \to \infty$: $\eta y \to 0$. If $F(x) = 0$, then we have simply, $\eta = y$ for $k > h$ or even for $k > 0$, depending on whether $BF_{n_1 \ldots n_h}$ is the last non-vanishing set or $B\,F_{n_1} = 0$ to begin with. This proves the first half of III.

For the proof of the second half, we remark that the set of x for which

$F(x)$ is non-empty is closed in A or that the set of the x for which $F(x)=0$ is open. For if $F(x)=0$ and if $F_{n_1\ldots n_k}$ is the first vanishing set, then all ξ for which $\xi x < 1/k$ ($F_{\nu_1\ldots\nu_k}=F_{n_1\ldots n_k}$) also have the property $F(\xi)=0$. Therefore, as before, we represent the Borel set B as a Suslin set with *disjoint* summands, and restrict the definition of $y=\varphi(x)$ to non-empty $F(X)$; B then becomes the one-to-one continuous image of a set closed in A. Moreover, it is obvious that in both parts of III the set A can be replaced by the homeomorphic set I.

The Suslin (Borel) sets in separable complete spaces are thus continuous (one-to-one continuous) images of absolutely closed sets or real sets G_δ — but not, however, of real or closed Euclidean sets (whose continuous images are always merely absolute F_σ). In a corresponding way, they can also be represented as *projections*. Let the Suslin set B of the separable complete space Y be the continuous image under the mapping $y=\varphi(x)$, and the Borel set B the one-to-one continuous image, of the set A of the separable complete space X. The pairs of points (x, y) with $x \varepsilon X$, $y \varepsilon Y$ constitute the separable complete space $Z=(X, Y)$, with the distance defined, say, by $\sqrt{x\xi^2+y\eta^2}$. The set C of the points $(x, \varphi(x))$, that is, the set defined by $x \varepsilon A$, $y=\varphi(x)$, is closed in the space (A, Y) because of the continuity of $\varphi(x)$; B is its projection (one-to-one projection if $\varphi(x)$ is one-to-one) on Y. Now we could take A to be absolutely closed (the Baire null space or a subset thereof); then (A, Y) and C are also absolutely closed. Or we could take A as a G_δ in the set X of the real numbers; then (A, Y) is a G_δ in (X, Y) and therefore an absolute G_δ, and similarly for C. B is therefore a (one-to-one) projection of a separable absolute F or G_δ.

The case that B is a *Euclidean* set in the space $y=E_n$ is especially interesting; if we make the second choice for A, then B can be represented as a projection of C, where C is a G_δ in $(X, Y)=(E_1, E_n)$, that is, in the space E_{n+1}. Therefore, if we confine ourselves only to Euclidean sets and, as regards continuous mappings, only to the projections of spaces of higher dimension on spaces of lower dimension, we have:

IV. *The (one-to-one) projection of a Suslin (Borel) set is a Suslin (Borel) set; every Suslin (Borel) set in E_n can be represented as a (one-to-one) projection of a set G_δ in E_{n+1}.*

We know that in Euclidean space there exist Suslin sets that are not Borel sets (§ 33). The (not one-to-one) projection of a Borel set is thus certainly a Suslin set but need not be a Borel set; for example, even the planar G_δ have as their projections all the one-dimensional Suslin sets, and so the non-Borel sets as well. A one-to-one projection of a Borel set is indeed a Borel set, but the class is nevertheless not necessarily conserved; the planar G_δ under one-to-one projection give rise to one-dimensional Borel sets of arbitrarily high class. Thus even the simple problem of the nature of the projections of Borel sets leads as a matter of course past the Borel sets to the Suslin sets.

§ 38. Homeomorphism

A homeomorphism between two sets A and B ($A \approx B$) was defined as a one-to-one mapping $y = \varphi(x)$, $x = \psi(y)$, continuous in both directions, between the two sets. Despite the symmetry of this relation, we shall continue to use the names image and inverse image. Starting from the considerations of the preceding section, which will be considerably recast here, we first prove a theorem approximately analogous to Theorem I of that section.

I. *Let $A \approx B$, where A lies in a complete space X, and B in any space whatever. Suppose a sequence of open sets $P_1, P_2, \ldots$ given in X. Open sets $Q_1, Q_2, \ldots$ of the space Y can be made to correspond to these sets in such a way that, for every increasing sequence $\nu = (n_1, n_2 \ldots)$ of natural numbers for which $P_\nu = P_{n_1} P_{n_2} \ldots \leqq A$, $Q_\nu = Q_{n_1} Q_{n_2} \ldots$ will at the same time be the image of P_ν.*

In order to see what it is that is actually to be proved, we note the following: The sets $A_n = AP_n$ are open in A and their images B_n in B are open (because the function $x = \psi(y)$ is continuous); and since the image of the intersection is here the intersection of the images, it follows that $B_\nu = B_{n_1} B_{n_2} \ldots$ is the image of $A_\nu = A_{n_1} A_{n_2} \ldots$. If therefore we represent $B_n = BQ_n$ in any way whatever as the intersection of B with an open set Q_n, then BQ_ν is the image of AP_ν; we have to show that these open sets[1] Q_n can be taken so "small" that $Q_\nu \leqq B$ whenever $P_\nu \leqq A$. We proceed as follows: For every point $x \varepsilon A_n$ we choose a neighborhood $U_n(x)$ such that it and its closed hull lie inside the open set P_n, and for the image point $y = \varphi(x) \varepsilon B_n$ we choose a neighborhood $V_n(y)$ such that the inverse image of $BV_n(y)$ lies in $U_n(x)$ (which can be done because of the continuity of the function $x = \psi(y)$); in addition, we require that the radii of both neighborhoods be $< 1/n$. We shall then take Q_n to be the sum of the neighborhoods $V_n(y)$ taken over $y \varepsilon B_n$. It is clear that $BQ_n = B_n$; for the set $BV_n(y)$ has an inverse image lying in $AU_n(x) \leqq A_n$ and is therefore itself $\leqq B_n$, so that $BQ_n \leqq B_n$, while at the same time BQ_n contains all the points $y \varepsilon B_n$.

---

[1] In the analogous case of Theorem I, § 37, Q_n was the closed hull of B_n; but there is no such thing as an open hull.

Now as a matter of fact $Q_\nu \leqq B$ for $P_\nu \leqq A$. Let $m < n$ be numbers of the sequence ν. If $z \,\varepsilon\, Q_\nu$ then, for every n, $z \,\varepsilon\, Q_n$; thus $z \,\varepsilon\, V_n(y_n)$ for suitable $y_n \,\varepsilon\, B_n$, $zy_n < 1/n$, and $y_n \to z$. If m is held fixed, y_n as well as z lies *ultimately* in $V_m(y_m)$. Then the inverse image $x_n = \psi(y_n) \,\varepsilon\, A_n$ ultimately lies in $U_m(X_m)$, so that $x_m x_n < 1/m$ for sufficiently large n, and thus the x_n form a fundamental sequence whose limit $x \,\varepsilon\, X$ lies in the closed hull of $U_m(x_m)$ and therefore in P_m. Since this holds for every m, $x \,\varepsilon\, P_\nu \leqq A$; x therefore has an image $y = \varphi(x) \,\varepsilon\, B$, and it follows from $x_n \to x$ that $y_n \to y$, so that $z = y \,\varepsilon\, B$, which is what we wished to prove.

Now we consider, as we have done several times before, a set N of increasing sequences $\nu = (n_1, n_2, \ldots)$ of natural numbers and form from the sets P_n open in X the set (δs-function)

$$A = \mathop{\mathfrak{S}}_{\nu}^{N} P_\nu = \mathop{\mathfrak{S}}_{\nu}^{N} P_{n_1} P_{n_2} \ldots = \Phi(P_1, P_2, \ldots);$$

then, by I, every set B homeomorphic to A can be represented in the form

$$B = \mathop{\mathfrak{S}}_{\nu}^{N} Q_\nu = \mathop{\mathfrak{S}}_{\nu}^{N} Q_{n_1} Q_{n_2} \ldots = \Phi(Q_1, Q_2, \ldots),$$

where the Q_n are open sets of the space $Y \geqq B$ (X is to be complete; Y is arbitrary). *The function Φ is thus conserved under homeomorphism.* For suitable N, A now represents all the Borel sets G^ξ ($\xi \geqq 1$, fixed) of the space X, or even all the Suslin sets. Accordingly we obtain:

II. *The homeomorphic image of an absolute Suslin set is itself such a set; the homeomorphic image of an absolute Borel set G^ξ ($\xi \geqq 1$) is itself such a set (with the same index ξ).*

Comparing this with Theorem II of the preceding section, we see that the hypothesis of separability has been dropped, and we note particularly the conservation of the Borel class.

As regards the absolute sets F^ξ, Theorem II merely informs us that, as special sets $G^{\xi+1}$, they have sets $G^{\xi+1}$ as their homeomorphic images. We shall later be able to improve on this result and demonstrate the conservation of the sets F^ξ for $\xi \geqq 2$; even for $\xi = 1$ we can obtain a somewhat stronger result. But for $\xi = 0$ it is not possible to get beyond Theorem II; we have rather:

III. *The homeomorphic image of an absolutely closed set is an absolute G_δ, and every absolute G_δ is homeomorphic to some absolutely closed set.*

The first half follows from II, since every absolute F is an absolute $G_\delta = G^1$. The second half still to be proved can be stated as follows:

A Young set A, that is, a G_δ in a complete space E, is homeomorphic to a complete space.

To begin with, let E be merely a metric space, let F be closed ($0 < F < E$), and let $\delta(x, F)$ be the lower distance of the point x from the set F. We consider points x, y, and z of the complement $G = E - F$ and define

$$\varphi(x, y \mid F) = \frac{xy}{xy + \delta(x, F) + \delta(y, F)}. \tag{1}$$

This expression, symmetric in x and y, has the attributes of a distance: it vanishes for $x = y$, is otherwise positive (< 1), and *satisfies the triangle inequality*. To prove the latter, we abbreviate $\delta(x, F)$ by δ_x and, taking into account that $\delta_y \leqq \delta_z + yz$ and $\delta_y \leqq \delta_x + xy$, we have

$$\frac{xy}{xy + \delta_x + \delta_y} + \frac{yz}{yz + \delta_y + \delta_z} \geqq \frac{xy + yz}{xy + yz + \delta_x + \delta_z} \geqq \frac{xz}{xz + \delta_x + \delta_z}.$$

Applying $\delta_y \leqq \delta_x + xy$ also in (1), we obtain

$$\frac{xy}{xy + \delta(x, F)} \geqq \varphi(x, y \mid F) \geqq \tfrac{1}{2} \frac{xy}{xy + \delta(x, F)}. \tag{2}$$

Now let $A = G_1 G_2 \ldots$ be a G_δ and the complement $B = F_1 \dotplus F_2 \dotplus \ldots$ an F_σ. Then we take a convergent series $c_1 + c_2 + \ldots$ of positive numbers and define $\overline{xy}$ by

$$\overline{xy} = \Sigma c_n \varphi(x, y \mid F_n)$$

for the points of A.

This also has the attributes of a distance, and with these distances A becomes a metric space $\overline{A}$ (distinct from A) that is mapped one-to-one on A (to every point $x \in A$ there corresponds the same point $x \in \overline{A}$). We wish to show that under this mapping A and $\overline{A}$ become homeomorphic, that is, that for fixed x, $xy \to 0$ implies $\overline{xy} \to 0$, and conversely. In fact, it follows from (2) that

$$\overline{xy} \leqq \Sigma\, c_n \frac{xy}{xy + \delta(x, F_n)};$$

since $\delta(x, F_n) > 0$, every term in the series converges to zero for $xy \to 0$, and because of the uniform convergence, so does the sum of the series. On the other hand, from (2)

$$\overline{xy} \geqq \frac{c_1}{2} \frac{xy}{xy + \delta(x, F_1)} \tag{3}$$

and the convergence of $\overline{xy}$ to zero entails that of xy.

Finally, let

$$\widehat{xy} = \max\,[xy, \overline{xy}].$$

This too is a distance and generates a third space A homeomorphic to $\bar{A}$ and A. This space A is complete, provided E is complete – which concludes the proof of III. For let x_n be a fundamental sequence in $\hat{A}$, so that (since $\widehat{xy} \geqq xy$) it is also a fundamental sequence in A and in $\bar{A}$. Then it has a limit, in the sense of the original distance xy, in E. This limit cannot be a point t of B; for if, say $t \varepsilon F_1$, then for $m < n$ it would follow from (3) that

$$\overline{x_m x_n} \geqq \frac{c_1}{2} \frac{x_m x_n}{x_m x_n + \delta(x_n, F_1)},$$

so that for $n \rightarrow \infty$ $(x_m x_n \rightarrow x_m t > 0,\ \delta(x_n, F_1) \rightarrow 0)$

$$\liminf_n \overline{x_m x_n} \geqq \frac{c_1}{2}.$$

But then x_n would not be a fundamental sequence in A nor, all the more, would it be a fundamental sequence in $\hat{A}$, since otherwise even $\limsup \overline{x_m x_n}$ would have to converge to 0 with increasing m. Therefore there exists a point $x \varepsilon A$ for which $x x_n \rightarrow 0$ and $\widehat{x x_n} \rightarrow 0$, and the space $\hat{A}$ is complete.

One example we already know (p. 239) : the set of irrational numbers, an absolute G_δ, is homeomorphic to the absolutely closed Baire null space.

If a set A and a set B both lying in Euclidean spaces are homeomorphic and if A is closed, then B is a G_δ; but it is an F_σ (a K_σ, § 35, 2) at the same time and is therefore reducible. The irreducible set of the irrational numbers therefore cannot be homeomorphic with any closed Euclidean set.

Let us prove Theorem II in another, and more fruitful, way.

IV. (Lavrentiev's Theorem). *A homeomorphism between A and B can be extended to a homeomorphism between two sets $X \geqq A$ and $Y \geqq B$, where X and Y are both absolute G_δ.*

For the time being let B be merely the continuous image of A under the continuous function $y = \varphi(x)$ and let A_0 and B_0 be complete hulls of A and B. Let us consider a point $x \varepsilon A_0$, which is thus the limit of at least one sequence of points $a_n \varepsilon A$; let $b_n = \varphi(a_n)$ be the images of these points. The b_n may or may not form a fundamental sequence; in the first case, they converge to a point $y \varepsilon B_0$. It may now happen that for *all* a_n convergent to x there correspond fundamental sequences b_n (as is the case, for example, for all $x \varepsilon A$, where we always have $b_n \rightarrow y = \varphi(x)$) ; then all these fundamental sequences b_n converge to *one and the same* point $y \varepsilon B_0$; for if two sequences $b_n \to y$ and $\bar{b}_n \to \bar{y}$ for which $\bar{y} \neq y$ were to correspond to the two sequences $a_n \to x$ and $\bar{a}_n \to x$, then the sequence $a_1, \bar{a}_1, a_2, \bar{a}_2, \ldots$ would converge to x, and the corresponding images $b_1, \bar{b}_1, b_2, \bar{b}_2, \ldots$ would not form a fundamental sequence. Let the set of the points $x \varepsilon A_0$ having the above property (that to all sequences $a_n \to x$ there correspond fundamental sequences b_n) be called A_1; then there corresponds to each point $x \varepsilon A_1$ a completely determined point $y = \varphi_1(x)$ of B_0, namely one for which $a_n \to x$ always entails $b_n \to y$. We have thus defined a single-valued function $\varphi_1(x)$ in A_1, where $A \leqq A_1$, and $\varphi_1(x) = \varphi(x)$ for $x \varepsilon A$. This extended function, which we may again call $\varphi(x)$, is continuous in A_1; for if $x_n \to x$ $(x_n, x \varepsilon A_1)$ and $y_n = \varphi(x_n)$, $y = \varphi(x)$, then it is possible to determine some $a_n \varepsilon A$ for which $a_n x_n < 1/n$ in such a way that $b_n y_n < 1/n$ as well; then $a_n \to x$, so that $b_n \to y$ and $y_n \to y$.

The set A_1 is a G_δ in A_0 — that is, an absolute G_δ. In fact, the condition that whenever a_n approaches arbitrarily close to x the image b_n shall form a fundamental sequence may also be expressed as follows: For every $\sigma > 0$ there exists some $\varrho > 0$ such that for $xa < \varrho$ and $x\bar{a} < \varrho$ the distance $b\bar{b}$ of the images is $\leqq \sigma$; or, For every σ there exists a neighborhood U_x (with respect to A_0 as the space) such that the image $\Phi(AU_x)$ has diameter $\leqq \sigma$. If, first, we hold σ fixed, then the set $G(\sigma)$ of the points x that have such a neighborhood is open (in A_0); for every point of U_x itself has such a neighborhood ($\leqq U_x$). The set of x that have such a neighborhood for every σ, or for $\sigma = 1, \frac{1}{2}, \frac{1}{3}, \ldots$, is $A_1 = G(1)G(\frac{1}{2})\ldots$ and is thus a G_δ.[1]

We have therefore proved the following: A function $\varphi(x)$ continuous in A can be extended to a function continuous in A_1 (in such a way that both agree in A); A_1 is an absolute G_δ and is contained in the complete hull A_0 of A.

If A and B are now homeomorphic, then we also extend the function $\psi(y)$ continuous in B to a function continuous in B_1, where B_1 is a G_δ in B_0.

The function $\varphi(x)$ gives rise to the continuous image $B_2 \leqq B_0$ of A_1, which need not coincide with B_1 (compare the example below). That is, when x ranges over the set A_1, then $\varphi(x)$ ranges over the set B_2. Similarly, let A_2 be the continuous image of B_1 under the mapping $\psi(y)$; that is, when y ranges over the set B_1, $\psi(y)$ ranges over the set A_2.

Finally, let A_3 be the set of the points $x \varepsilon A_1$ for which $\varphi(x) \varepsilon B_1$;

[1] This would also hold, by the way, without the hypothesis regarding the continuity of $\varphi(x)$, although A would then not have to be contained in A_1.

that is, let it be the inverse image of B_1B_2 under the continuous mapping of A_1 on B_2; obviously $A \leqq A_3 \leqq A_1$. Since B_1B_2 is a G_δ in B_2, then, from § 35, II, A_3 is a G_δ in A_1, and so it too is an absolute G_δ. In the same way, let B_3 be the set of the points $y \varepsilon B_1$ for which $\psi(y) \varepsilon A_1$; we have $B \leqq B_3 \leqq B_1$, and B_3 is an absolute G_δ.

The sets A_3 and B_3 are mapped homeomorphically on each other by the functions $y = \varphi(x)$ and $x = \psi(y)$. For, let $x \varepsilon A_3$ and $y = \varphi(x) \varepsilon B_1$; because of the definition of B_1, this means: For an arbitrary sequence $b_n \rightarrow y$ $(b_n \varepsilon B)$, $a_n = \psi(b_n)$ converges to $\psi(y)$. But if we take an arbitrary sequence $a_n \rightarrow x$ $(a_n \varepsilon A)$, then $b_n = \varphi(a_n)$ converges to $y = \varphi(x)$; therefore a_n must converge to $\psi(y)$; that is, we must have $x = \psi(y)$. Since $\psi(y) \varepsilon A_1$, we have, furthermore, that $y \varepsilon B_3$. Therefore: from $x \varepsilon A_3$ and $y = \varphi(x)$ it follows that $y \varepsilon B_3$ and $x = \psi(y)$, and conversely; by virtue of $y = \varphi(x)$ it follows that $y \varepsilon B_3$ and $x = \psi(y)$, and conversely; by virtue of $y = \varphi(x)$, B_3 is the continuous image of A_3, and likewise, by virtue of $x = \psi(y)$, A_3 is the continuous image of B_3. This proves IV $(X = A_3, Y = B_3)$.

Moreover, $A_3 = A_1A_2$ and $B_3 = B_1B_2$. For from $A_3 \leqq A_1$ it follows by virtue of the mapping $y = \varphi(x)$ that $B_3 \leqq B_2$, so that $B_3 \leqq B_1B_2$ and $A_3 \leqq A_1A_2$. Conversely, we also have $A_1A_2 \leqq A_3$; for from $x \varepsilon A_1A_2$ it follows (because $x \varepsilon A_2$), that $x = \psi(y)$, with $y \varepsilon B_1$, and then (because $\psi(y) \varepsilon A_1$) that $y \varepsilon B_3$ and $x \varepsilon A_3$. Finally it should also be remarked that A_3 and B_3 are the *greatest* sets X, Y $(\leqq A_0, B_0)$ to which the homeomorphism between A and B can be extended; for if x and y are points of X and Y that correspond to each other, then we must have $x \varepsilon A_1$, $y = \varphi(x)$ and $y \varepsilon B_1$, $x = \psi(y)$, so that $x \varepsilon A_3$, $y \varepsilon B_3$.

Example. Let

$$A = (0, 1) + (1, 2) + (2, 3)$$

be the sum of the three open real intervals $(0, 1)$, $(1, 2)$, and $(2, 3)$; let the function $y = \varphi(x)$ be defined on these intervals by

$$\varphi(x) = 1 - x, \quad 3 - x, \quad \text{and} \quad x.$$

This function maps A homeomorphically onto itself $(B = A)$ in such

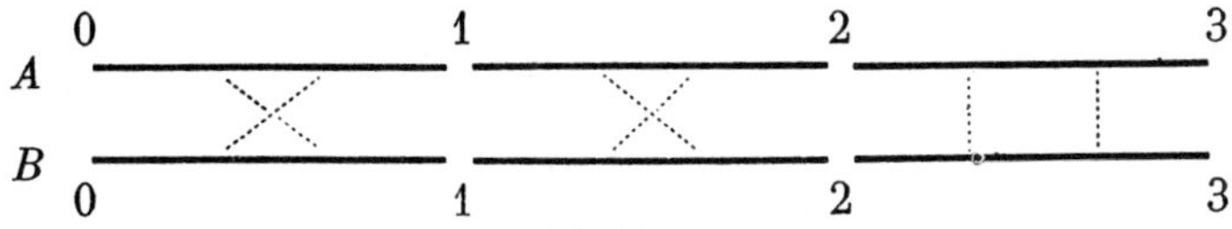

Fig. 11

a way (Fig. 11) that the first two intervals are reflected in their midpoints, while the third remains fixed point by point. Since the mapping is an involution (that is, the function $\varphi(y)$ is identical with its inverse $\psi(y)$), the sets A_0, A_1, A_2, and A_3 coincide with B_0, B_1, B_2, and B_3. We have

$$\begin{aligned} A_0 &= A + \{0, 1, 2, 3\} \\ A_1 &= A + \{0, 3\} \\ A_2 &= A + \{1, 3\} \\ A_3 &= A + \{3\}. \end{aligned}$$

The second formula is obtained thus: For $x \to 0$, we have $y \to 1$, and for $x \to 3$, we have $y \to 3$; the points 0 and 3 are thus to be included in A_1, and their images 1 and 3 are to be included in A_2. 1 and 2, however, are not to be included in A_1, for if x converges to 1 either from the left or from the right, then y converges to 0 or 2, so that a fundamental sequence does not correspond to every sequence $x \to 1$; the point 2 behaves analogously.

From Theorem IV, Theorem II now follows once more, together with the corollary:

II*. *The homeomorphic image of an absolute Borel set* F^ξ $(\xi \geqq 2)$ *is itself such a set (with the same index* ξ).

For after the homeomorphism has been extended to the absolute G_δ-sets X and Y, we can apply Theorem II of § 35. If A is an absolute G^ξ $(\xi \geqq 1)$, then it is a G^ξ in X. Then, by virtue of the continuity of $x = \psi(y)$, B is a G^ξ in Y, and is therefore an absolute G^ξ, since Y is an absolute G^1.

In the same way, if A is an absolute F^ξ $(\xi \geqq 2)$, then B is an F^ξ in Y and is therefore an absolute F^ξ, since Y is an absolute G^1 and F^2. The proof for the absolute Suslin sets proceeds along similar lines.

Some further set characteristics invariant under homeomorphism can be obtained from IV by considering the complements $X - A$ and $Y - B$. For example, the complements of absolute Suslin sets (in a complete space) map under homeomorphism into this same type of set. The difference of two absolute G_δ map into such differences; for if $A = A_1 - A_2$ is the difference of two absolute G_δ which, because of $XA = XA_1 - XA_2$, may be taken as subsets of X, then $B = B_1 - B_2$ is also such a difference. This applies in particular to the absolute sets $F^1 = F_\sigma$.

In the short table below we collect the most important results that refer to continuous, one-to-one continuous, and homeomorphic images of sets. K denotes a set compact in itself; the symbols F (closed), F^ξ, G^ξ, B (Borel set), and S (Suslin set) are to be understood as meaning absolute F, absolute F^ξ, etc. The abbreviation sep. means separable; a blank entry means that there is nothing that can be said.

A	Image of A		
	Continuous	One-to-one Continuous	Homeomorphic
K	K	K	K
F			G_δ
F^ξ			$F^\xi (\xi \geqq 2)$
G^ξ			$G^\xi (\xi \geqq 1)$
S			S
sep. F	S	B	G_δ
sep. B	S	B	B
sep. S	S	S	S

§ 39. Simple Curves

1. Conditions for simple curves. Our interval-image, that is, the continuous map of a closed interval or of the interval $T = [0, 1]$ of the real numbers did not necessarily have much resemblance to our intuitive notion of a curve. Somewhat closer to this conception comes the *simple curve*,[1] namely the *homeomorphic image of* T. In order that C be such a curve, the following properties are certainly necessary, and the list could easily be extended; the concepts closed, continuum, and so forth, refer to C itself as the space.

(a) C is compact in itself.

(b) C has two points a and b between which it is an *irreducible continuum*; that is, C itself is a continuum, but no continuum $< C$ contains the points a and b.

(c) C has two points a and b between which it is *irreducibly connected*; that is, C itself is connected, but no connected set $< C$ contains the points a and b.

(d) C is connected and has two points a and b of the following kind: For every point $x \varepsilon C$ there exists a decomposition $C = A \dot{+} B$ for which A and B are closed and have only the point x in common, and $a \varepsilon A$, $b \varepsilon B$.

(e) C is locally connected.

As a matter of fact, the necessity of (a) and (e) follows from III of § 36. The remaining conditions result if we take a and b to mean the images of the end-points of 0 and 1; no connected sets $< T$ contain the

[1] Also called a simple arc, or a Jordan arc. The homeomorphic map of the circumference of a circle is called a simple closed curve or a closed Jordan curve. (In the "Fundamenta Mathematicae," ligne de Jordan and the like mean the same as our interval-image.)

points 0 and 1, whence (c) and, a fortiori, (b) follows: and for every $t \varepsilon T$, $T = [0, t] \dotplus [t, 1]$ yields a decomposition which, carried over to C, has the property (d) ($[0, 0]$ and $[1, 1]$ are to mean the sets $\{0\}$ and $\{1\}$ consisting of a single point).

We shall now show that conditions (a), (b), and (e), or (a) and (c), or (a) and (d) are also sufficient.

I. *Conditions* (c) *and* (d) *are equivalent.*

That (c) follows from (d) is very easy to see. If $D < C$ contains the points a and b, let $x \varepsilon C - D$, and let $C = A \dotplus B$ be, in accordance with (d), a decomposition belonging to x; then $DAB = 0$, and $D = DA + DB$ is a partition, and so D is not connected.

Conversely, let (c) – or even merely the following partial assumption – be satisfied: Let C be a continuum irreducible between a and b in the sense of (b), and let it become disconnected by elimination of a point other than a or b. In order to prove (d) from this, we may suppose x different from a and b, since for $x = a$ and $x = b$ the decompositions $C = a \dotplus C = C \dotplus b$ satisfy the given conditions (we now denote a set $\{x\}$ consisting of one point simply by x). Then $C - x$ is disconnected and can therefore be partitioned into $C - x = P + Q$, where P and Q are closed in $C - x$. Then the sets $A = P + x$ and $B = Q + x$ are closed (in C) and in addition, by III of § 29, they are connected, since their sum C and their intersection x are connected. Neither of the continua $A < C$ and $B < C$ can contain both of the points a and b; therefore we have, say, $a \varepsilon A$ and $b \varepsilon B$, and $C = A \dotplus B$ is a decomposition satisfying (d). I is thus proved.

II. *If C is separable and satisfies the condition* (c) *or* (d), *then the real interval $T = [0, 1]$ is a one-to-one continuous image of C.*

The separability of C will not play any role until the end; let us ignore this condition for the moment. The sets A and B in (d), as we have just seen, are connected (continua).

If x_1 and x_2 are two (not necessarily distinct) points and $C = A_1 \dotplus B_1 = A_2 \dotplus B_2$ are decompositions belonging to them, then

(1) $\qquad$ for $x_1 \varepsilon A_2$ we have $A_1 \leqq A_2$.

For, as a sum of connected sets with the common point x_1, $A_2 + B_1$ is connected; since it contains the points a and b, it follows, by (c), that $C = A_2 \dotplus B_1$; and forming the intersection of this with A_1 yields $A_1 = A_1 A_2 \dotplus x_1 = A_1 A_2$.

For $x_1 = x_2$ it follows from this that $A_1 = A_2$ and, of course, in the same way, $B_1 = B_2$; that is, the decomposition $C = A \dotplus B$ belonging to

x is *uniquely determined* by x. Let us call A the *initial portion* of C belonging to x (B, the final portion). To $x = a$ there belongs the initial portion a and to $x = b$ the initial portion C.

If, however, $x_1 \neq x_2$ then

$$(2) \qquad A_1 < A_2, \; x_2 \,\varepsilon\, A_2 - A_1.$$

For if we had both $x_1 \,\varepsilon\, A_2$ and $x_2 \,\varepsilon\, A_1$, then it would follow that $A_1 = A_2$ and thus $B_1 - x_1 = B_2 - x_2$ and $B_1 + x_2 = B_2 + x_1$. In this last equation, which expresses a decomposition into components, $B_1 = x_1$ and $B_2 = x_2$ would have to hold; but B_1 and B_2 contain b, and we arrive at the contradiction $x_1 = x_2 = b$. Therefore: If x_1 and x_2 are distinct and $x_1 \,\varepsilon\, A_2$, then we cannot have $x_2 \,\varepsilon\, A_1$, proving (2).

Of course, for $x_1 \neq x_2$ the relations $x_1 \,\varepsilon\, B_2$ and $x_2 \,\varepsilon\, B_1$ also cannot both hold at the same time. Thus one and only one of the relations

$$x_1 \varepsilon A_2, \quad A_1 < A_2, \quad x_2 \varepsilon A_2 - A_1$$

or

$$x_2 \varepsilon A_1, \quad A_2 < A_1, \quad x_1 \varepsilon A_1 - A_2$$

can hold. The initial portions belonging to different points are therefore always related by $A_1 \lesseqgtr A_2$. We make C into an *ordered set* by the definition

$$x_1 < x_2 \quad \text{for} \quad A_1 < A_2.$$

This is equivalent with $x_1 \,\varepsilon\, A_2$, $x_1 \neq x_2$; in addition, A_2 also contains the point x_2.

Once the ordering has been accomplished, A becomes the set of points $\leqq x$ and B the set of points $\geqq x$; in analogy with our notation in the case of real intervals, we write for this:

$$A = [a, x], \qquad B = [x, b].$$

These sets are closed, as is, in general, the set $[x_1, x_2]$ of the points $x_1 \leqq x \leqq x_2$ (the intersection A_2B_1). Sets such as $C - B = A - x = [a, x)$ (the set of points $< x$), $(x, b]$, and (x_1, x_2) are open (in C). Of course, we set $[a, a] = a$ and $[a, a) = 0$.

The ordered set C has a as its first element and b as its last element. It is *dense* (p. 58); that is, if $x_1 < x_2$, there always exists still another element x for which $x_1 < x < x_2$. For the connected set A_2 cannot be $= A_1 + x_2$, so that $A_2 - A_1$ certainly contains a point x different from x_2. Furthermore, it is *continuous* (p. 62). For, suppose $C = C_1 + C_2$ to be split into two disjoint non-empty sets for whose elements we always have $x_1 < x_2$. If C_1 has no last element, then it is equal to the sum (for all $x_1 \,\varepsilon\, C_1$) of the sets $[a, x_1)$, and it is therefore open. Similarly, C_2 is open, provided it has no first element. Both at once would mean a partition of C, so that either C_1 has a last element or C_2 a first element.

If, furthermore, C is separable, so that a countable set R is dense in C (in the metric sense), then R is also dense in C in the ordinal sense (p. 63). For (x_1, x_2), where $x_1 < x_2$, is open and therefore contains a point r of R; that is, $x_1 < r < x_2$. By Theorem V of § 11, $C - \{a, b\}$ is therefore of the type λ of the open interval $(0, 1)$ and C itself of the type of the closed interval $T = [0, 1]$. There exists, in consequence, a *similarity* transformation

$$x = \varphi(t), \quad t = \psi(x)$$

of C on T $(0 \leqq t \leqq 1)$, with $a = \varphi(0)$ and $b = \varphi(1)$. Here the function $t = \psi(x)$ is continuous. For, to every interval open in T (the intersection of T with an open interval), namely $[0, t)$, $(t, 1]$, and (t_1, t_2), there corresponds a set open in C, namely $[a, x)$, $(x, b]$, and (x_1, x_2); and thus to every set open in T there corresponds a set open in C — which is precisely the condition for the continuity of $\psi(x)$ of Theorem I of § 35. This proves II.

In the nature of a converse to Theorem II, moreover, we have the following:

If C is connected and T is a one-to-one continuous image of C, then C satisfies condition (c) *or* (d). For the decomposition $T = [0, t] + [t, 1]$ gives a decomposition $C = A + B$ such as is required by (d). From the mere fact that T is a one-to-one continuous image of C, neither connectedness nor separability of C follows. C can, after all, be (p. 223) any set of cardinality $\aleph$ in which the distance between every two points is 1.

If C now is compact in itself and T is a one-to-one continuous image of C, then the mapping is a homeomorphism (§ 35, III). Thus:

III. *In order that C be a simple curve, the conditions* (a) *and* (c) *or the conditions* (a) *and* (d) *are necessary and sufficient.*

Conditions (a) and (c) are due to Lennes; (a) and (d) to Sierpiński.

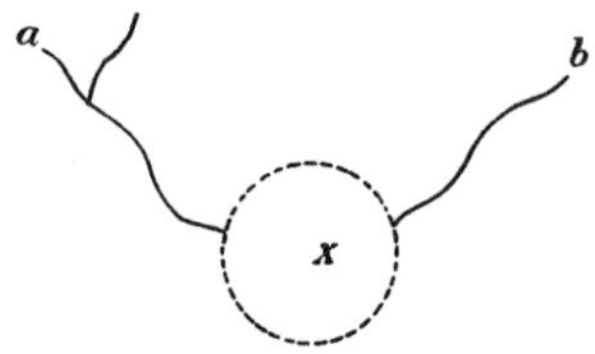

Fig. 12

If condition (c) is weakened to (b), then strengthening in some other respect is necessary; this is accomplished by the condition of local connectedness; and we have:

IV. *In order that C be a simple curve, conditions* (a), (b), *and* (e) *are both necessary and sufficient.*

It is only necessary to show that for every point x a decomposition $C = A + B$ in accordance with (d) is possible, where x is again assumed to be distinct from a and b. Let U_n $(n = 1, 2, 3, \ldots)$ be the neighborhood of x of radius $1/n$, and let $F_n = C - U_n$ be closed. For n sufficiently large, a and b belong to F_n, but, by virtue of (b), not to the same component of F_n; let P_n be the component of F_n containing a, and Q_n the one containing b (as long as $a \varepsilon U_n$, we set $P_n = 0$, and analogously for Q_n). The sets

$$P = \mathfrak{S}P_n, \quad Q = \mathfrak{S}Q_n$$

(where the summands increase with n) are disjoint and connected. Because of the Border Theorem (Theorem XVIII) of § 29, P_n contains a point that is on the border of F_n and so is at distance $1/n$ from x; x is a point of accumulation of P and Q; and $P + Q + x$, as the sum of the connected sets $A = P + x$ and $B = Q + x$, is connected. If we now show, in addition, that A and B are closed, then the proof is complete; for it then follows from the irreducibility (b) that $C = P + Q + x = A + B$, which is the desired decomposition. Therefore what we must show is that, if $c \neq x$ is an α-point of P, then $c \varepsilon P$. Let R_n be the component of F_n containing c, and let $R = \mathfrak{S}R_n$ (ultimately $c \varepsilon F_n$; until this occurs we again let $R_n = 0$). Now c ultimately becomes an interior point of F_n and, by virtue of the local connectedness, an interior point of R_n(the component of F_{ni} containing c already has c as an interior point); R_n thus contains points of P. Therefore R_nP is non-empty, RP is non-empty and, for sufficiently large n, R_nP_n is non-empty as well; that is, $R_n = P_n$ and $R = P$, so that $c \varepsilon P$.

This proves IV. A compact, locally connected continuum was always the continuous image of an interval; if, in addition, it is irreducible between a certain two of its points, then it is the homeomorphic image of an interval.

2. Prime parts of a continuum.[1] Let us take C to have more than one point, and to be connected, and let us again take it as the space to which the relative concepts refer. The points r at which C is locally connected may be called *regular* points and the remaining s, *singular* points; if R is the set of regular points and S that of singular points, then

$$C = R + S = R_i + S_\alpha.$$

The points (sets of one point) *of* R_i *and the components of* S_α are called *the prime parts of* C (Hahn). In case $R_i = 0$ and S is dense in C, C has itself as its only prime part and will be called a *prime continuum.* If $R_i > 0$, then this dense-in-itself set is locally connected, since any one

[1] Compare Appendix C.

of its points may be joined to one sufficiently near it by a connected set of arbitrarily small diameter $\leq C$ and therefore $\leq R_i$; its components are open in R_i and have more than one point, so that R_i is thus (by § 29, VII) of cardinality at least $\aleph$. In this case C therefore has at least $\aleph$ prime parts and will be called a *composite continuum*; the prime parts are themselves continua.

Let us introduce for two points x and y a concept analogous to the (always vanishing) separation in C, the *singular separation*, which we denote once more by $\overline{xy}$. A ϱ-chain (p. 180)

$$(3) \qquad (x, s_1, s_2, \ldots, s_{n-1}, y),$$

the "inside" points $s_1, s_2, \ldots, s_{n-1}$ of which are singular points – we also include, for $xy \leqq \varrho$, the chain (x, y) without any inside points – will be called a *singular ϱ-chain.* Let us join x and y by all possible singular ϱ-chains; the greatest lower bound of the numbers ϱ so defined will be called the *singular separation* $\overline{xy}$. We have $\overline{xy} \leqq xy$, and the triangle inequality $\overline{xy} + \overline{yz} \geqq \overline{xz}$ holds; for if x and y can be joined by a singular ϱ-chain, and y and z by a singular σ-chain, then x and z can be joined by a singular $(\varrho + \sigma)$-chain. If, instead of the singular ϱ-chains, we use chains

$$(4) \qquad (x, t_1, t_2, \ldots, t_{n-1}, y)$$

whose inside points are taken from S_α, then the greatest lower bound of the ϱ is unchanged; for a ϱ-chain (3) is a special ϱ-chain (4) and, on the other hand, to a given ϱ-chain (4) there belongs a $(\varrho + \delta)$-chain (3) obtained by choosing, for each t_k, a s_k for which $s_k t_k < \delta/2$ ($\delta > 0$ arbitrarily small).

The singular separation $\overline{xy}$ of course vanishes for $x = y$; for $x \neq y$ it does so if and only if both points belong to S_α and have separation 0 in this set. If from now on we take C to be a *compact* continuum, then $\overline{xy} = 0$ means the same as, x and y belong to the same prime part.

By virtue of these separations, C becomes a new metric space Γ in which the points belonging to the same prime part are to be considered identical. This can also be expressed as follows: To every point $x \varepsilon C$ there is made to correspond a uniquely defined point $\xi = \varphi(x)$ with the stipulation that $\varphi(x) = \varphi(y)$ if and only if x and y belong to the same prime part; the set Γ of the points ξ becomes the single-valued image of C while, conversely, the inverse image of ξ is an entire prime part. With the distance $\xi\eta = \overline{xy}$, Γ becomes a metric space and – since $\overline{xy} \leqq xy$ – the *continuous* image of C and so, once more, a compact continuum. Let us call it the *continuum of the prime parts of C.*

The inverse image of a continuum $\Delta \leqq \Gamma$ is a continuum $D \leqq C$. For D is closed; if $D = D_1 + D_2$ can be partitioned, then no prime part can have points in common with both summands (because it is a continuum). The images Δ_1 and Δ_2 of D_1 and D_2 are then disjoint and are compact closed sets, and $\Delta = \Delta_1 + \Delta_2$ can be partitioned. From this it follows that: *If C is irreducible between x and y, then Γ is irreducible between the image points ξ and η* (irreducible in the sense of (b), and thus an irreducible continuum). We assume here that $\xi \neq \eta$, with x and y belonging to different prime parts; in the excluded case, C would be a prime continuum and Γ would consist of a single point.

The image $\Phi(G)$ of a set G open in C need not be open in Γ. But if G contains the entire prime part A, the inverse image of the point ξ, then $\Phi(G)$ has ξ as an interior point. For if $F = C - G$, then the image $\Phi(F)$ is closed (since it is the continuous image of a compact closed set), does not contain ξ, and therefore has a positive lower distance ϱ from ξ; therefore all the points η for which $\xi\eta < \varrho$ belong to $\Phi(G)$.

We should now like to get to the true goal of this investigation, which is, to prove that the continuum of the prime parts is *locally connected.*

V. *If C is a compact continuum and if F is closed (in C) and P is a component of F, then every point x of $F_i P(F-P)_\alpha$ is singular, and the prime part belonging to x intersects the border F_b of F.*

Let us first note the following. In order that this theorem have content, that is, that a point x exist, we must have $F_i > 0$ and $F > P$, so that F is not connected, and in particular $F < C$. Since the space C is connected, F cannot be open at the same time, and therefore F_b is non-empty. The Border Theorem (Theorem XVII of § 29) on which the proof of the present theorem mainly rests, states that every component of $CF = F$ meets the border F_b, and further, that if Q is a continuum intersecting F_b and F_i, then every component of QF_i has points of accumulation in F_b.

Now x cannot be regular; for if $U_x \leqq F_i$, then x must be an interior point of the component of U_x containing it, and all the more of P, and so could not be a point of accumulation of $F - P$.

Further, let $F = P + \Sigma Q_m$ be the decomposition of F into components. Since x is supposed to be an accumulation point of $F - P$ and $\delta(x, Q_m) >$ 0, there must be a sequence of components Q_n for which $\delta(x, Q_n) \rightarrow 0$; by the Axiom of Choice, we can assume that the *closed limit* $Q = \mathrm{Fl}\, Q_n$ exists. It is, again, a continuum $\leqq F$ (Zoretti's Theorem) and contains x and is therefore contained in P and, furthermore, of course in $(F-P)_\alpha$; from what has already been proved it is clear that all the points of QF_i (which includes x) are thus singular, $QF_i \leqq S$. As we have already remarked above, all the Q_m intersect the border F_b, so that QF_b is non-empty also, and X, the component containing x of QF_i, has points of accumulation in F_b; $X_\alpha F_b$ is non-empty.

Now since $X \leqq S, X_\alpha \leqq S_\alpha$, and X_α is connected, X_α is contained in the prime part A belonging to x, and AF_b is non-empty.

VI. *If A is a prime part of the compact continuum C, F the set of the points for which $\delta(x, A) \leqq \varrho$ ($\varrho > 0$), and P the component of F containing A, then $A \leqq P_i$.*

For if $x \varepsilon A \leqq F_i P$, then x must not belong to $(F - P)_\alpha$, since otherwise, by V, A would have to intersect the border of F; therefore, a neighborhood $U_x \leqq F_i$ exists which is disjoint from $F - P$, so that $U_x \leqq P$, and x is an interior point of P.

VII. (MOORE'S THEOREM). *The continuum of the prime parts of a compact continuum is locally connected.*

Let $\xi \varepsilon \Gamma$, and let the inverse image of ξ be the prime part A of C; let Γ_0 be a neighborhood of ξ and its inverse image a set $G_0 \geqq A$ open in C. If ϱ is positive and smaller than the lower distance between A and the boundary[1] of G_0 (both are compact continua), then the set F of Theorem VI is contained in G_0; as in that theorem, let P be the component of F containing A, and let $A \leqq G \leqq P \leqq G_0$, where $G = P_i$ is open. For the images it follows that $\Phi(G) \leqq \Phi(P) \leqq \Phi(G_0) = \Gamma_0$. $\Phi(G)$, as we saw above, contains the point ξ as an interior point, $\Phi(P)$ is a continuum $\leqq \Gamma_0$, containing ξ as an interior point, and we have thus proved the local connectedness of Γ at ξ.

VIII. (HAHN'S THEOREM). *If C is a compact, composite continuum irreducible between certain two of its points, then the continuum of its prime parts is homeomorphic with the interval T ($0 \leqq t \leqq 1$). T is the continuous image of C, and the mapping is such that the inverse images of the points t are the prime parts of C.*

For: Γ, the continuum of the prime parts, is compact, has more than one point, is irreducible between two points, is locally connected, and thus by IV, is homeomorphic to T. T is a continuous image of Γ, Γ a continuous image of C, and therefore T a continuous image of C, where there corresponds to each point t exactly one point of Γ and one prime part of C.

A simple example in the (x_1, x_2)-plane is the set $C = R + S$ formed from the two sets

[1] When this vanishes ($G_0 = C$), then $\varrho > 0$ may be arbitrary.

$$R: \quad 0 < x_1 \leqq 1, \; x_2 = \sin \pi / x_1,$$

$$S: \quad x_1 = 0, \; -1 \leqq x_2 \leqq 1,$$

where at the same time, R is the set of regular points and S the set of singular points.[1] The prime parts are S and the points of R; the projection on the x_1-axis gives $[0, 1]$ as the continuous image of C. C is an irreducible continuum between every point $a \varepsilon S$ and the point b ($x_1 = 1$, $x_2 = 0$); and between all other pairs of points, it is reducible. But it is not irreducibly connected even between a and b, in the sense of (c), since $a + R$ is connected; the set $a + R$, however, is irreducibly connected between a and b and, by II, T is its one-to-one continuous image (again by projection).

§ 40. Topological Spaces

Homeomorphisms are also called *topological* mappings and homeomorphic sets are called *topologically equivalent*; properties common to homeomorphic sets are called topological invariants. Thus, the property of being an absolute G^{ξ} ($\xi \geqq 1$) is topologically invariant, but that of absolute closure (completeness) is not; relative closure and relative openness, on the contrary, are topologically invariant; that is, if A is closed (open) in E and E is homeomorphic to $\bar{E}$, while A is homeomorphic to a corresponding subset $\bar{A}$, then $\bar{A}$ is closed (open) in $\bar{E}$.

The mathematical discipline concerned with these matters is called Topology, or Analysis Situs. (The latter term, due to Leibniz, was re-introduced by Riemann.) We have not been able to go very deeply into this subject nor to prove more than a very few general theorems about it. But this seems like a suitable occasion to touch, in all brevity, on those point-set theories that emphasize the topological point of view from the very beginning and work only with topologically invariant concepts; a *topological space* defined in this way is to be distinguished from its homeomorphs in the same way in which, in our own theory, we distinguished between a metric space and the spaces isometric with it. It is not a mere matter of a formal transformation of the metric theory but rather of a new and wider conception of a space; the *metrizable* spaces – that is, those spaces that are homeomorphic to metric spaces – constitute merely a special class among the topological spaces.

[1] The same holds for the set in Fig. 6 (p. 180).

What are primary in the topological space E are the sets that are *closed* (in E) and their complements, the *open* sets; on this is based the *concept of continuity* – namely, the following (§ 35, I): The single-valued function $\bar{x} = f(x)$ that maps the space E on the space $\bar{E}$ is called continuous if a set closed (open) in E corresponds as inverse image to every set closed (open) in $\bar{E}$. A one-to-one mapping continuous in both directions is called a homeomorphism. The closed or open sets can be taken as our starting point and left undefined, or they can be derived from related concepts (closed hull, limit point, point of accumulation, open kernel, neighborhood), but always derived in such a way as to keep invariant their topological character; the more detailed nature of the space is then determined by a suitable choice of *axioms*, of which we shall take just three main groups into account: *sum and intersection axioms, separation axioms,* and *axioms on cardinality*. Such axioms may be obtained, for example, by borrowing them from the theory of metric spaces, where they appear as provable theorems.

I. SUM AND INTERSECTION AXIOMS. The closed sets must, regardless of anything else, satisfy the following conditions:

(1) The space E and the null set 0 are closed.

(2) The sum of two closed sets is closed.

(3) The intersection of any number of closed sets is closed.

As a consequence, the closed hull A_α can be defined as the intersection of all the closed sets $\geqq A$ (which in any case includes E); it has the following properties:

(a) $$0_\alpha = 0$$
(b) $$A_\alpha \geqq A$$
(c) $$A_{\alpha\alpha} = A_\alpha$$
(d) $$(A \dotplus B)_\alpha = A_\alpha \dotplus B_\alpha.$$

It would also be possible to make these properties our starting point (Kuratowski) by taking them as our axioms for the set function A_α, defining closed sets by means of $A_\alpha = A$, and proving in this way the theorems about closed sets; for example, (3) follows from the fact that because of (d), A_α is a monotone set function, that is, if $A < B$ then $A_\alpha \leqq B_\alpha$.

For the open sets, the corresponding theorems hold:

(1) The space E and the null set 0 are open.

(2) The intersection of two open sets is open.

(3) The sum of any number of open sets is open.

The sum of all the open sets $\leqq A$ is called the open kernel A_i and has properties (a), (b), (c), and (d) analogous to those of A_α. Of course, these properties also, or the theorems about open sets, could be taken as our axiomatic starting point. One modification of this is formed by the axioms about *neighborhoods.* If we denote by G_x the open sets containing x (including, of course, E) and select from them a subsystem U_x in such a way that every G_x contains a U_x, then these U_x are called neighborhoods of x, and the neighborhoods of all the points constitute a *complete system of neighborhoods* for the space E. In general, there will be many such systems possible; the largest of them consists of all the nonempty open sets; in metric spaces, the spherical neighborhoods $U_x(\varrho)$ with the positive radii ϱ, introduced in § 22, form such a system, and they do so even if we restrict ϱ to rational values or to the values 1, 1/2, 1/3, ... ; in separable spaces, the "special" neighborhoods V of § 25 form a complete system of neighborhoods; in locally connected spaces, there exists a complete system of connected neighborhoods. Two such complete systems, with the neighborhoods U_x and V_x, are related as follows: Every U_x contains some V_x, and every V_x contains some U_x. If the space E with the neighborhoods U_x is homeomorphic to $\bar{E}$, then the images of the U_x give rise to a complete system of neighborhoods for $\bar{E}$. From the theorems about open sets we derive the following properties of the neighborhoods:

(A) Every point x has at least one neighborhood U_x; and U_x always contains x.

(B) For any two neighborhoods U_x and V_x of the same point, there exists a third, $W_x \leqq U_x V_x$.

(C) Every point $y \varepsilon U_x$ has a neighborhood $U_y \leqq U_x$.

It is now again possible to treat neighborhoods as unexplained concepts and to use them as our starting point, postulating Theorems (A), (B), and (C) as *neighborhood axioms.*[1] Open sets G are then defined as sums of neighborhoods or as sets in which every point $x \varepsilon G$ has a neighborhood $U_x \leqq G$ (the null set included). Theorems (1), (2), and (3) about open sets are then provable.

Whether one form or another is preferred of the axioms discussed so far, the space defined by them is of course still very deficient in properties. We have not even seen to it thus far that sets consisting of one point (and consequently, by (2), sets consisting of any finite number of points)

---

[1] Such a program was carried through in the first edition of this book. [*Grundzüge der Mengenlehre.* (Leipzig, 1914; repr. New York, 1949).]

are closed. This can be achieved either by an axiom requiring just this or, better still, by imposing the following condition:

For two distinct points x and y there exists a closed set containing x but not y.

For, the closed hull of the set $\{x\}$ containing only one point is then this set itself.

In this condition, the word closed can also be replaced by open; it then goes over into the first of the following separation axioms.

II. SEPARATION AXIOMS.

(4) If $x_1 \neq x_2$, then there exists an open set G_1 containing x_1 but not x_2.

(5) If $x_1 \neq x_2$, then there exist two disjoint open sets G_1 and G_2 for which $x_1 \varepsilon G_1$ and $x_2 \varepsilon G_2$.

(6) If F_2 is a closed set not containing the point x_1, then there exist two disjoint open sets G_1 and G_2 for which $x_1 \varepsilon G_1$ and $F_2 \leqq G_2$.

(7) If F_1 and F_2 are two disjoint closed sets, then there exist two disjoint open sets G_1 and G_2 for which $F_1 \leqq G_1$ and $F_2 \leqq G_2$.

(8) If A_1 and A_2 are two disjoint sets closed in their sum, then there exist two disjoint open sets G_1 and G_2 for which $A_1 \leqq G_1$ and $A_2 \leqq G_2$.

Each of these axioms, retaining (4), is a strengthening of the preceding one, and in this way topological spaces of increasing specialization are obtained. In metric spaces the last separation axiom holds, and therefore so do all of them (compare p. 186; the proof also suffices for (8)).

III. AXIOMS ON CARDINALITY. Here we are concerned primarily (if the trivial finite spaces are excluded) with the relations to the countable; we express them by means of neighborhoods in the two *Axioms of Countability*.

(9) There exists a complete system of neighborhoods for which every point has at most a countable number of neighborhoods.

(10) There exists a countable complete system of neighborhoods.

The first is satisfied in every metric space, the second in every separable space.

The list of axioms we have given can of course be extended; but the axioms of Group I and at least one of the separation axioms are perhaps the least that can be required of a topological space if it is not to become

[1] First Axiom of Countability and Second Axiom of Countability are the commonly accepted terminology for (9) and (10), respectively.

altogether pathological. It is possible to base on the second separation axiom and on the "First Axiom of Countability," that is, on (1), (2), (3), (5), and (9) a theory close to the theory of metric spaces. But in order to metrize the space, the strongest separation axiom, and so at least (1), (2), (3), (8), and (9) are necessary; we mention here without proof that for homeomorphism to a separable metric space the validity of Axioms (1), (2), (3), (6), and (10) is both necessary *and sufficient.* (Urysohn's Theorem, somewhat sharpened by Tychonoff).

An interesting category of topological spaces has been defined by Fréchet; it is based on the concept of a convergent sequence or of a limit (limit point). To certain sequences $(x_1, x_2, \ldots)$ of points of the space E, there are to correspond uniquely defined points x of the space E; such a sequence is called *convergent* (to x), and the corresponding point $x = \lim x_n$ is called its limit. The following two *limit axioms* are required to hold:

(α) Every constant sequence $(x, x, x, \ldots)$ converges to x.

(β) Every subsequence of a sequence converging to x converges to x.

A space having such a definition of limit will be called an *L-space.*

If $A \leqq E$ and a sequence of points of A converges to x, then x will be called a limit point[1] of A; let the set of the limit points of A be called A_λ. Because of Axiom (α), we have $A_\lambda \geqq A$; the sets for which $A_\lambda = A$ are defined to be *closed.* Then Theorems (1), (2), and (3) concerning closed sets hold; this follows easily from the fact that A_λ is a monotone set function and that, because of (β), we obviously have $(A \dotplus B)_\lambda = A_\lambda \dotplus B_\lambda$. The closed hull A_α of A is then found, by § 30, 2, as the greatest set of the sequence $A^0, A^1, \ldots, A^\omega, \ldots$ defined inductively by

$$A^0 = A, \quad A^{\xi+1} = A^\xi_\lambda, \quad A^\eta = \mathfrak{S}_{\xi<\eta} A^\xi \qquad (\eta \text{ a limit number})$$

and which begins with $A, A_\lambda, A_{\lambda\lambda}, \ldots$; moreover, because of the same considerations as in the case of the Baire system of functions (p. 192) we have in any case $A_\alpha = A^\Omega$; that is, the greatest set $A_\alpha = A^\eta$ is already reached for some index $\eta \leqq \Omega$.

Incidentally, the *systems of functions* just referred to constitute the simplest example of L-space — an example that shows immediately that in general A_λ is not closed, as it is in metric spaces, and that the limit points constitute only some of the α-points that are obtained when the formation of limits is repeated without bound. Let the elements of E

[1] The limit points here, as we shall see at once, are not necessarily identical with the α-points (points of the closed hull) but constitute only a part of them.

('points') be the real functions $x = x(t)$ defined in a space T, and define convergence $x = \lim x_n$ by means of $x(t) = \lim x_n(t)$; that is, $x_n(t)$ is to converge – in the ordinary sense – to $x(t)$ everywhere, for $t \varepsilon T$. A set A, contained in E, is thus a system of functions, a closed set a Baire system of functions (p. 191 and § 43), and the closed hull the smallest Baire system over A. If now T is, for example, the set of real numbers, A the system of *continuous* functions x, A_λ that of the functions $y = \lim x_n$, $A_{\lambda\lambda}$ that of the functions $z = \lim y_n$, then $A_\lambda < A_{\lambda\lambda}$; for, as we shall see in § 42, the functions y still have points of continuity, whereas the functions z can already be everywhere discontinuous. The closed hull $A_\alpha = A^\eta$ is here reached only for $\eta = \Omega$. The metric counterpart should be kept in mind; if we make the system E of bounded functions into a ***metric*** space by means of the distance $xy = \sup | x(t) - y(t) |$, then $\lim x_n = x$ means the *uniform* convergence of $x_n(t)$ to $x(t)$ for all t; A_λ is then always closed, and

$$A_\lambda = A_{\lambda\lambda} = \cdots = A_\alpha.$$

Another departure of the L-spaces from the metric spaces is that even the second separation axiom may fail to hold (the first, (4), does hold, since the sets containing just one point are closed, because of Limit Axiom (α)). It may even be violated in a completely flagrant way. Let us call the space E *decomposable* if it can be represented as a sum $F_1 \dotplus F_2$ of two closed sets (properly) contained in E (if, in addition F_1 and F_2 are disjoint, then we have a partition, so that unconnected spaces are certainly decomposable and indecomposable ones certainly connected, although not conversely). In our theory we had no occasion to mention this concept because, apart from one-point spaces, which are, of course, indecomposable, every metric space is decomposable. As a matter of fact, every space in which the second separation axiom (5) holds is decomposable between any two of its points $x_1 \neq x_2$; that is, decomposable in such a way that x_1 belongs only to F_1 and not to F_2, and x_2 only to F_2 and not to F_1: one need only take F_1 and F_2 to be the complements ($F_1 = E - G_2$ and $F_2 = E - G_1$) of the open sets named in (5).

Since clearly the continuous image of an indecomposable space is itself indecomposable (just as that of a connected space was itself connected), then this image, in case it is a metric space, must consist of a single point: in particular, *in an indecomposable space every real continuous function is constant.* With the indecomposable spaces having this paradoxical nature, it is especially remarkable that an *L-space* (consisting of more than one point) *can be indecomposable,* as the following example shows.

Let E be the periphery of a circle, with a positive sense chosen for its rotations about the center; let the symbol φ denote a rotation through the fixed angle $2\pi\delta$, where δ is irrational; let the point x go into the point x_φ under this rotation and the set A, contained in E, into A_φ. We define as convergent, first, the constant sequences $(x, x, x, \ldots)$ having the limit x, second, the sequences consisting entirely of distinct points that converge in the ordinary sense — on the basis of the distances of elementary geometry — to a point x, and to these sequences we assign the limit x_φ. The two limit axioms are satisfied.

Then $A_\lambda = A \dot{+} (A')_\varphi$, where A' denotes the set of points of accumulation of A in the ordinary sense. We now claim that for $E = A \dot{+} B$ at least one of the equations $A_\alpha = E$ and $B_\alpha = E$ holds, which will show the indecomposability of E. If on each circular arc there are points of A, then $A' = E$ and $A_\lambda = E$ and, a fortiori, $A_\alpha = E$. If the opposite is the case, then B contains a circular arc C (including its endpoints). Then $C' = C, C_\lambda = C \dot{+} C_\varphi, C_{\lambda\lambda} = C \dot{+} C_\varphi \dot{+} C_{\varphi\varphi}$, etc., $C_\alpha \geqq C \dot{+} C_\varphi \dot{+} C_{\varphi\varphi} \dot{+} \ldots$, and this set is the whole periphery of the circle, for if x is the point half way along the arc C, then the set $\{x, x_\varphi, x_{\varphi\varphi}, \ldots\}$ is dense in E (in the ordinary sense). Thus $C_\alpha = E$ and $B_\alpha = E$.

CHAPTER IX

REAL FUNCTIONS

§ 41. Functions and Inverse Image Sets

1. Inverse image sets. Let a single-valued, real function $f(x)$ be defined in the space A (which, for the time being, may be a pure set and not a metric space), so that a real number $f(x)$ is made to correspond to every point $x \varepsilon A$. The set of points x at which $f(x) > y$ (y a given real number) will be denoted for brevity, as in § 22, by $[f > y]$; we define similarly sets such as $[f \geqq y]$, $[y < f < z]$, and so on. If B is the *set of values*, or *range*, of $f(x)$, that is, the set of numbers taken on by $f(x)$, then these sets are nothing but the inverse images of certain subsets of B, in the terminology of § 35. Since real functions can exhibit[1] different kinds of behavior "from above" and "from below" — e.g., they may be bounded from above and unbounded from below — it seems advisable to consider simultaneously the sets $[f > y]$ and $[f < y]$, say; in place of the latter, we prefer their complements and call the sets

$$[f > y] \text{ and } [f \geqq y]$$

the *inverse image sets* (or *Lebesgue sets*) belonging to the function f. But the two kinds of sets are related, for we have

$$(1) \quad \begin{cases} [f \geqq y] = \mathfrak{D}_n \left[f > y - \dfrac{1}{n}\right] \\ [f > y] = \mathfrak{S}_n \left[f \geqq y + \dfrac{1}{n}\right] \end{cases} \qquad (n = 1, 2, 3, \ldots).$$

A function determines its inverse image sets, but the converse is also true, and in fact we can see from (1) that the sets $[f > y]$ are themselves sufficient to determine f; for, having them, we then also know the sets $[f \geqq y]$ and, as differences, the sets $[f = y]$. Neither need all the sets $[f > y]$ be known, since further relations hold among them: for example, it suffices to know the sets $[f > r]$ for rational r, since

$$[f > y] = \mathfrak{S}_{r > y} [f > r].$$

[1] If, in addition, x is a real variable, then a further distinction has to be made as between left and right.

Among the sets $[f > r]$ there subsist, further, the relations

$$[f > r] = \mathfrak{S}_{\varrho > r} [f > \varrho], \quad A = \mathfrak{S}_{r} [f > r], \quad 0 = \mathfrak{D}_{r} [f > r],$$

and the reader can easily convince himself that a system of sets $M(r)$ satisfying these conditions really defines one (and only one) function f for which $[f > r] = M(r)$.

The interrelations between the properties of a function and those of its inverse image sets will be the principal subject of this chapter. We are already familiar with one result of this kind: If f is a continuous function, then every set $[f > y]$ is open (in A) and every set $[f \geqq y]$ is closed. The converse of this also holds: If all the sets $[f > y]$ and $[f < z]$ are open, then so are their intersections $[y < f < z]$ and, since every one-dimensional open set G is a sum of open intervals, the inverse image of BG is open and, by I of § 35, $f(x)$ is thus continuous (B is again the range (set of values) of f).

We now consider a system of functions f *all of which are defined in the same space* A.

Given two functions f_1 and f_2 we obtain, by considering at each point x the maximum and minimum of the two numbers $f_1(x)$ and $f_2(x)$, the two additional functions

$$\bar{f} = \max [f_1, f_2] \quad \text{and} \quad \underline{f} = \min [f_1, f_2].$$

Then we obviously have

$$(2) \qquad \begin{cases} [\bar{f} > y] = [f_1 > y] \dotplus [f_2 > y] \\ [\bar{f} \geqq y] = [f_1 \geqq y] \dotplus [f_2 \geqq y] \\ [\underline{f} > y] = [f_1 > y]\,[f_2 > y] \\ [\underline{f} \geqq y] = [f_1 \geqq y]\,[f_2 \geqq y]. \end{cases}$$

For the sum

$$f = f_1 + f_2$$

$f > y$ or $f_1 > y - f_2$ asserts the existence of a rational number r (which depends on the point x under consideration) satisfying $f_1 > r > y - f_2$, or $f_1 > r$ and $f_2 > y - r$, from which the first of the two formulas

$$(3) \qquad \begin{cases} [f > y] = \mathfrak{S}_{r} [f_1 > r]\,[f_2 > y - r] \\ [f \geqq y] = \mathfrak{D}_{r} [f_1 \geqq r] \dotplus [f_2 \geqq y - r] \end{cases}$$

is obtained; the second results from the corresponding treatment of $[f < y]$ and formation of complements.

In addition, let $f_1, f_2, \ldots$ be a *sequence of functions,* and let its *least upper bound* and *greatest lower bound* be

$$(4) \qquad \begin{cases} g = \sup\,[f_1, f_2, \ldots] = \sup f_n \\ h = \inf\,[f_1, f_2, \ldots] = \inf f_n \end{cases}$$

where, for every x, the sequence of the numbers $f_n(x)$ is, in the first case, bounded from above, and, in the second case, bounded from below. (We consider only finite functions and so exclude the improper values $\pm\infty$, which we can discuss separately whenever necessary.) Here we have

$$(5) \qquad \begin{cases} [g > y] = \mathfrak{S}_n\,[f_n > y] \\ [h \geqq y] = \mathfrak{D}_n\,[f_n \geqq y], \end{cases}$$

whereas the two middle formulas in (2) cannot be carried over to an infinite number of functions. (5) would seem to suggest that it is not unsuitable to denote the functions $\sup f_n$ by f_σ and the functions $\inf f_n$ by f_δ. The least upper bound $f_{\sigma\sigma}$ of a sequence of functions f_σ is itself an f_σ, for in place of

$$g = \sup_m g_m, \quad g_m = \sup_n f_{mn}$$

we can write

$$g = \sup_{mn} f_{mn} = \sup\,[f_{11}, f_{12}, f_{21}, \ldots]$$

with the double sequence transformed into a simple one; similarly, $f_{\delta\delta}$ is an f_δ.

The *upper limit* and the *lower limit* of a sequence, as is well known, are defined by:

$$(6) \qquad \begin{cases} \overline{\lim} f_n = \lim g_n, & g_n = \sup\,[f_n, f_{n+1}, f_{n+2}, \ldots] \\ \underline{\lim} f_n = \lim h_n, & h_n = \inf\,[f_n, f_{n+1}, f_{n+2}, \ldots]. \end{cases}$$

In the first case, f_n is to be assumed bounded from above, and g_n from below; in the second, f_n from below and h_n from above (these assumptions about boundedness will not always be repeated in future). We have $g_1 \geqq g_2 \geqq \ldots$ and $h_1 \leqq h_2 \leqq \ldots$, so that it is also possible to write

$$\overline{\lim} f_n = \inf g_n, \quad \underline{\lim} f_n = \sup h_n;$$

the g_n are functions f_σ, $\overline{\lim} f_n$ is thus an $f_{\sigma\delta}$ and, similarly, $\underline{\lim} f_n$ is an $f_{\delta\sigma}$. The limit function $\lim f_n$ of a convergent sequence is both at the same time.

In the case of uniform convergence, an essential simplification appears: *The limit function* $\lim f_n$ *of a uniformly convergent sequence is both an* f_σ *and an* f_δ, assuming that the functions f are taken from a system which contains $f +$ constant whenever it contains f. For if $|\varphi - f_n| \leqq \varepsilon_n$ and $\varepsilon_n \to 0$, then $\varphi = \inf (f_n + \varepsilon_n) = \sup (f_n - \varepsilon_n)$.

In order to put our statements about inverse image sets in convenient form, let us agree as follows: The sets M and N are to range over given systems of sets $\mathfrak{M}$ and $\mathfrak{N}$. If then $[f > y]$ is an M for every y, we say that *the function f is of the class* $(M, *)$. If $[f \geqq y]$ is always an N, then we say that f *is of the class* $(*, N)$. When both hold, we say f *is of the class* (M, N). For example, the continuous functions of the metric space A are of the class (G, F), where G ranges over the open sets of the space A and F over the closed sets, and vice versa. When, in particular, the N are the complements $A - M$ of the M, then the statements "f is of the class $(M, *)$" and "$-f$ is of the class $(*, N)$" have the same meaning.

Let us now assume that the M as well as the N form a *ring* (the sum and the intersection of two M is an M; the sum and the intersection of two N is an N). Then we can state the following theorems:

I. *If the functions f are of the class* $(M, *)$, *then*

max $[f_1, f_2]$ *and* min $[f_1, f_2]$ *are also of the class* $(M, *)$;

$f_\delta = \inf f_n$ *are of the class* $(*, M_\delta)$;

$f_\sigma = \sup f_n$ *and* $f_1 + f_2$ *are of the class* $(M_\sigma, *)$.

II. *If the functions f are of the class* $(*, N)$, *then*

max $[f_1, f_2]$ *and* min $[f_1, f_2]$ *are also of the class* $(*, N)$;

$f_\sigma = \sup f_n$ *are of the class* $(N_\sigma, *)$;

$f_\delta = \inf f_n$ *and* $f_1 + f_2$ *are of the class* $(*, N_\delta)$.

All these assertions follow immediately from (2), (3), and (5), although for the two middle ones we must also make use of (1). If the f are of the class $(M, *)$, then they are at the same time of the class $(*, M_\delta)$, and f_δ is of the class $(*, M_{\delta\delta}) = (*, M_\delta)$. If the f are of the class $(*, N)$, then they are also of the class $(N_\sigma, *)$, and f_σ is of the class $(N_{\sigma\sigma}, *) = (N_\sigma, *)$.

We shall call a system of functions f an *ordinary function system* if it satisfies the following axioms:

(α) *Every constant function is an f.*

(β) *The maximum and the minimum of two f is an f.*

(γ) *The sum, difference, product, and quotient* (with nowhere-vanishing denominator) *of two f is an f.*

Because of the identities

$$|f| = \max[f, -f]$$

$$\max_{\min}[f_1, f_2] = \tfrac{1}{2}(f_1 + f_2) \pm \tfrac{1}{2}|f_1 - f_2|$$

condition (β) can be replaced by: *The absolute value of every f is an f.*

An ordinary function system is called *complete* if it also satisfies the following postulate:

(δ) *The limit of a uniformly convergent sequence of functions f is an f.*

We then have the following theorem:

III. *Let the sets M, to which there belong the whole space and the null set, form a σ-ring,*[1] *their complements $N = A - M$ therefore forming a δ-ring. Then all the functions f of the class (M, N) form a complete system.*

For (α) is satisfied, since A and 0 are sets M and N; (β) holds because, by I and II, $\max[f_1, f_2]$ and $\min[f_1, f_2]$ are of the class (M, N). Next, f_σ and $f_1 + f_2$ are of the class $(M, *)$ and f_δ and $f_1 + f_2$ are of the class $(*, N)$, so that $f_1 + f_2$ and the uniform limit of functions f are of the class (M, N); (δ) is satisfied. That the difference of two f is also an f follows from the corresponding statement for the sum, since $-f$ is an f. The square of an f is an f; for, $[f^2 > y]$ is the whole space for $y < 0$, is the sum of the two sets $[f > \sqrt{y}]$ and $[f < -\sqrt{y}]$ for $y \geqq 0$, and is thus an M; in the same way, $[f^2 \geqq y]$ is an N. Therefore the product of two f,

$$f_1 f_2 = \left(\frac{f_1 + f_2}{2}\right)^2 - \left(\frac{f_1 - f_2}{2}\right)^2,$$

is an f. Provided $f \neq 0$, $1/f$ is an f; for $[1/f > y]$ is identical with $[0 < f < 1/y]$ for $y > 0$, the latter set being the intersection of two M; for $y = 0$, it is identical with $[f > 0]$; and for $y < 0$, with the sum of the sets $[f > 0]$ and $[f < 1/y]$. Thus $1/f$ and $-1/f$ are of the class $(M, *)$ and $1/f$ is of the class (M, N). The validity of (γ) is thus proved.

2. Extension of ordinary systems. Let f range over an ordinary function system. Next let f^* denote the limit of an (everywhere) convergent sequence of functions f, let g denote the particular case of an increasing sequence ($f_1 \leqq f_2 \leqq \ldots$), let h denote that of a decreasing sequence ($f_1 \geqq f_2 \geqq \ldots$), and let k denote a function which is both a g and an h. In the table

$$f \quad k \quad \begin{matrix} g \\ h \end{matrix} \quad f^*$$

every function is a special case of the one that follows to the right. Incidentally, this scheme is identical with the following one:

$$-f \quad -k \quad \begin{matrix} -h \\ -g \end{matrix} \quad -f^*.$$

From now on, of the two halves of the results concerning g and h, we shall most of the time prove only one.

Every g is an $f_\sigma = \sup f_n$, and also conversely, inasmuch as

[1] That is, a ring and a σ-system (every M_σ is an M).

$$\sup f_n = \lim \max [f_1, f_2, \ldots, f_n].$$

Included among the k (which are simultaneously f_δ and f_σ) are, in particular, the limits of uniformly convergent sequences f_n. The limit of uniformly convergent g_n, h_n, and k_n is a g, h, and k ($\lim g_n$ is a $g_\sigma = g$; $\lim h_n$ is an $h_\delta = h$).

The maximum, the minimum, and the sum of two g is a g. For if f_n and f'_n are increasing sequences that converge to g and g', then $\max [f_n, f'_n]$, $\min [f_n, f'_n]$, and $f_n + f'_n$ are increasing sequences that converge to $\max [g, g']$, $\min [g, g']$, and $g + g'$.

The maximum, the minimum, the sum, the difference, and the product of two f^* is each, of course, an f^*, and so is their quotient (with nowhere-vanishing denominator). It suffices to show that $1/\varphi$ is an f^* whenever $\varphi \neq 0$ is an f^*. If $\varphi > 0$ everywhere and $\varphi = \lim f_n$, then it is possible also to assume that $f_n > 0$ by replacing it by $\max [f_n, 1/n]$, which converges to $\max [\varphi, 0] = \varphi$, and then we have $\varphi = \lim 1/f_n$. If $\varphi \gtrless 0$, then $\frac{1}{\varphi} = \varphi \cdot \frac{1}{\varphi^2}$ is the product of two f^* and is thus an f^*.

The f^* therefore form an ordinary system, but over and above this we have:

IV. *The limit of a uniformly convergent sequence of functions f^* is an f^*; the f^* form a complete system.*

First, it should be noted that if $f^* = \lim f_n$ has absolute value $\leqq \varepsilon$, then we may assume that $|f_n| \leqq \varepsilon$; for $f'_n = \max [f_n, -\varepsilon]$ and $f''_n = \min [f'_n, \varepsilon]$ as well converge to f^*.

Now let F be the uniform limit of the functions $F_0, F_1, \ldots$ that are functions f^*; by restriction to a subsequence, it is possible to assume that F_m deviates from all the following F by at most ε_{m+1} ($m = 0, 1, 2, \ldots$) where $\varepsilon_1 + \varepsilon_2 + \ldots$ is a convergent series of positive numbers and, in consequence, to write

$$F - F_0 = (F_1 - F_0) + (F_2 - F_1) + \cdots$$

or

$$\varphi = \varphi_1 + \varphi_2 + \cdots,$$

where the φ_m ($m = 1, 2, \ldots$) are functions f^* of norm $\leqq \varepsilon_m$; it is to be shown that φ is an f^*. By what was said above, we can suppose that

$$\varphi_m = \lim_n f_{mn}, \quad |f_{mn}| \leqq \varepsilon_m.$$

But then

$$f_n = f_{1n} + f_{2n} + \cdots + f_{nn}$$

converges to φ, which proves our result. In fact, for $n > m$, the absolute value of

$$f_n - (f_{1n} + \cdots + f_{mn}) = f_{m+1,n} + \cdots + f_{nn}$$

is $\leqq \varepsilon_{m+1} + \cdots + \varepsilon_n < \delta_m$, if we set $\delta_m = \varepsilon_{m+1} + \varepsilon_{m+2} + \cdots$; from

$$f_{1n} + \cdots + f_{mn} - \delta_m < f_n < f_{1n} + \cdots + f_{mn} + \delta_m$$

it follows, for $n \to \infty$, that

$$\varphi_1 + \cdots + \varphi_m - \delta_m \leqq \underline{\lim}\, f_n \leqq \overline{\lim}\, f_n \leqq \varphi_1 + \cdots + \varphi_m + \delta_m$$

and from this, for $m \to \infty$, that

$$\lim f_n = \varphi_1 + \varphi_2 + \cdots = \varphi.$$

Now we denote the inverse image sets

	$[f > y]$	$[f \geqq y]$	$[g > y]$	$[h \geqq y]$	$[f^* > y]$	$[f^* \geqq y]$
by	M	N	P	Q	M^*	N^*,

so that M, for example, denotes all the sets appearing among the sets $[f > y]$ when f ranges over the system of functions under consideration and y over all the real numbers and where, moreover, y can be assumed to have a fixed value, say $y = 0$, since $f - y$ is also an f.

By definition, the functions f, g, h, k, and f^* are of the classes (M, N), $(P, *)$, $(*, Q)$, (P, Q), and (M^*, N^*). *It will be our task to invert these statements insofar as possible,* first expressing the P, Q, M^*, and N^* in terms of the M and the N.

The M and the N are complements of each other, as are the P and the Q, and also the M^* and the N^*. All six systems of sets are *rings*; the sum and the intersection of two P, for example, are themselves sets P, by (2), because the maximum and the minimum of two g is a g.

In addition, there follows from I and II:

V. *The sets P, Q, M^*, and N^* are sets M_σ, N_δ, Q_σ, and P_δ.*

For, $g = f_\sigma$ is of class $(M_\sigma, *)$, so that every P is an M_σ; f_σ is of the class $(P, *)$ so that $f_{\sigma\delta}$ is of the class $(*, P_\delta)$; the latter holds in particular for $\overline{\lim}\, f_n$ and a fortiori for f^*, so that every N^* is a P_δ. The other statements are proved in the same way.

We give four simple lemmas that will lead to the converse of V.

(A) *For every M, there exists an f that is positive in M and otherwise* (that is, in $A - M$) *vanishes.*

For there exists a function f for which $M = [f > 0]$; then $f' = \max[f, 0]$ satisfies the condition. Moreover $f'' = \min[f', \varepsilon]$ with $\varepsilon > 0$ serves the same purpose; that is, the function called for in (A) may be assumed in addition to be as small as we please $(0 \leqq f \leqq \varepsilon)$.

(B) *For every M_σ there exists a function F which is the limit of a uniformly convergent sequence of functions f and which, in addition, is positive in M_σ and otherwise vanishes.*

Let $M_\sigma = M_1 \dot{+} M_2 \dot{+} \ldots$, and let $\varepsilon_1 + \varepsilon_2 + \ldots$ be a convergent series of positive numbers; in accordance with (A) we determine a function f_n for which $0 \leqq f_n \leqq \varepsilon_n$ and which is positive in M_n and otherwise vanishes. Then

$$F = f_1 + f_2 + \ldots$$

is a function of the required kind.

(C) *For every M there exists a g which equals* 1 *in M and is otherwise* 0.

We choose f as in (A); then

$$g = \lim_n \frac{nf}{1+nf}, \qquad g = \lim_n \min\,[nf, 1],$$

say, are functions of the kind required.

(D) *For every M_σ there exists a g which is* 1 *in M_σ and is otherwise* 0.

If $M_\sigma = M_1 \dot{+} M_2 \dot{+} \ldots$, then let g_n be a function which, in accordance with (C), is 1 in M_n and is otherwise 0; then

$$g = \sup g_n$$

(which is also a g) is a function of the kind required.

Now we can form the converse of V.

VI. *The sets M_σ, N_δ, Q_σ, and P_δ are sets P, Q, M^*, and N^*.*

By (D), every $M_\sigma = [g > 0]$ is a P; and also, of course, every N_δ is a Q. But at the same time $M_\sigma = [g \geqq 1]$ is an N^* (since g is an f^*), and thus every P is an N^*, every Q an M^* and every Q_σ an M_σ^*. If we apply (B), not to the f but rather to the f^*, where the function F named in (B) is now, by IV, an f^*, then it follows that every $M_\sigma^* = [F > 0]$ is an M^*. Thus every Q_σ is an M^* and similarly every P_δ an N^*.

Thus the	P, Q, M^*, and N^*
are identical with the	M_σ, N_δ, Q_σ, and P_δ

or (eliminating the P and Q) the M^* and N^* are identical with the $N_{\delta\sigma}$ and the $M_{\sigma\delta}$; the transition from the f to the f^* induces the σ and δ process in the inverse image sets.

3. Inversion of the theorems on class. We now come to the principal result of the whole theory, namely:

VII. *The functions of the class (P, Q) are identical with the functions v that form the smallest complete system containing the system of the f.*

One half of the statement follows from III. The P form a ring which – because of postulate (α) for ordinary systems – contains the space A and the null set. In addition, because of their identity with the M_σ, they form a σ-system (P_σ is a P). The corresponding result holds for their complements $Q = A - P$. The functions of the class (P, Q) therefore constitute a complete system containing the system of the f; the smallest complete system of this kind must be contained in this system; that is, every function v is of the class (P, Q).

In order to show that, conversely, every function φ of the class (P, Q) is a v, we first prove the following: If $y_1 < y_2$, then there always exists a function v such that for

$$\varphi \leqq y_1, \quad y_1 < \varphi < y_2, \quad \varphi \geqq y_2$$

we have

$$v = 0, \quad 0 < v < 1, \quad v = 1.$$

For let $P_1 = [\varphi > y_1]$ and $P_2 = [\varphi < y_2]$. Corresponding to these sets $P = M_\sigma$ there exist, by Lemma (B), functions v_1 and v_2 (limits of uniformly convergent sequences f_n) that are positive in these sets and vanish in their complements $Q_1 = [\varphi \leqq y_1]$ and $Q_2 = [\varphi \geqq y_2]$. Since $Q_1 Q_2 = 0$, the v_1 and v_2 do not vanish simultaneously, we have $v_1 + v_2 > 0$, and the function $v = v_1/(v_1 + v_2)$ satisfies the required conditions.[1] In fact, in the three sets above we have

Q_1P_2	P_1P_2	P_1Q_2
$v_1 = 0$	$v_1 > 0$	$v_1 > 0$
$v_2 > 0$	$v_2 > 0$	$v_2 = 0$
$v = 0$	$0 < v < 1$	$v = 1$.

If, for the time being, φ is now *bounded* – say, $0 \leqq \varphi \leqq 1$ – then we choose a natural number n, as large as we wish, determine a function v_m for $m = 1, 2, \ldots, n$, such that for

$$\varphi \leqq \frac{m-1}{n}, \quad \frac{m-1}{n} < \varphi < \frac{m}{n}, \quad \varphi \geqq \frac{m}{n}$$

$$v_m = 0, \qquad 0 < v_m < 1, \qquad v_m = 1$$

and set $v = (v_1 + \ldots + v_n)/n$. (The meaning of v_1, v_2, and v differs from that above.) If, at some point x, we find $(m-1)/n \leqq \varphi \leqq m/n$, then we have

$$v_1 = \cdots = v_{m-1} = 1, \quad 0 \leqq v_m \leqq 1, \quad v_{m+1} = \cdots = v_n = 0$$

[1] v need no longer be the uniform limit of functions f but belongs to the smallest complete system generated by the f.

at that point, so that $(m-1)/n \leqq v \leqq m/n$, and therefore $|\varphi - v| \leqq 1/n$ everywhere. Therefore it is possible to approximate φ uniformly by some v, so that φ must itself be a v.

If Φ is of the class (P, Q) but is not bounded, then

$$\varphi = \frac{\Phi}{1+|\Phi|} \tag{7}$$

is bounded $(-1 < \varphi < 1)$ and is of the same class. For

$$y = \frac{Y}{1+|Y|}, \quad Y = \frac{y}{1-|y|}$$

is a similarity mapping of the open interval $-1 < y < 1$ onto the set of all the real numbers Y (in the ordinal sense, so that it is a continuous and monotone mapping). Every set $[\varphi > y]$ is, for $-1 < y < 1$, a set $[\Phi > Y]$, and conversely; the former also contains, for $y \leqq -1$ and $y \geqq 1$, the whole space and the null set, which — as already remarked — are also sets P. Thus φ is of the class $(P, *)$ whenever Φ is of this class, and conversely; the same holds for $(*, Q)$. Therefore, once again, φ is a v, and consequently

$$\Phi = \frac{\varphi}{1-|\varphi|} \tag{8}$$

is also a v, and Theorem VII is proved. This "bounding" transformation, the replacing of the unbounded function Φ by the bounded function φ, will be made use of later on also.

VIII. *If the functions f form a complete system, then the M form a σ-ring and the N a δ-ring, and the functions of the class (M, N) are identical with the f.*

For, Lemma (B), where F is now an f, shows that every M_σ is an M. The P and Q then become identical with the M and N, the functions v with the f, and the balance of the result follows from VII.

Theorem VIII, is, at the same time, the converse of III.

By IV, the hypothesis of completeness certainly holds for the f^*, and therefore:

IX. *The functions of the class (M^*, N^*) are identical with the f^*.*

Let us now look for the converse to the fact that every g is of the class $(P, *)$. By definition, for every g there exists a $f \leqq g$ — a *minorant* f. Conversely, we have:

X. *Every function of the class $(P, *)$ that has a minorant f is a g.*

Let φ be of the class $(P, *)$ and $\varphi \geqq f$ or, if we write $1-f$ in place of f, $\varphi + f > 0$. $\varphi + f$ is also of the class $(P, *)$, as follows from (3) with $P = M_\sigma$, and so — altering our notation slightly — we can assume that $\varphi > 0$. For some $\delta > 0$ and $n = 1, 2, \ldots$, noting that the set $[\varphi > n\delta]$ is a $P = M_\sigma$, we look for a g_n that, by Lemma (D), is 1 in this set and is 0 otherwise. The everywhere-convergent series

$$g = \delta(g_1 + g_2 + \ldots),$$

whose elements in fact ultimately vanish for every x, represents a g, since it is the limit of increasing g. If at some point

$$(n-1)\delta < \varphi \leqq n\delta,$$

then at that point

$$g_1 = \cdots = g_{n-1} = 1, \quad g_n = g_{n+1} = \cdots = 0, \quad g = (n-1)\delta$$

and therefore the relation

$$0 < \varphi - g \leqq \delta$$

holds everywhere. Thus φ can be uniformly approximated by functions g and is itself a g.

XI. *Every function of the class $(P, *)$ is the limit of an increasing sequence of functions v of the class (P, Q).*

For a bounded function, this is contained in X. If Φ is unbounded and of the class $(P, *)$, then once more we make the "bounding" transformation (7); φ is of the class $(P, *)$ and is bounded $(-1 < \varphi < 1)$, and it is therefore a g; $\varphi = \lim f_n$ with $f_1 \leqq f_2 \leqq \ldots$, where we may assume $-1 \leqq f_n \leqq \varphi < 1$ by replacing f_n by max $[f_n, -1]$. To return to Φ however, we must have, instead of the functions f_n, functions that do not attain the lower bound -1. If we set

$$v_n = \tfrac{1}{2} f_n + \tfrac{1}{4} f_{n+1} + \tfrac{1}{8} f_{n+2} + \cdots,$$

then this function, as the sum of a uniformly convergent series of functions f, is a v (and even a k). Obviously $f_n \leqq v_n \leqq v_{n+1} \leqq \varphi$, and v_n is an increasing sequence converging to φ. In $v_n \geqq f_n$, the equality can hold only if $f_n = f_{n+1} = f_{n+2} = \cdots$, so that $v_n = \varphi > -1$; otherwise $v_n > f_n \geqq -1$. Therefore since $-1 < v_n < 1$ always holds, we can form the functions

$$V_n = \frac{v_n}{1 - |v_n|}$$

which, once more, are functions v and converge from below to $\dfrac{\varphi}{1-|\varphi|} = \Phi$.

The corresponding theorems hold for the functions of the class $(*, Q)$; if they have a majorant f, they are functions h, and, in any case, they are limits of decreasing sequences of functions v. Every function f that lies entirely between two functions v of the class (P, Q) is both a function g and a function h, and is thus a function k. Since, in particular, every bounded function v is a k, it follows from the bounding transformation that every function v can be represented in the form $\frac{k}{1-|k|}$ with $|k| < 1$. In this representation, moreover, $|k| = \max[k, -k]$, as the maximum of two k, is itself a k, and the same is true of $1 - |k|$; that is, *the functions v can be represented as quotients of two k.* Conversely, every quotient of two k, as the quotient of two v, is itself a v.

If the system of the f is complete, then it follows from XI that every function of the class $(M, *)$ is a g. We summarize here all the simplifications that occur in this case:

XII. *If the f form a complete system, then the f, g, h, and f^* are identical with the functions of the classes (M, N), $(M, *)$, $(*, N)$, and (N_σ, M_δ), respectively.*

Here the k and v are identical with the f and the sets P, Q, M^*, and N^* with the sets M, N, N_σ, and M_δ.

If the f form merely an ordinary system, then XII is applicable to the v: the v, v_σ, v_δ, and v^* are identical with the functions of the classes (P, Q), $(P, *)$, $(*, Q)$, and (Q_σ, P_δ). The f^* here are, by IX, identical with the v^*, while the f, g, and h (or the f, f_σ and f_δ) constitute only some of the v, v_σ and v_δ; the g are identical with those v_σ that have a minorant f; the h, with those v_δ that have a majorant f; and the k (of which, again, the f constitute only a subclass), with those v that lie between two f.

We suggest that the reader now review the discussion up to this point, keeping in mind some simple example like the following: Let the f be the functions that take on only a finite number of values; then the g are the functions that are bounded from below, the h those bounded from above, the k those bounded from both above and below, and the v and f^* the completely arbitrary functions. That every function bounded from below, say $\varphi \geqq 0$, is in fact a g — the converse is trivial — is seen as follows: In the set $R_n = \left\{\frac{0}{n}, \frac{1}{n}, \frac{2}{n}, \ldots, \frac{n^2-1}{n}, \frac{n^2}{n}\right\}$ let $f_n(x)$ be the greatest number $\leqq \varphi(x)$; f_n is an f and converges to φ since, for $n > \varphi$, we have $f_n \leqq \varphi < f_n + 1/n$. Since $R_n < R_{2n}$, $f_n \leqq f_{2n}$; the functions $f_1, f_2, f_4, f_8, \ldots$ converge to φ from below. The rest is easy to see. The sets M and N are already the arbitrary subsets of A, and all the more is this true of

P, Q, M^*, and N^*. After this, it is advisable to follow through the converses of the theorems on classes – for example, that not every function of the class (M, N) is an f, or that the restriction, in X, that the function under consideration have a minorant (i.e., is to be bounded from below) cannot be dispensed with.

4. Interposition and Extension Theorem.

XIII. (Interposition Theorem). *If g is a function g, h a function h, and $g \geqq h$ everywhere, then there exists a function k for which $g \geqq k \geqq h$.*

For brevity, we set

$$\{t\} = \max\,[t, 0] = \tfrac{1}{2}\,|\,t\,| + \tfrac{1}{2}\,t \tag{9}$$

for real t; this is a continuous function of t which is non-negative and which increases (more exactly: does not decrease) with increasing t. We now make the following analysis, which we shall have occasion to revert to later (in the proof of XVI). Let

$$\varphi = \lim \varphi_n, \quad \varphi_1 \leqq \varphi_2 \leqq \cdots,$$
$$\psi = \lim \psi_n, \quad \psi_1 \geqq \psi_2 \geqq \cdots,$$

and $\varphi \geqq \psi$. Then

$$\psi_1 - \varphi_1 \geqq \psi_1 - \varphi_2 \geqq \psi_2 - \varphi_2 \geqq \psi_2 - \varphi_3 \geqq \cdots, \tag{10}$$

so that, in addition,

$$\{\psi_1 - \varphi_1\} \geqq \{\psi_1 - \varphi_2\} \geqq \{\psi_2 - \varphi_2\} \geqq \{\psi_2 - \varphi_3\} \geqq \cdots,$$

and these functions converge to $\{\psi - \varphi\} = 0$. The alternating series

$$\omega = \varphi_1 + \{\psi_1 - \varphi_1\} - \{\psi_1 - \varphi_2\} + \{\psi_2 - \varphi_2\} - \{\psi_2 - \varphi_3\} + \cdots \tag{11}$$

therefore converges everywhere. We claim that $\varphi \geqq \omega \geqq \psi$. Let us distinguish between the points for which $\varphi = \psi$ and $\varphi > \psi$. If $\varphi = \psi$, then all the members of the sequence (10) are $\geqq 0$, the braces may be removed, and we have

$$\begin{aligned}\omega &= \varphi_1 + (\psi_1 - \varphi_1) - (\psi_1 - \varphi_2) + (\psi_2 - \varphi_2) - (\psi_2 - \varphi_3) + \cdots \\ &= \lim \varphi_n = \lim \psi_n = \varphi = \psi.\end{aligned}$$

If $\varphi > \psi$, then the terms in (10) ultimately become negative. If the first negative term is $\psi_n - \varphi_n$, so that $\varphi \geqq \varphi_n > \psi_n \geqq \psi$, then

$$\omega = \varphi_1 + (\psi_1 - \varphi_1) - \cdots - (\psi_{n-1} - \varphi_n) = \varphi_n, \ \varphi \geqq \omega > \psi.$$

If the first negative term is $\psi_n - \varphi_{n+1}$, so that $\varphi \geqq \varphi_{n+1} > \psi_n \geqq \psi$, then

$$\omega = \varphi_1 + (\psi_1 - \varphi_1) - \cdots + (\psi_n - \varphi_n) = \psi_n, \ \varphi > \omega \geqq \psi.$$

Now, in order to prove XIII, let $\varphi = g$ and $\psi = h$; let the functions

φ_n and ψ_n be functions f. The individual terms and the partial sums of series ω are also functions f; since the partial sums with an odd number of terms form an increasing sequence while those with an even number of terms form a decreasing sequence, ω is both a g and an h and is thus a k.

In the following theorem we are concerned with the question of "extending" a function φ defined in the set $B < A$ to a function ψ defined in A (which of course means that $\psi = \varphi$ in B). We say that φ is of the class $(M, *)$ if every set $[\varphi > y]$ is the intersection of B with an M; and correspondingly for the classes $(*, N)$ and (M, N).

XIV. (EXTENSION THEOREM). *If Q_0 is a set Q, then a function of the class (P, Q) defined in Q_0 can be extended to a function of the class (P, Q) defined in the whole space A; that is, it can be extended to a function v.*

Let $P_0 = A - Q_0$; let φ be defined in Q_0, let it be of the class (P, Q), and let it, for the time being, be bounded – say, $-1 \leqq \varphi \leqq 1$. We define the function h by:

$$h = \varphi \text{ in } Q_0, \quad h = -1 \text{ in } P_0,$$

and we claim that this is an h. For it is of the class $(*, Q)$ since, for $y > -1$, $[h \geqq y]$ coincides with $[\varphi \geqq y]$ (which is a $Q_0 Q$ and thus a Q) and, for $y \leqq -1$, is the whole space; furthermore, h is bounded and therefore, by X, is an h. In the same way, we conclude that the function g,

$$g = \varphi \text{ in } Q_0, \quad g = 1 \text{ in } P_0,$$

is a g ($-g$ is an h). Since $g \geqq h$, a function k can be interposed between them, $g \geqq k \geqq h$; in Q_0, $k = \varphi$; φ can, in particular, be extended here to a k.

We now wish to show that for $|\varphi| < 1$ we can also make $|k| < 1$. If we determine k as we did just now, then $|k| \leqq 1$; the equality can hold only at points of P_0. Now, using Lemma (B), we determine for P_0, which is an M_σ, a function k_0 (also a k) which is positive in P_0 and vanishes in Q_0. The function $v = k/(1 + k_0)$ is certainly a v (by virtue of its boundedness it is still a k, however); in Q_0 we have $v = k = \varphi$, in P_0 $|v| < |k|$ or $v = 0$, and thus, everywhere, $|v| < 1$.

If, finally, Φ is defined in Q_0, is of the class (P, Q), and is not bounded, then we make the bounding transformation (7). The previous assumptions apply to φ; it can be extended to a v for which $|v| < 1$; and Φ can be extended to $V = v/(1 - |v|)$, that is, to a function v.

5. Absolute convergence. The functions f^* can be represented as sums of convergent *series* of functions f:

$$f^* = \lim f_n = f_1 + (f_2 - f_1) + (f_3 - f_2) + \cdots = \varphi_1 + \varphi_2 + \varphi_3 + \cdots.$$

If we require *absolute convergence* here rather than simple convergence (that is, $|\varphi_1| + |\varphi_2| + \cdots$ is to converge everywhere), then we obtain only some of the functions f^*; we denote these functions by d. *They, also, constitute an ordinary system.* For, to begin with, the sum, difference, and product of two d is itself a d Next, the absolute value $|d|$ of a d is a d, for by virtue of $||\beta| - |\alpha|| \leqq |\beta - \alpha|$ the series obtained from the absolutely convergent series $f_1 + (f_2 - f_1) + \ldots$ by interchanging f_n with $|f_n|$ is absolutely convergent when $f_1 + (f_2 - f_1) + \ldots$ is absolutely convergent. It remains only to prove that $1/d$, with $d \neq 0$, is also a d. First, let $d = \lim f_n > 0$; if f'_n is set equal to max $[f_n, 1/n]$, which is a function that also converges to d, then we obtain the estimate $|f'_{n+1} - f'_n| \leqq |f_{n+1} - f_n| + (1/n - 1/(n+1))$ most easily from the obvious inequality

$$\max[\alpha_1, \beta_1] - \max[\alpha, \beta] \leqq \max[\alpha_1 - \alpha, \beta_1 - \beta] \\ \leqq |\alpha_1 - \alpha| + |\beta_1 - \beta|;$$

f_n can therefore be replaced by f'_n, or f_n may be taken > 0 to begin with. For $1/d = \lim 1/f_n$, and $\dfrac{1}{f_{n+1}} - \dfrac{1}{f_n} = \dfrac{f_n - f_{n+1}}{f_n f_{n+1}}$ is the general term of an absolutely convergent series whenever this is true of $f_{n+1} - f_n$; $1/d$ is a d. If, finally $d \gtrless 0$, then $\dfrac{1}{d} = d \cdot \dfrac{1}{d^2}$, as the product of two d, is itself a d.

From the decomposition

$$t = \frac{|t| + t}{2} - \frac{|t| - t}{2} = \{t\} - \{-t\}$$

it follows that, in the case of absolute convergence,

$$d = \Sigma\varphi_n = \Sigma\{\varphi_n\} - \Sigma\{-\varphi_n\}$$

is the difference of two convergent series with terms $\geqq 0$; that is, every function d can be represented as the *difference* $g - g'$ *of two functions* g, in place of which it is also possible to set $h - h'$ or $g + h$ (with $g = -h'$ and $g' = -h$) — the difference of two functions h or the sum of a g and an h. (Whereas $g - h = g + g'$ is again a g and $h - g = h + h'$ again an h.) Conversely, it is clear that the functions g and h and their sums and differences are functions d. With the restriction to absolute convergence, the f thus give rise to the functions

$$(12) \qquad d = g - g' = h - h' = g + h.$$

Let us call any function whose range is *isolated* a *step function*. Then we have:

XV. *Every function f^* which is also a step function is a function d.*

We preface the proof by the following remark. If we denote by R those sets that are both M^* and N^*, then every function φ which is a step function f^* is of the class (R, R).

For the set $[\varphi > y]$ is identical with $[\varphi \geqq y]$ if φ does not take on the value y; and otherwise, for sufficiently small $\delta > 0$, it is identical with $[\varphi \geqq y + \delta]$; similarly, the set $[\varphi \geqq y]$ is identical with $[\varphi > y]$ or with $[\varphi > y - \delta]$; both sets are M^* and N^* at one and the same time. The sets R obviously form a field. For every function of the class (R, R), the sets $[\varphi = y]$ are sets R as well.

Now let φ be a step function f^* or, more generally, a function of the class (R, R) with a range consisting of at most a countable number of values; let $c_1, c_2, \ldots$ be the various values taken on by φ. The sets $[\varphi = c_m]$ are sets R and, in particular, sets $M^* = Q_\sigma$, and they can therefore be represented with increasing summands Q as follows:

$$\begin{aligned}[\varphi = c_m] &= Q_{m1} \dot{+} Q_{m2} \dot{+} Q_{m3} \dot{+} \cdots \\ &= Q_{m1} + (Q_{m2} - Q_{m1}) + (Q_{m3} - Q_{m2}) + \cdots \\ &= D_{m1} + D_{m2} + D_{m3} + \cdots.\end{aligned}$$

We now set $c_m = a_m - b_m$, where the positive numbers a_m and b_m increase without bound together with m, for example,

$$a_m = \tfrac{1}{2}\,|\,c_m\,| + \tfrac{1}{2}\,c_m + m, \quad b_m = \tfrac{1}{2}\,|\,c_m\,| - \tfrac{1}{2}\,c_m + m$$

and define the functions g and g' by means of

$$g(x) = a_m + n, \quad g'(x) = b_m + n \ \text{ for } x \,\varepsilon\, D_{mn},$$

so that $\varphi = g - g'$ everywhere. But these functions are functions g. For if y is given, then the inequality $g \leqq y$ can hold for only a finite number of m $(a_m \leqq y - 1)$ and then for only a finite number of $n \leqq y - a_m$; therefore, if n_m denotes the greatest integer $\leqq y - a_m$,

$$[g \leqq y] = \sum_{a_m \leqq y-1} \sum_{n \leqq n_m} D_{mn} = \sum_{a_m \leqq y-1} Q_{m n_m}$$

is the sum of a finite number of Q and is thus itself a Q (or 0, if no $a_m \leqq y - 1$ exists). g is thus of the class $(P, *)$ and is > 0 and therefore, by X, is a function g; the same is true for g', so that XV is proved.

The functions g, h, and d can be approximated as close as we please by means of step functions of the same kind. Let g be a function g, and let $\delta > 0$ and $m = 0, \pm 1, \pm 2, \ldots$; the set $[g > m\delta] = P_m$ is a P. We define the function g_0 to be equal to $m\delta$ in the set $P_{m-1} - P_m = [(m-1)\,\delta < g \leqq m\delta]$. We see at once that every set $[g_0 > y]$ is a P_m, so that g_0 is of the class $(P, *)$; since g has a minorant f, so does $g_0 \geqq g$, and g_0 is a g (Theorem X). Furthermore, $0 \leqq g_0 - g < \delta$, and g_0 is a special step function taking on only the values $m\delta$. By means of step functions h_0 and $d_0 = g_0 + h_0$ of the same kind, we can approximate the functions h and $d = g + h$.

On the other hand, the general functions f^* can be approximated by functions d. For another interposition theorem holds:

XVI. *If φ and ψ are two functions f^*, and $\varphi > \psi$ everywhere, then there exists a function $\omega = d$ for which $\varphi \geqq \omega \geqq \psi$.*

We can refer back to the proof of XIII. By (6), every f^* can be represented as a limit of decreasing g or increasing h; let us therefore take the functions ψ_n of the above proof to be functions g and the φ_n to be functions h. The functions (10) are again functions g and retain this property upon being enclosed in braces, since max $[g, 0]$ is a g. Because this time we made the stronger assumption $\varphi > \psi$ (rather than $\varphi \geqq \psi$), the terms of the sequence (10) ultimately become negative at every point and those of the series (11) ultimately become 0; therefore both of the series

$$g = \{\psi_1 - \varphi_1\} + \{\psi_2 - \varphi_2\} + \cdots$$

and

$$g' = -\varphi_1 + \{\psi_1 - \varphi_2\} + \{\psi_2 - \varphi_3\} + \cdots$$

converge and, as limit functions of increasing g, represent functions g; then we have $\omega = g - g'$ and $\varphi \geqq \omega \geqq \psi$, proving the theorem.

If we apply it, in particular, to the case $\psi = \varphi - \delta$ ($\delta > 0$ constant), then it follows that *every function f^* can be approximated by functions d, and therefore also by step functions d, as closely as we please.* It can therefore also be represented by an *absolutely convergent* series with terms d; that is, restricting ourselves to absolute convergence, we reach the f^* from the f in two steps, with the d intermediate between the two.

§ 42. Functions of the First Class

1. Introduction. We assume the space A to be metric and identify the functions f of the preceding paragraph with the *continuous* functions; since they constitute a complete system — the limit of a uniformly convergent sequence of continuous functions is itself continuous — Theorem XII above is applicable. The M are identical with the *open* sets G of the space and the N with the *closed* sets F (§ 22, I and II). Therefore:

I. *The continuous functions f and the limit functions g, h, and f^* of increasing, decreasing, and convergent sequences of continuous functions are identical with the functions of the classes (G, F), $(G, *)$, $(*, F)$, and (F_σ, G_δ), respectively.*

The f^* are called *functions of the first* (Baire) *class*, and in § 43 this will be extended to higher classes. The functions of the classes $(G, *)$, $(*, F)$ are called *semi-continuous* and, specifically, those of the class $(G, *)$ *lower semi-continuous* and those of the class $(*, F)$ *upper semi-continuous*. The significance of these names will be made clear shortly. In view of the fact that the sets P and Q coincide here with the M and N and the functions k with the f, the Interposition and the Extension Theorems take on the following forms:

II. *If g is lower semi-continuous, h upper semicontinuous, and $g \geqq h$ everywhere, then there exists a continuous function f for which $g \geqq f \geqq h$.*

III. *A continuous function defined in the closed set F can be extended to a function continuous in the whole space A.*

The names "upper semi-continuous" and "lower semi-continuous" derive from the fact that the conditions for continuity are here split into two parts. A function $f(x)$ is continuous at the point a if, for every $\sigma > 0$, there exists a neighborhood U_a for whose points $x \varepsilon U_a$

$$| f(x) - f(a) | < \sigma.$$

If, for every $\sigma > 0$, a neighborhood U_a exists in which

$$f(x) - f(a) < \sigma,$$

then $f(x)$ is said to be *upper semi-continuous* at the point a; if there is always one in which

$$f(x) - f(a) > -\sigma,$$

then $f(x)$ is said to be *lower semi-continuous* at a. To make this more intuitive, we remark that, e.g. an upper (lower) semi-continuous function can be obtained from a continuous function by increasing (decreasing) the functional value $f(a)$ alone, without alteration of the neighboring values $f(x)$. If $f(a) = \pm 1$ and if $f(x) = 0$ everywhere else, then $f(x)$ is $\left\{\begin{matrix}\text{upper}\\ \text{lower}\end{matrix}\right.$ semi-continuous at the point a. If $f(x)$ is upper semi-continuous, then $-f(x)$ is lower semi-continuous.

If $f(x)$ is lower semi-continuous at the point a, then a is an interior point of every set $[f > y]$ to which it belongs, and vice versa. For if $f(a) > y$ and if we choose $0 < \sigma < f(a) - y$, then in a certain neighborhood U_a, $f(x)$ is still $> f(a) - \sigma > y$, so that a is an interior point of $[f > y]$. If, conversely, this condition is met, then for every $\sigma > 0$ a is an interior point of $[f > f(a) - \sigma]$, and there exists a neighborhood U_a in which $f(x) > f(a) - \sigma$; and $f(x)$ is lower semi-continuous at a. From this it follows that, for $f(x)$ to be lower semi-continuous at every point, it is necessary and sufficient that every set $[f > y]$ be open. And for an upper semi-continuous function f, that is, for a lower semi-continuous function $-f$, it is necessary and sufficient that $[f < y]$ be open and $[f \geqq y]$ closed. The reason for the nomenclature "lower semi-continuous" and "upper semi-continuous" for functions of the classes $(G, *)$, $(*, F)$ is thus made clear. These functions were introduced by Baire, who was also the first to prove that every lower semi-continuous function is the limit of an increasing sequence of continuous functions or, in our notation, that every function of the class $(G, *)$ is a g. The converse, that every g is of the class $(G, *)$, moreover, holds here in a much wider sense than is ordinarily the case; the least upper bound not only of a countable number but of an *arbitrary* number of continuous or lower semi-continuous functions

$$g = \sup g_n$$

remains lower semi-continuous, since

$$[g > y] = \mathfrak{S}[g_n > y],$$

as a sum of open sets, is itself open (of course, the $g_n(x)$ are supposed to be bounded from above at every point x). Consider, for example, the lower semi-continuous minorants $g \leqq \varphi$ belonging to an arbitrary function φ; if such functions exist at all, then there is one among them that is the greatest, namely the least upper bound of all of them. Corresponding results hold for upper semi-continuous functions.

One might perhaps wish to see Theorem I supplemented by a method of construction in accordance with which the functions of the classes $(G, *)$, $(*, F)$, and (F_σ, G_δ) can actually be represented as the limit functions of increasing, decreasing, and convergent sequences of continuous functions. Such methods of construction, valid for the general case of an arbitrary initial function f, are of course, already implicit in the proofs of the converses of the theorems on classes (§ 41, 3); there remains, however, the possibility that they here can be simplified. For the Baire Theorem, that a lower semi-continuous function φ is a limit of an increasing sequence of continuous functions, it is in fact possible to give an exceedingly simple proof, at least when φ is bounded from below — say $\varphi \geqq 0$. Let t be a positive number and

$$f(x) = \inf_z [\varphi(z) + t \cdot xz],$$

where the greatest lower bound is taken for all points z of the space;

obviously $0 \leqq f \leqq \varphi$ ($f(x) \leqq \varphi(x)$ is obtained by choosing $z = x$). For two points x and y of the space,

$$\varphi(z) + t \cdot xz \leqq \varphi(z) + t \cdot yz + t \cdot xy,$$

and thus, taking the greatest lower bound with respect to z,

$$f(x) \leqq f(y) + t \cdot xy$$

or, interchanging the two points, $| f(x) - f(y) | \leqq t \cdot xy$; the function f is therefore continuous. If we now let t range over all the natural numbers, the functions

$$f_n(x) = \inf_z [\varphi(z) + n \cdot xz]$$

form an increasing sequence for which $f_n \leqq \varphi$, and thus $g = \lim f_n \leqq \varphi$; we show that also $g \geqq \varphi$, so that $g = \varphi$. For preassigned $\sigma > 0$, let us choose the point z_n so that

$$f_n(x) > \varphi(z_n) + n \cdot x z_n - \sigma$$

holds; then (since $\varphi \geqq f_n$, $\varphi \geqq 0$), $\varphi(x) > n \cdot x z_n - \sigma$, so that $xz_n \to 0$; But since φ is lower semi-continuous, we finally have

$$\varphi(z_n) > \varphi(x) - \sigma, \quad f_n(x) > \varphi(x) - 2\sigma,$$

so that $g(x) \geqq \varphi(x)$.

2. Examples of functions of the first class. Immediately after the lower semi-continuous functions g and the upper semi-continuous functions h, the functions

$$d = g + h = g - g' = h - h'$$

– which we discussed in some generality in § 41, 5 – are worthy of our attention; they arise from the summation of absolutely convergent series of continuous functions. Every function of the first class can be approximated with arbitrary closeness by functions d and, in particular, by step functions d.

Every function with at most a countable number of points of discontinuity is of the first class. Let C be the set of the points of continuity of f and D the set of the points of discontinuity[1] of f; let M be the set $[f > y]$. If now $x \in MC$, then the inequality $f > y$ still holds in a certain neighborhood of x, and thus $MC \leq M_i$ and $MD \geqq M_b$. If D is at most countable, then so is M_b, and $M = M_i + M_b$ is composed of an open set

[1] We now drop the requirement that the letter f shall always stand for a continuous function.

and an at most countable set and is thus an F_σ. Since the same is true for $[f < y]$, f is of the class (F_σ, G_δ).

Worthy of special mention among the functions of the first class of a real variable x are, on the one hand the derivatives $\varphi'(x) = \lim n[\varphi(x + 1/n) - \varphi(x)]$ of differentiable functions and, on the other hand, the functions $f(x)$ for which the left-hand and right-hand limiting values $f(x + 0)$ and $f(x - 0)$ exist at all points (and so, in particular, the monotone functions and their sums and differences: the functions of bounded variation). As a little reflection will show, these functions with one-sided limiting values have at most a countable number of points of discontinuity and are thus indeed functions of the first class; moreover, they are even functions d. For since $f(x + 0)$, as a function of x, has the same one-sided limiting values as $f(x)$, and $\max[f(x), g(x)]$ has the right-hand limiting value $\max[f(x + 0), g(x + 0)]$, we have for the function

$$\varphi(x) = \max[f(x), \quad f(x + 0), \quad f(x - 0)]$$

that $\varphi(x \pm 0) = f(x \pm 0) \leqq \varphi(x)$, and $\varphi(x)$ is upper semi-continuous; similarly,

$$\psi(x) = \min[f(x), \quad f(x + 0), \quad f(x - 0)]$$

is lower semi-continuous; $\varphi + \psi$ is a function d. If in this $f(x)$ is replaced by

$$f(x + 0), \quad f(x + 0) - f(x), \quad f(x - 0) - f(x),$$

then we obtain

$$f(x + 0) + f(x - 0), \quad f(x + 0) - f(x), \quad f(x - 0) - f(x)$$

as functions d and then, by means of linear combinations, $f(x)$ itself as well.

3. Point of continuity. If f is, for the time being, any real function defined in the space A, let C be the set of its points of continuity and $D = A - C$ the sets of its points of discontinuity. *C is a G_δ; D is an F_σ* (with respect to the space A). For, continuity can also be characterized in this way: $f(x)$ is continuous at the point a if and only if for every $\sigma > 0$ there exists a neighborhood U_a for whose points x and y

$$|f(x) - f(y)| < \sigma$$

always holds. For fixed σ let $C(\sigma)$ be the set of the points a having such a neighborhood U_a; every point $b \varepsilon U_a$ then also has such a neighborhood U_b $(\leqq U_a)$, so that $U_a \leqq C(\sigma)$, and $C(\sigma)$ is open. Then C is the intersection of all the $C(\sigma)$ for $\sigma > 0$, or

$$C = C(1)C(1/2)C(1/3)\ldots,$$

and C is a G_δ (W. H. Young).

One extreme is represented by the (everywhere) continuous functions, with $C = A$ and $D = 0$; the other extreme, by the everywhere discontinuous functions, with $C = 0$ and $D = A$. An example of the latter is given, for example, by the so-called Dirichlet function of the real variable x, which is 1 for rational x and 0 for irrational x. Closest to the continuous functions are the functions for which C is *dense in* A; following Hankel, we call them *pointwise discontinuous* (or better, at most pointwise discontinuous, thus including the continuous functions as well).

As an F_σ with a dense complement, D is – by the result on p. 166 – *of the first category* in A (an A_{I}); and if thus A itself is of the second category in itself (an A_{II}) – say, a Young set – then C is an A_{II}. It may also happen here that D is dense in A, but that the two sets are of different categories and cannot possibly exchange roles. Thus it can happen – for example, if A is the set of real numbers – that C is the set of irrationals and D the set of rationals (if $D = \{r_1, r_2, \ldots\}$ and Σc_n is a convergent series of positive numbers, then

$$f(x) = \sum_{r_n < x} c_n$$

is a monotone function of this kind), but not conversely.

Next, let $f_n \to f$ be a sequence of functions convergent everywhere (in A); we ask, under what circumstances can we infer the continuity of the limit function from that of the f_n. We say that a sequence converges *uniformly* at the point a if for every $\sigma > 0$ there exists a natural number m and a neighborhood U_a such that

$$|f_m(x) - f(x)| \leqq \sigma \qquad (x \varepsilon U_a). \tag{1}$$

Then we have:

IV. *If $f_n \to f$ and every f_n is continuous at the point a, then f is continuous at the point a if and only if a is a point of uniform convergence.*

Proof. If a is a point of uniform convergence, we satisfy (1) by a suitable choice of m and U_a, where because of the continuity of f_m at a, it is possible to choose U_a so small that

$$|f_m(x) - f_m(a)| \leqq \sigma \qquad (x \varepsilon U_a).$$

Since, by (1), we have in particular that

$$|f_m(a) - f(a)| \leqq \sigma$$

it follows from these three inequalities that

$$| f(x) - f(a) | \leqq 3\sigma \qquad (x \varepsilon U_a),$$

that is, that f is continuous at a.

If, conversely, f is continuous at a, we first determine an m for which

$$| f_m(a) - f(a) | \leqq \sigma;$$

next, using the continuity of both functions, a U_a for which

$$| f_m(x) - f_m(a) | \leqq \sigma, \quad | f(x) - f(a) | \leqq \sigma \qquad (x \varepsilon U_a);$$

from these three inequalities it now follows that

$$| f_m(x) - f(x) | \leqq 3\sigma \qquad (x \varepsilon U_a),$$

which is precisely uniform convergence at a.

The set K of the points of uniform convergence may be formed in this way: *Let $G(\sigma)$ be the set of the points a for which* (1) *may be satisfied by a suitable choice of m and U_a.* We see once again that $G(\sigma)$ is open ($U_a \leqq G(\sigma)$) and K is the intersection of all the $G(\sigma)$ for $\sigma > 0$, or

$$K = G(1)\ G(\tfrac{1}{2})\ G(\tfrac{1}{3}) \cdots;$$

the set of the points of uniform convergence, again, is a G_δ.

4. The Theorem of Baire. If the functions f_n are everywhere continuous and $f = \lim f_n$ is a function of the first class, then the points of continuity of f coincide with the points of uniform convergence: $C = K$. Let us retain this as our assumption. Then for some fixed $\sigma > 0$, let $F_m(\sigma)$ or, more concisely, F_m be the set of the points x that satisfy all the inequalities

$$(2) \qquad | f_n(x) - f_m(x) | \leqq \sigma \qquad \text{for } n > m.$$

For each particular n, this inequality defines a closed set; F_m is the intersection of these closed sets for $n = m + 1, m + 2, \ldots$, and therefore is itself closed. Because of the convergence of the sequence, every point x satisfies the inequalities (2) for sufficiently large m and thus

$$(3) \qquad A = F_1 \dotplus F_2 \dotplus \cdots.$$

On the other hand, if a is an *interior* point of F_m, so that the inequalities (2) and the inequality

$$| f(x) - f_m(x) | \leqq \sigma$$

that follows from it for $n \to \infty$ hold not only for $x = a$ but also for a certain neighborhood $(x \varepsilon U_a)$, then a belongs to the set $G(\sigma)$ defined earlier, and so

$$(4) \qquad G(\sigma) \geqq F_{1i} \dotplus F_{2i} \dotplus \cdots.$$

From this, it follows that: If $G(\sigma) = 0$, then every $F_{mi} = 0$, and F_m, as a closed set without interior points, is *nowhere dense* in A and, by (3), A is of the first category in itself. Therefore, conversely:

If A is an A_{II}, then every $G(\sigma)$ is non-empty.

Furthermore: If A is a G_{II}-set (p. 165), so that every non-empty set G open in A is of the second category in itself, then we consider the partial functions $f_n(x \mid G)$ and $f(x \mid G)$ (the restrictions to G); the $G(\sigma)$ mentioned above then has to be replaced by $GG(\sigma)$. We thus find that for non-empty G, $GG(\sigma)$ is also non-empty, that is, $G(\sigma)$ *is dense in* A. The closed complement $F(\sigma)$ of this set is thus nowhere dense in A, the set

$$D = F(1) \dotplus F(\tfrac{1}{2}) \dotplus F(\tfrac{1}{3}) \dotplus \cdots$$

of the points of discontinuity of f is an A_{I}, and the set C of the points of continuity is dense in A and is an A_{II}. We have thus discovered the theorem:[1]

V. *If the space A is a G_{II} set* (that is, every non-empty open set G is of the second category in itself or in A), *then every function of the first class is at most pointwise discontinuous, and the set of its points of continuity is dense in A.*

This thus applies in particular if A is a Young set and, specifically, a complete space. Thus, if A is the set of real numbers, a function of the first class can only be pointwise discontinuous; the Dirichlet function $f(x)$ $\left(= \begin{matrix} 1 \\ 0 \end{matrix} \text{ for } \begin{matrix} \text{rational} \\ \text{irrational} \end{matrix}\ x\right)$ is not of the first class, although it is of the second class (§ 43); that is, it is a limit of functions of the first class, as the formula

$$f(x) = \lim_m \lim_n (\cos m!\, \pi x)^{2n}$$

shows.

Theorem V fails when the assumption about A does not hold. In the countable set $A = \{a_1, a_2, \ldots\}$ of real numbers, every function is of the first class since, for any arbitrarily prescribed $b_n = f(a_n)$ it is always possible to determine a continuous function $f_n(x)$ – a polynomial, for example – such that $f_n(a_1) = b_1, \ldots, f_n(a_n) = b_n$ and $f_n \to f$. If A is the

[1] Compare § 45, 3.

set of rational numbers and, say, $f(x) = 1$ or 0 depending on whether x is a dyadic rational number ($x = m/2^n$, m an integer) or not, then f is everywhere discontinuous.

A flat converse to Theorem V, in the sense that pointwise discontinuous functions are of the first class as well, is out of the question, if only because of considerations of cardinality. If, for instance, A is the set of real numbers, then there are only $\aleph$ continuous functions and $\aleph^{\aleph_0} = \aleph$ functions of the first class; but there are $\aleph^{\aleph} = 2^{\aleph}$ pointwise discontinuous functions. For if D is a perfect, nowhere-dense set (of cardinality $\aleph$) and C its open complement dense in A, then every function which vanishes in C and does not vanish in D (and which is thus continuous at $x \,\varepsilon\, C$ and discontinuous at $x \,\varepsilon\, D$) is pointwise discontinuous.

But let us apply V to the partial functions $f(x \mid B)$ contained in $f(x) = f(x \mid A)$ which are, after all, themselves functions of the first class in their space B; if B is a G_{II}-set, then the points of continuity of the partial function (which need not be points of continuity of the total function) are dense in B. This holds, in particular, if A is an F_{II}-set (p. 165) and B is closed in A and is thus also an F_{II}-set. Therefore we can deduce from V:

VI. *If the space A is an F_{II}-set* (that is, if every non-empty closed set F is of the second category in itself) *and if f is a function of the first class, then every non-empty closed set F (closed in A) contains at least one point of continuity of the partial function $f(x \mid F)$.*

We next have the following counterpart to VI:

VII. *If the space A is separable, if f is a function defined in A, and if every non-empty set F closed in A contains at least one point of continuity of the partial function $f(x \mid F)$, then f is of the first class.*

We have to prove that f is of the class (F_σ, G_δ), that is, that all the sets $B = [f > y]$ and $C = [f < z]$ are sets F_σ. Let us consider two such sets for which $y < z$, so that $A = B \dotplus C$. Now suppose F non-empty and closed and a a point of continuity of $f(x \mid F)$. If $a \,\varepsilon\, B$ and $f(a) > y$, then there exists a neighborhood U_a for which $f > y$ remains true in FU_a, that is, $FU_a \leqq B$; in the same way, there exists for $a \,\varepsilon\, C$ a neighborhood for which $FU_a \leqq C$, and at least one of these cases holds (and both when $a \,\varepsilon\, BC$). If we set $F - FU_a = F_1$, then it follows that:

Every non-empty closed set F contains a smaller closed set $F_1 < F$ such that the difference $F - F_1$ is contained either in B or in C. If, in addition, F_1 is non-empty, then we find in the same way a set F_2 properly contained in F_1 and, continuing the procedure transfinitely, we define the closed sets F_ξ for all the ordinal numbers $\xi < \Omega$ in the now familiar manner, namely (except for $F_0 = F$): If F_ξ is non-empty, we let $F_{\xi+1}$ be a set properly contained in F_ξ such that the difference $D_\xi = F_\xi - F_{\xi+1}$ is contained either in B or in C (and possibly in both); for $F_\xi = 0$, we let $F_{\xi+1} = 0$; for a limit ordinal η, we let $F_\eta = \mathfrak{D}_{\xi<\eta} F_\xi$. Since the space is supposed to be separable, there must exist (§ 30, IV) a smallest set $F_\eta = F_{\eta+1} = F_{\eta+2} = \ldots$; because of the method of construction, this must be the null set, and with this, $F = \sum_{\xi<\eta} D_\xi$ is split into at most countably many summands, which are contained in B or in C and which, furthermore, as differences of closed sets, are special sets F_σ. If we recombine the summands belonging to B and to C, we obtain a decomposition $F = Y + Z$ into two disjoint sets F_σ for which $Y \leqq B$ and $Z \leqq C$; in particular, the whole space admits such a decomposition $A = Y + Z$.

Finally, we hold y fixed while allowing z to describe a sequence $z_1 > z_2 > \ldots$ with $z_n \to y$. Corresponding to $B = [f > y]$ and $C_n = [f < z_n]$, we determine a decomposition of the space $A = Y_n + Z_n$ into two disjoint sets F_σ for which $Y_n \leqq B$, $Z_n \leqq C_n$. Let

$$Y = \mathfrak{S} Y_n, \quad Z = \mathfrak{D} Z_n, \quad C = \mathfrak{D} C_n;$$

then we find $C = [f \leqq y] = A - B$. From $A = B + C = Y + Z$ and $Y \leqq B$, $Z \leqq C$ it follows that $Y = B$ and $Z = C$; that is, the set $B = [f > y]$ is an F_σ. The same, of course, holds for the sets $[f < z]$, and we have thus proved VII.

From VI and VII, we obtain:

VIII. (BAIRE'S THEOREM). *If the space A is a separable F_{II}-set, then the function f defined in A is of the first class if and only if every non-empty set F closed in A contains at least one point of continuity of the partial function $f(x \mid F)$.*

The word *closed* can be replaced here without further ado by *perfect,* since an isolated point of F is *eo ipso* a point of continuity of $f(x \mid F)$.

5. Application of Baire's Theorem. Let A be the set of real numbers; $f(x)$ is thus a real function of the real variable x; in the plane E with the rectangular coordinates x, y we consider the set ("curve") C defined by $y = f(x)$. We denote the points of the plane by $z = (x, y)$ and those of C by $z = (x, f(x)) = \varphi(x)$. We then ask when C is *connected.* For this to be the case, the following condition is surely necessary:

(α) *Every point of C is a point of accumulation, both from the left and from the right*; that is, for every x there exists a sequence $x_n < x$ for which $\varphi(x_n) \to \varphi(x)$ and another such sequence $x_n > x$.

For if we split the set C by means of $x < x_0$ and $x \geqq x_0$ into C_1 and C_2, where C_2 is closed in C, then in order that no partition occur, C_1 must have a point of accumulation in C_2, which obviously can be none other than $\varphi(x_0)$. That condition (α) does not suffice by itself is shown by a function such as the Dirichlet function, which takes on only the values 0 and 1, each in a set dense in A.

If, however, $f(x)$ is of the first class, then (α) is also sufficient.

Let us suppose that $C = C_1 + C_2$ can be partitioned into two relatively closed sets; projected onto the x-axis, this gives

$$A = A_1 + A_2 = G_1 + G_2 + F,$$

where we have set $G_1 = A_{1i}$, $G_2 = A_{2i}$, $F = A_{1\alpha} A_{2\alpha} > 0$.[1] According to VI, the partial function $f(x \mid F)$ has a point of continuity x, say $x \varepsilon A_1$. Then x cannot be a limit of points $x_n \varepsilon A_2 F$, since otherwise $\varphi(x) \varepsilon C_1$ would be a limit of points $\varphi(x_n) \varepsilon C_2$; thus there must exist a neighborhood U of x disjoint from $A_2 F$. But this U cannot then be also disjoint from G_2, since x is, after all, an α-point of $A_2 = A_2 F + G_2$, and so UG_2 is non-empty. But condition (α) prohibits this. For if the open interval (a, b) is a component of the open set $UG_2 < U$, then at least one of the end points, say a, lies in U; now since the point $\varphi(a)$, because of (α), is a point of accumulation of C from the right and thus of C_2, we would have $a \varepsilon A_2$ and $a \varepsilon A_2 - G_2 = A_2 F$, and U would actually not be disjoint from $A_2 F$. Therefore C cannot be partitioned.

We can form here still another example (other than that of § 31, 2) of a connected discontinuous set. Let us ask, independent of the foregoing, When does C contain a continuum consisting of more than one point (relative to the plane E and thus a connected set perfect in E)? The answer is: If and only if the points of continuity fill up a whole interval. One part of this statement is trivial: If $f(x)$ is continuous for $a \leqq x \leqq b$, then C contains a simple curve. The other we formulate thus: If K is a continuum of more than one point contained in C, and if $\varphi(a)$ and $\varphi(b)$ are two points of K ($a < b$), then $f(x)$ is continuous in $[a, b]$ (continuous from the right at a, from the left at b, from both sides in between).

For suppose we let K_a, ${}_aK_b$ and ${}_bK$ be the subsets of K defined by $x \leqq a$, $a \leqq x \leqq b$, and $x \geqq b$. They are closed (in K, and therefore in E) and, by § 29, III, they are continua because K_a and ${}_aK$ have the sum K and a one-point intersection and similarly, K_a and ${}_aK_b$ have the sum K_b and a one-point intersection. The projection of ${}_aK_b$ on the y-axis is connected, and $f(x)$ therefore takes on in (a, b) every value

[1] If the relative terms are not qualified, they refer to the space A.

between $f(a)$ and $f(b)$, if these are distinct; the same is true for every subinterval. But then $f(x)$ must be *bounded* in $[a, b]$. For if, as we may assume, we had $f(x_n) \to +\infty$, $x_n \to x$, and $f(x_n) > y > f(x)$, then at some point ξ_n between x_n and x, f would have to take on the value y; this would give $f(\xi_n) = y$ and $\xi_n \to x$, and the point (x, y) distinct from $\varphi(x)$ would have to belong to the closed set K, which is not the case. Therefore ${}_aK_b$ is a *bounded* (compact) continuum. We now consider its projection on the x-axis; this, again, is connected, and therefore identical with the entire interval $[a, b]$; it is the one-to-one continuous image of ${}_aK_b$ and so, conversely (§ 35, III), ${}_aK_b$ is also the one-to-one continuous image of $[a, b]$. This means precisely that $f(x)$ is continuous in $[a, b]$, in the sense defined above.

From all this we can see that C is *discontinuous* (in E) if and only if the points of discontinuity of $f(x)$ are dense in A. And C is simultaneously connected and discontinuous if $f(x)$ is a function of the first class, satisfies the condition (α), and has its points of discontinuity dense in A. Such a function is easy to construct. The function defined by

$$s(x) = \sin \pi/x \qquad (x \neq 0), \quad s(0) = 0$$

is discontinuous only at the point $x = 0$, but even there it satisfies the condition (α), since $s(1/n) = s(-1/n) = 0$ for $n = 1, 2, 3, \ldots$. If $\{r_1, r_2, r_3, \ldots\}$ is the set of rational numbers and $c_1 + c_2 + c_3 + \ldots$ is a convergent series of positive numbers then, as follows easily from the uniform convergence, the function

$$f(x) = \Sigma c_n s(x - r_n)$$

is discontinuous only at the rational points, although even there it satisfies the condition (α) and is a function of the first class (since it has only countably many points of discontinuity).

§ 43. Baire Functions

1. Baire systems. We consider real functions all of which are defined in the same space A (which, for the time being, can be taken as a pure set). A system of such functions f is called a *Baire system if the limit of every convergent sequence of functions f belonging to the system itself belongs to the system.* For a given system Φ of functions f there exists a Baire system — for instance, that of all the functions defined in A — and a smallest such system, the intersection of all the Baire systems containing Φ; the functions of this system are called the *Baire functions* generated by f.

Let us, for the time being, represent them in the following form, corresponding to the representation of Borel sets of pp. 97-98. Letting $i, k, l, \ldots$ range over the natural numbers, we consider all the functions of the form

$$g = \lim_i g_i, \quad g_i = \lim_k g_{ik}, \quad g_{ik} = \lim_l g_{ikl}, \ldots$$

with the requirement that for every sequence of natural numbers $i, k, l, \ldots$ in the sequence of the functions $g_i, g_{ik}, g_{ikl}, \ldots$ there are ultimately to occur only functions f. These functions g are identical with the Baire functions b generated by the f. For, on the one hand, the g obviously form a Baire system over Φ, so that every b is a g. On the other hand, every g is also a b; if some g were not a b, there would also have to be at least one g_i which is not a b, and then at least one g_{ik}, and then a g_{ikl}, etc., each of which is not a b, in contradiction with the fact that the sequence of these functions is ultimately to contain only terms f.

A step-by-step construction, again, is preferable to this representation. Among the Baire functions are the functions themselves, next the functions $f^1 = \lim f_n$, then the functions $f^2 = \lim f_n^1$, and so forth, with finite or infinite repetition, which need not, however, extend beyond the ordinal numbers $\xi < \Omega$. In the inductive definition of the f^ξ it is advisable, in order to arrive at as polished a final result as possible, to proceed as follows (a complete system of functions has been defined on pp. 267-8):

The f^0 are the functions of a complete initial system Φ^0;
The $f^{\xi+1}$ are the limits of convergent sequences of functions f^ξ;
The f^η (η a limit ordinal) are the functions of the smallest complete system to which all the functions f^ξ ($\xi < \eta$) belong.

Accordingly, the functions $f^0, f^1, f^2, \ldots$, with finite indices, for example, are not followed immediately, as functions f^ω, by the limits of convergent sequences of functions f^ξ, but rather by the functions of the smallest complete system containing the f^ξ. This departure from the otherwise usual notation — which we assumed provisionally even in § 30, 2 — is justified, as we shall see, by better agreement between the function indices and the set indices. For the f^ξ now constitute a complete system for *every* index (and not only for the $f^{\xi+1}$, § 41, IV) and this, as we know, entails simplification.

Every f^ξ is a special f^η for $\xi < \eta$. The f^ξ of all indices constitute the smallest Baire system over Φ^0; for fixed ξ they form a *Baire class of functions* which is also called, for brevity, the *class* ξ. The classes increase with increasing indices, equality not excluded; but if $\Phi^\xi = \Phi^{\xi+1}$, then Φ^ξ

is already the whole Baire system, and $\Phi^\xi = \Phi^\eta$ for $\eta > \xi$. A function belongs *exactly* to the class ξ if it belongs to this class but to no earlier one.

We make the further definitions:

$g^\xi =$ limit of an increasing sequence of functions f^ξ,
$h^\xi =$ limit of a decreasing sequence of functions f^ξ;

in addition, for a limit ordinal η,

$g_\eta =$ limit of an increasing sequence of functions f^ξ $(\xi < \eta)$,
$h_\eta =$ limit of a decreasing sequence of functions f^ξ $(\xi < \eta)$.

The inverse image sets are to be denoted by

$$(1) \qquad M^\xi = [f^\xi > y], \quad N^\xi = [f^\xi \geqq y];$$

we shall see in a moment that no others are needed.

If we identify the f of § 41 with the f^ξ which, after all, always form a complete system, then Theorem XII of that section yields:

I. *The functions f^ξ, g^ξ, and h^ξ, are identical with the functions of the classes (M^ξ, N^ξ), $(M^\xi, *)$ and $(*, N^\xi)$.*

In addition, the functions $f^{\xi+1}$ (the former functions f^*) are identical with those of the class $(N^\xi_\sigma, M^\xi_\delta)$; hence this gives

$$(2) \qquad M^{\xi+1} = N^\xi_\sigma, \quad N^{\xi+1} = M^\xi_\delta.$$

Furthermore, let η be a limit ordinal; we identify the earlier f with the functions f^ξ of all the classes $\xi < \eta$. The M are now the M^ξ, the N are the N^ξ; the P and Q, however, are the M^η and N^η, since the functions f^η have now taken on the role of the earlier v. We conclude thus from $P = M_\sigma$ and $Q = N_\delta$ that:

$$(3) \quad \begin{cases} M^\eta = \text{sum of a sequence of sets } M^\xi & (\xi < \eta) \\ N^\eta = \text{intersection of a sequence of sets } N^\xi & (\eta \text{ a limit ordinal}). \end{cases}$$

In this, as follows from the remarks made in connection with Theorem XII of § 41, 3, the limits of convergent sequences of function f^ξ are identical with the $f^{\eta+1}$; the g_η are those g^η that have a minorant f^ξ; the h_η are those h^η that have a majorant f^ξ; the k_η (which are both g_η and h_η) are those f^η that remain between two functions f^ξ. The f^η are the quotients of two k_η. On the other hand, the k^ξ (which are both g^ξ and h^ξ) are always identical with the f^ξ.

Formulas (2) and (3) determine the M^ξ and N^ξ inductively, starting from the sets $M^0 = [f^0 > y]$ and $N^0 = [f^0 \geqq y]$ of the initial system. If we leave off the superscript 0, we thus have

$$(4)\quad \begin{cases} M^0 = M & N^0 = N \\ M^1 = N^0_\sigma = N_\sigma & N^1 = M^0_\delta = M_\delta \\ M^2 = N^1_\sigma = M_{\delta\sigma} & N^2 = M^1_\delta = N_{\sigma\delta} \\ M^3 = N^2_\sigma = N_{\sigma\delta\sigma} & N^3 = M^2_\delta = M_{\delta\sigma\delta} \\ \dots & \dots \\ M^\omega = \mathfrak{S}\, M^{\xi_n} & N^\omega = \mathfrak{D}\, N^{\xi_n} \qquad (\xi_n < \omega) \\ M^{\omega+1} = N^\omega_\sigma & N^{\omega+1} = M^\omega_\delta \\ \dots & \dots \end{cases}$$

In addition, we make note of the Interposition and Extension Theorems:

II. *If* $g^\xi \geqq h^\xi$, *then there exists a function* f^ξ *for which* $g^\xi \geqq f^\xi \geqq h^\xi$.

For limit ordinals η we have, in addition: If $g_\eta \geqq h_\eta$, then there exists a function k_η for which $g_\eta \geqq k_\eta \geqq h_\eta$.

III. *If* N *is a set* N^ξ, *then a function of the class* (M^ξ, N^ξ) *defined in* N *can be extended to a function* f^ξ *defined in the whole space.*

2. The Baire functions of the space. If, in particular, the functions *continuous* in the space A are taken as the initial functions $f^0 = f$, then the Baire functions generated by them are called the *Baire functions* (or the *analytically representable functions*) *of the space* A. The functions M and N are here the G and F, and the M^ξ and N^ξ become the *Borel sets* of the space A; by the definition of the G^ξ and F^ξ (§ 32, (α) and (β)), we find from (4) that

$$(5)\quad \begin{cases} M^0 = G = G^0 & N^0 = F = F^0 \\ M^1 = F_\sigma = F^1 & N^1 = G_\delta = G^1 \\ M^2 = G_{\delta\sigma} = G^2 & N^2 = F_{\sigma\delta} = F^2 \\ M^3 = F_{\sigma\delta\sigma} = F^3 & N^3 = G_{\delta\sigma\delta} = G^3 \\ \dots & \dots \\ M^\omega = G^\omega & N^\omega = F^\omega \\ M^{\omega+1} = F^{\omega+1} & N^{\omega+1} = G^{\omega+1} \\ \dots & \dots \end{cases}$$

and in general,

$$(6)\quad \begin{cases} M^\xi = G^\xi, \quad N^\xi = F^\xi \quad (\xi \text{ even}) \\ M^\xi = F^\xi, \quad N^\xi = G^\xi \quad (\xi \text{ odd}). \end{cases}$$

It should be remarked here that for a limit ordinal η it is quite indifferent whether M^η is considered as a sum of sets M^ξ or N^ξ or G^ξ or F^ξ ($\xi < \eta$) since, indeed, every M^ξ is a special $N^{\xi+1}$, etc.

IV. *The Baire functions of the space* A *are identical with the functions of the class* (B, B), *where* B *ranges over the Borel sets of the space* A.

For every Baire function is of the class (B, B). If, conversely, f is of the class (B, B), then we consider for rational r the countably many

Borel sets $[f > r]$ and $[f \geqq r]$ and choose the ordinal number ξ so large that all these sets are simultaneously sets G^ξ and sets F^ξ and hence are simultaneously sets M^ξ and sets N^ξ. Then for every y

$$[f > y] = \mathfrak{S}_{r>y} [f > r]$$

is an $M^\xi_\sigma = M^\xi$ and

$$[f \geqq y] = \mathfrak{D}_{r<y} [f \geqq r]$$

is an $N^\xi_\delta = N^\xi$, so that f is of the class (M^ξ, N^ξ), or is an f^ξ.

From Theorem I of § 33, there follows directly the *Existence Theorem* for Baire functions:

V. *In a complete space whose dense-in-itself kernel does not vanish, there exist for every $\xi < \Omega$ Baire functions f^ξ that belong exactly to the class ξ (and to no earlier class).*

In a separable space there exists $\aleph$ continuous functions (at least $\aleph$, because the constant functions – which are of this cardinality – are included among them, and at most $\aleph$, because a continuous function is already determined by its values at a countable dense subset). There then exist also only $\aleph$ functions f^ξ for every ξ, as follows by induction, and $\aleph$ (more specifically, at most $\aleph_1 \aleph \leqq \aleph \aleph = \aleph$) Baire functions altogether. Thus, in case the space has cardinality $\aleph$ (for example, if it is complete and has a non-empty dense-in-itself kernel), the Baire functions constitute a vanishingly small subsystem of the system of all $(\aleph^\aleph = 2^\aleph)$ functions.

That the Baire functions, even apart from considerations of cardinality, are still very close to the continuous functions and, in fact, if sets of the first category are neglected, are themselves continuous, is shown by the following theorem:[1]

VI. *If the space A is a G_{II}-set, then for every Baire function f there exists a set $C = G_\delta$ dense in A such that the partial function $f(x \mid C)$ is continuous.*

This is true for the continuous functions themselves $(C = A)$ and can be extended to all the Baire functions by going from the functions f_n of a convergent sequence to their limit f. Let $f_n(x \mid C_n)$ be continuous and let C_n be a G_δ dense in A, so that $D_n = A - C_n$ is an F_σ of the first category in A; then $D_0 = D_1 \dotplus D_2 \dotplus \ldots$ is an F_σ and an A_{I}; $C_0 = A - D_0 = C_1 C_2 \ldots$ is a G_δ dense in A and, again, is a G_{II} set (p. 165). Now all the functions $f_n(x \mid C_0)$ are continuous; their limit $f(x \mid C_0)$ is thus, by V of § 42, at most pointwise discontinuous – that is, the set C of its points

[1] Compare this with § 45, 3.

of continuity is dense in C_0 and is a G_δ in C_0, so that it is dense in A and is a G_δ in A; $f(x \mid C)$ is continuous.

For example, the Dirichlet function f (p. 287) is constant and equal to 0 in the set C of the irrational numbers and is thus continuous; that is, the irrational numbers are points of continuity of the partial function $f(x \mid C)$ – but not of the total function.

VI can be expressed concisely as follows: Every Baire function is *continuous "up to" sets of the first category*; we mean by this that the space allows of a decomposition $A = C + D$ in which D is an A_{I} and $f(x \mid C)$ is continuous. It is then possible *eo ipso* to assume C a G_δ and D an F_σ by replacing the nowhere-dense sets whose sum is D by their closed hulls.

Theorem VI has a certain resemblance to Theorem V of § 42 about functions of the first class, and also admits of an analogue to Theorem VI of § 42:

If the space A is an F_{II}-set and f is a Baire function, then for every non-empty set F closed in A the partial function $f(x \mid F)$ is also continuous up to sets of the first category.

That is, there exists a decomposition $F = C + D$ for which D is an F_{I} and $f(x \mid C)$ is continuous. This follows from the fact that F is itself an F_{II}-set and therefore (p. 165) a G_{II}-set and $f(x \mid F)$ a Baire function of the space F.

One might now conjecture that, corresponding to Theorem VII of § 42, in a separable space the above continuity property might perhaps also suffice; but this conjecture is false. To begin with, let us note that the continuity property is not weakened if, instead of for all *closed* sets, it is required to hold merely for all *perfect* sets – for it then holds for all closed sets. For let

$$F = F_h + F_\beta = F_h + (F_s - F_h) + F_k$$

be closed, and let $F_h > 0$ be the isolated part, F_s the separated part, F_k the dense-in-itself (perfect) kernel, and F_β the derived set. The derived set $F_{h\beta} \leqq F_\beta$ of the isolated part is nowhere dense in F (its complement $F - F_{h\beta} \geqq F_h$ is dense in F, since its closed hull contains $F_{h\alpha} \dot{+} (F - F_{h\beta}) = F$) and it is therefore an F_{I}; it consists of $F_s - F_h$ and of those points of F_k that are points of accumulation of F_h. Now since $f(x \mid F_k)$ is by hypothesis continuous up to sets of the first category, there exists a set D, of the first category in F_k, and a fortiori in F, such that $f(x \mid F_k - D)$ is continuous. If we now remove from F the set $F_{h\beta} \dot{+} D$ of the first category, then there remains $F_h + C$, where $f(x \mid C)$ is continuous and C contains no point of accumulation of F_h; as a result,

$f(x \mid F_h + C)$ is also continuous at the points of C and also, of course, at the (isolated) points of F_h; that is, $f(x \mid F)$ is continuous up to sets of the first category. (In the case $F_k = 0$, $f(x \mid F_h)$ is continuous, and F_β is an F_{I}).

We now show, following Lusin, that it is possible (in the space A of the real numbers) for $f(x \mid P)$ to be continuous up to sets of the first category for all non-empty perfect sets P, while f is nevertheless not a Baire function. To do this, we construct an *uncountable* set L such that LP is always a P_{I}. Assuming this to have been done, we see that L is not a Borel set (nor even a Suslin set), for otherwise it would have to contain a non-empty perfect set P, and $LP = P$ would be a P_{II}. The characteristic function f of L ($f = 1$ in L; $f = 0$ in $A - L$) is thus not a Baire function, whereas $f(x \mid P)$ is nevertheless always continuous up to sets of the first category; specifically, $f(x \mid P - LP) = 0$ is continuous.

In order to form such a set L, we consider sequences of natural numbers

$$X = (x_1, x_2, \ldots, x_n, \ldots)$$

and define $X < Y$ (X "finally" smaller than Y) if ultimately, for $n \geqq n_0$, we have $x_n < y_n$; the smallest number n_0 for which this is the case will be denoted by $n(X, Y)$. This relation is transitive: If $X < Y$ and $Y < Z$, then $X < Z$ and, in fact, it is obvious that

$$n(X, Z) \leqq \max\,[n(X, Y),\ n(Y, Z)].$$

For every finite or countable set of number sequences $X, Y, Z, \ldots$ there exists a "finally greater" U; it is necessary only to choose

$$u_1 > x_1, \quad u_2 > \max\,[x_2, y_2], \quad u_3 > \max\,[x_3, y_3, z_3], \ldots .$$

Accordingly, it is possible to construct a set of number sequences $X_0 < X_1 < \ldots < X_\omega < \ldots$ of type Ω.

On the other hand, we assign to each number sequence X the continued fraction

$$t = \frac{1|}{|x_1} + \frac{1|}{|x_2} + \frac{1|}{|x_3} + \cdots$$

(t an irrational number between 0 and 1), and to the above sequences X_ξ the numbers t_ξ ($\xi < \Omega$). Then the set $L = \{t_0, t_1, \ldots, t_\omega, \ldots\}$ has the required properties.

Writing $n_{\xi\eta}$ as an abbreviation for $n(X_\xi, X_\eta)$ ($\xi < \eta$), let us remark the following: If a sequence of numbers t_η converges to t_ξ, then the number of initial numerals common to the two continued fractions, and consequently $n_{\xi\eta}$ as well, tends to ∞. We now choose some $\eta > 0$ and set

$$M = \{t_0, \ldots, t_\eta\}, \quad N = \{t_{\eta+1}, t_{\eta+2}, \ldots\},$$

and $L = M + N$; furthermore, we split up the set N of the numbers t_ζ $(\zeta > \eta)$ into $N = N_1 + N_2 + \ldots$, where N_n is the set of the t_ζ for which $n_{\eta\zeta} = n$. *Then no point of M is a point of accumulation of N_n.* For if $\xi < \eta$, then

$$n_{\xi\zeta} \leqq \max[n_{\xi\eta}, n_{\eta\zeta}],$$

so that for $t_\zeta \varepsilon N_n$,
$$n_{\xi\zeta} \leqq \max[n_{\xi\eta}, n],$$

$n_{\xi\zeta}$ is bounded, so that t_ζ cannot converge to t_ξ. The same holds for $\xi = \eta$.

We can now (L separable) choose η so great that M is dense in L; then N_n is nowhere dense in L. For $MN_{n\alpha} = 0$, and $\boldsymbol{L - LN_{n\alpha} \geqq M}$ is dense in L. Therefore N is of the first category in L; that is, there exists a decomposition $L = M + N$, where M is countable and N is an L_{I}.

Finally, suppose $P > 0$ perfect. If LP is uncountable, then this is a set of the same kind as L itself (corresponding to a set of number sequences $X_{\xi_0} < X_{\xi_1} < \cdots < X_{\xi_\omega} < \cdots$) and admits of a decomposition $LP = M + N$, where N is of the first category in LP and thus in P, and M is countable and therefore also of the first category in P (every countable set contained in Q_a is a Q_{I} (p. 164): LP is a P_{I}. The same holds when LP is at most countable. Our investigation has now reached its goal. A function f need not be a Baire function even if $f(x \mid F)$ is always continuous up to sets of the first category.

It should also be mentioned that the complement $K = A - L$ of the Lusin set is an F_{II}-set; that is (p. 165), every non-empty set perfect in K is of the second category in itself. Such a set, which is thus dense-in-itself and closed in K, is of the form KP, where P is perfect (in the set A of the real numbers); because of $P = KP + LP$, KP is of the second category in P and thus, all the more so, in itself. Thus there exists F_{II}-sets that are not absolute Borel sets, and thus a statement made earlier (p. 165) to the effect that an F_{II}-set need not be a Young set, is proved in a far wider context.

If a function f (whether a Baire function or not) is continuous up to sets of the first category in the space A, thought of as a G_{II}-set — so that at least one decomposition $A = C + D$ exists, where D is an A_{I} and $f(x \mid C)$ is continuous — then among all such decompositions $A = C_1 + D_1 = C_2 + D_2 = \ldots$ there exists (Sierpiński) one with greatest C and smallest D, namely

$$C = C_1 \dot{+} C_2 \dot{+} \ldots, \qquad D = D_1 D_2 \ldots.$$

It need only be shown that $f(x \mid C)$ is continuous (D is of course an A_{I}).

Let $x \varepsilon C$ and, say, $x \varepsilon C_1$; since $f(x \mid C_1)$ is continuous, there exists for any $\sigma > 0$ a neighborhood U_x for which

$$(7) \qquad | f(z) - f(x) | < \sigma \quad \text{for} \quad z \varepsilon C_1 U_x.$$

Next, let $y \varepsilon CU_x$; if, say, $y \varepsilon C_2$ (where C_2 can equal C_1), then there exists a neighborhood U_y for which

$$(8) \qquad | f(z) - f(y) | < \sigma \quad \text{for} \quad z \varepsilon C_2 U_y.$$

The non-empty (it contains y) open set $U_x U_y$ is an A_{II} and is therefore not contained in $D_1 \dot{+} D_2$; consequently $U_x U_y C_1 C_2$ is non-empty, and there exists at least one z satisfying both (7) and (8), so that

$$| f(x) - f(y) | < 2\sigma \quad \text{for} \quad y \varepsilon CU_x,$$

and since x was any point of C, it follows that $f(x \mid C)$ is continuous.

3. Extensions of the space. It is possible to characterize the Baire functions of a real variable by means of only two plane sets rather than by means of the system of its one-dimensional inverse image sets and, in general, to characterize the Baire functions of the space A by means of two sets of the *extended* space $A^* = (A, Y)$ – the product of A with the set Y of the real numbers in which distances may be defined by $\sqrt{x\xi^2 + (y - \eta)^2}$. Let the Borel sets (6) of the *extended* space be denoted by M^ξ and N^ξ. The inverse image sets

$$(9) \qquad M(\beta) = [f > \beta], \quad N(\beta) = [f \geqq \beta]$$

considered thus far were the sets of the points x satisfying the inequalities in brackets; by

$$(10) \qquad M = [f > y], \qquad N = [f \geqq y]$$

we now mean the sets (no longer depending on a parameter) of the points (x, y) satisfying the inequalities in question. In the same sense we let

$$(11) \qquad C = N - M = [f = y].$$

Geometrically interpreted – in the case in which x is a real variable also – C is the "curve" represented by $y = f(x)$, M is that part of the xy-plane lying below it, and $M(\beta)$ is the projection on the x-axis of that part of C lying in the half-plane $y > \beta$ (or of that part of M lying on the line $y = \beta$); corresponding statements can be made concerning N and $N(\beta)$. We now have the theorem:

VII. *$f(x)$ is a Baire function $f^\xi(x)$ if and only if the set M is an M^ξ and the set N is an N^ξ. If $f(x)$ is an $f^\xi(x)$, then the set C is an N^ξ.*

For the proof, we consider the Baire functions $f^\xi(x)$ of the space A and the Baire functions $f^\xi(x, y)$ of the extended space A^*. We have:

Every $f^\xi(x, 0)$ *is an* $f^\xi(x)$. This holds true for $\xi = 0$, since from a function continuous in both the variables x and y the substitution $y = 0$ produces a function continuous in x, and we then proceed by induction. The induction from ξ to $\xi + 1$ is trivial; furthermore, if η is a limit ordinal and the statement is proved for all $\xi < \eta$, then the conclusion follows for η via the representation of f^η as quotient of two k_η (p. 293). Similarly, there follows:

Every $f^\xi(x)$ *is an* $f^\xi(x, y)$, *and* $f^\xi(x) - y$ *is an* $f^\xi(x, y)$ – the latter because y is a continuous function of x and y and is thus an $f^\xi(x, y)$ of every class.

If, therefore, $f(x)$ is an $f^\xi(x)$ then $f(x) - y$ is an $f^\xi(x, y)$ and is therefore of the class (M^ξ, N^ξ); the set M is an M^ξ, N is an N^ξ and C is an N^ξ. If, conversely, M is an M^ξ and N is an N^ξ, then $f(x, y) = f(x) - y$ is of the class (M^ξ, N^ξ), for this function has the peculiarity that its inverse image sets (in A^*) arise from M and N by translations $\eta = y + \beta$ which transform the whole space A^* isometrically into itself. Therefore $f(x, y)$ is an $f^\xi(x, y)$, and $f(x, 0) = f(x)$ is an $f^\xi(x)$.

The last part of Theorem VII does not, in general, have a converse. Nevertheless, the following theorem provides a limited converse, which is remarkable because the sets $C(\beta) = [f = \beta]$ of the space A allow of no inference as to the character of the function $f(x)$:

VIII. *If the space A is a separable absolute Suslin set and if C is a Suslin set in the extended space (A, Y), then $f(x)$ is a Baire function.*

Let A be a Suslin set in the separable complete space X; then $A^* = (A, Y)$ is a Suslin set in the separable complete space (X, Y) and is thus a separable S ($S =$ absolute Suslin set). C and the half-space $y > \beta$ open in A^* are Suslin sets in A^*, and their intersection is therefore an at most separable S; $M(\beta)$ is the projection of this on the space A, is therefore a continuous image, and by Theorem II of § 37, thus is also an S. A consideration of the half-space $y \leqq \beta$ also shows the complement $A - M(\beta)$ to be an S; both sets are Borel sets in their sum A (§ 34, III). $N(\beta)$ turns out, just like $M(\beta)$, to be a Borel set in A; $f(x)$ is a Baire function. In fact, as we know from VII, C was therefore actually a Borel set in A^* and not merely a Suslin set. Incidentally, we cannot infer the Baire class of $f(x)$ from a knowledge of the Borel class of C; if C is an N^ξ, $f(x)$ can be an $f^\eta(x)$ with $\eta \geqq \xi$.

The projection of C on Y is the range B of the values of $f(x)$, the (real, single-valued) image of A under $y = f(x)$; we call this set, when

$f(x)$ is a Baire function, the *Baire image* of A.

We have the following:

IX. *The Baire image of a separable absolute Suslin set is a Suslin set. The one-to-one Baire image of a separable absolute Borel set is a Borel set. If B is the one-to-one Baire image of a real Suslin set A, then A is also the one-to-one Baire image of B.*

The proof is already contained for the most part in the proof of VIII. If A is a separable S, then we saw that A^* is a separable S, as are C and B (§ 37, II). If A is separable and is an absolute Borel set or a Borel set in X, then so is (A, Y) in (X, Y), so that A^* is a separable absolute Borel set and so are C (as a Borel set in A^*) and B, provided the projection is one-to-one. For the third statement, let $x = g(y)$ be the function, defined in B, inverse to $y = f(x)$. Now B was a separable S, and C was an S and therefore a Suslin set in the space $B^* = (X, B)$, where X is now the set of real numbers. Once more, therefore, with an interchange of the variables x and y, we have the condition of Theorem VIII, and $g(y)$ is a Baire function (whose class we cannot deduce from that of $f(x)$).

Theorem IX is a generalization of Theorem II of § 37, although, for the time being, only for real functions (compare XIII). Moreover, the (real) *continuous* functions defined in the Baire null space or in the space I of the irrational numbers already (§ 37, III) produce all the (real) Suslin sets as their ranges. But if x is to have as its domain the set A of *all* the real numbers, then the continuous functions $f(x)$ do not suffice to yield as their images all the Suslin sets (the continuous image of A is an F_σ); but the functions of the first class do suffice, and in fact:

X. *Every real Suslin set is the range of a function $f(x)$ of the first class of the real variable x* (and even of a function with an at most countable number of points of discontinuity).

For we were able to represent the real Suslin set B as the continuous image of I or, what amounts to the same, by means of a continuous function $f(i)$, where i ranges over the irrational numbers. We extend this function to all the real numbers (without extending its range) by arranging the rational numbers in a sequence $\{r_1, r_2, \ldots\}$, choosing for each r_n an irrational number i_n with $| i_n - r_n | < 1/n$, and setting $f(r_n) = f(i_n)$. Then the total function $f(x)$ is still continuous at every irrational point, since for $r_p \rightarrow i$ it follows that $i_p \rightarrow i$ and $f(r_p) = f(i_p) \rightarrow f(i)$. Therefore $f(x)$ is discontinuous at most at the rational points and so, by p. 283, is of the first class.

4. Non-real Baire functions. Let A and Y be metric spaces; we consider all the single-valued functions $y = \varphi(x)$ defined in A for which $y \,\varepsilon\, Y$, where thus the image $B = \Phi(A)$ is a subset of Y. Let us call A the *space*, and Y the *image space* of this system of functions. (When Y is the set of real numbers we have the real functions $\varphi(x)$, to which this chapter has been devoted.) A sequence of functions $y_n = \varphi_n(x)$ which converges for all x generates a new function $y = \varphi(x)$. Therefore we can again define the Baire functions φ^ξ for $\xi < \Omega$, with the exception that limit ordinals must be excluded wherever the concepts of an ordinary and a complete system of functions (§ 41,1) – formulated specifically for the real functions – cannot be carried over to an arbitrary image space. Let the φ^0 be the continuous functions; if the φ^ξ have already been defined, we let the $\varphi^{\xi+1}$ be the limit functions of convergent sequences of functions φ^ξ; if η is a limit ordinal, then we define (not the φ^η but) the $\varphi^{\eta+1}$ as the limit functions of convergent sequences of functions φ^ξ $(\xi < \eta)$. For real functions, the indices of these classes coincide with those defined earlier, except that the φ^η still allow of being interposed.

Since no distinction between above and below is necessary here, the Lebesgue inverse image sets are most expeditiously defined as follows. First, for Q contained in Y, we define $[y \,\varepsilon\, Q]$ to be the set of those x for which $y = \varphi(x) \,\varepsilon\, Q$, that is, the inverse image of BQ (B the image of A). The sets

$$[y \,\varepsilon\, G] \quad \text{and} \quad [y \,\varepsilon\, F],$$

where G ranges over all the sets *open* in Y and F over all the sets *closed* in Y, will then be called the inverse image sets of the function $y = \varphi(x)$; they are complements of each other, and it would suffice to consider only one kind. As M ranges over a given system of sets contained in A and $N = A - M$ over their complements, we say that the function φ is of the class (M, N) if every set $[y \,\varepsilon\, G]$ is an M and every set $[y \,\varepsilon\, F]$ is an N. The following theorem then holds, where among several possible statements as to class, we have chosen the one that takes on the simplest form in the case of Borel sets:

XI. *Let the functions $\varphi_n \to \varphi$ be of the class (M, N). Then φ is of the class $(N_{\delta\sigma}, M_{\sigma\delta})$ in the case of uniform convergence of the class (M_σ, N_δ). If the M form a σ-system and the N a δ-system, then φ is of the class (N_σ, M_δ) and, in the case of uniform convergence, of the class (M, N).*

Let the non-empty set F be closed in Y; for $\nu = 1, 2, 3, \ldots$, let F_ν be the closed set of the points y for which $\delta(y, F) \leqq 1/\nu$, G_ν the open set of the points $\delta(y, F) < 1/\nu$, and H_ν an arbitrary set between the two ($G_\nu \leqq H_\nu \leqq F_\nu$). Thus

$$F = \mathfrak{D} G_\nu = \mathfrak{D} H_\nu = \mathfrak{D} F_\nu .$$

Further, let $y_n = \varphi_n(x) \to y = \varphi(x)$. Then the following conditions on x are equivalent:

(a) $y \varepsilon F$;
(b) For every ν, $y_n \varepsilon H_\nu$ for almost all n;
(c) For every ν, $y_n \varepsilon H_\nu$ for infinitely many n.

(b) follows from (a). If $y \varepsilon F$ then, for every ν, $y \varepsilon G_\nu$ and thus (since G_ν is open) $y_n \varepsilon G_\nu \leqq H_\nu$ for almost all n.

(b) implies (c).

(c) implies (a). For every ν, $y_n \varepsilon H_\nu \leqq F_\nu$ holds for infinitely many n, so that (since F_ν is closed) $y \varepsilon F_\nu$, and consequently $y \varepsilon F$.

As a result, using (a) and (c), we obtain

$$[y \varepsilon F] = \mathfrak{D}_\nu \overline{\operatorname{Lim}}_n [y_n \varepsilon H_\nu] .$$

If we choose $H_\nu = F_\nu$, then the set $[y_n \varepsilon H_\nu]$ is an M, its upper limit for $n \to \infty$ is an $M_{\sigma\delta}$, and $[y \varepsilon F]$ is an $M_{\sigma\delta}$. The function φ is of the class $(*, M_{\sigma\delta}) = (N_{\delta\sigma}, M_{\sigma\delta})$.

If the convergence is uniform, then (a) is equivalent with the stronger statement:

(b*) for every ν, $y_n \varepsilon H_\nu$ for $n \geqq n_\nu$

(where n_ν depends only on ν and not on x). For if n_ν is so chosen that $y y_n < \frac{1}{\nu}$ for $n \geqq n_\nu$, then it follows from (a), for every ν and $n \geqq n_\nu$, that $\delta(y_n, F) \leqq y y_n < \frac{1}{\nu}$, $y_n \varepsilon G_\nu \leqq H_\nu$, and therefore (b*); conversely, (a) already follows from (b). Hence

$$[y \varepsilon F] = \mathfrak{D}_\nu \mathfrak{D}_{n \geqq n_\nu} [y_n \varepsilon H_\nu];$$

if we now choose $H_\nu = F_\nu$, $[y \varepsilon F]$ is then an N_δ, and φ is of the class (M_σ, N_δ). Thus XI is proved.

If once again we define the Borel sets (6) of the space A, then we have:

XII. *The Baire functions φ^ξ are of the class (M^ξ, N^ξ).*

This follows from XI by induction, because the M^ξ form a σ-system and their complements N^ξ form a δ-system. The induction from ξ to $\xi + 1$ is trivial; that from $\xi < \eta$ to $\eta + 1$ (η a limit ordinal) rests on the fact that all the functions φ^ξ are of the class (M^η, N^η).

In the case of real functions, it was possible to form the converse of XII: the functions of the class (M^ξ, N^ξ) are Baire functions φ^ξ. In the case of an arbitrary image space, not only do the methods of proof used in § 41, 3 fail, but the statement itself may be false (apart from $\xi = 0$; the functions of the class (G, F), by I of § 35, are always continuous, where G and F here denote the sets open and closed in A). When A is connected (and has more than one point) and Y is the set consisting only of the two numbers 0 and 1, then the two constant functions $\varphi = 0$ and $\varphi = 1$ are the only continuous functions, as well as the only Baire functions; a function which is 1 at a single point and otherwise is 0 everywhere is of the class (F_σ, G_δ) without being a φ^1. The question, in which spaces Y, or in which pairs of spaces A and Y, XII has a converse, deserves investigation.[1] In any event the converse holds for arbitrary A in case Y is a *Euclidean* space. For here convergence of points is equivalent with convergence of all their coordinates; to define $y = (y_1, \ldots, y_m)$ as a function $\varphi(x)$ means defining every coordinate y_k as a real function $f_k(x)$; φ is a function φ^ξ if and only if all the f_k are real f^ξ. If now φ is of the class (M^ξ, N^ξ), then every f_k is of the same class, because the half-space $y_k > \beta$ $(y_k \geqq \beta)$ is open (closed) in Y; therefore every f_k is a real f^ξ, and φ is a φ^ξ.

The first two results of IX, which referred earlier to real Baire images, hold for every image space Y whether the theorems on classes have converses or not. Thus:

XIII. *The Baire image, real or not, of a separable absolute Suslin set is an at most separable, absolute Suslin set. The one-to-one Baire image, real or not, of a separable absolute Borel set is a separable absolute Borel set.*

First we have to say: If $\varphi_n \to \varphi$ and if every φ_n gives rise to an image B_n of A which is at most separable, then φ also yields an at most separable image B, since B is obviously a subset of $(\mathfrak{S}B_n)_\alpha$ (B is already contained, by the way, in the lower closed limit $\underline{\mathrm{Fl}}\, B_n$). If, therefore, A is separable, then its continuous images (footnote, p. 238) and its Baire images are all at most separable. As a consequence, the image space Y of a Baire function $y = \varphi(x)$ can be replaced by an at most separable Y_0, and this can be done in such a way that not only does the image B of A lie in Y_0 but φ also remains a Baire function in the image space Y_0. To this end, we make use, say, of the representation

$$\varphi = \lim_p \varphi_p, \quad \varphi_p = \lim_q \varphi_{pq}, \quad \varphi = \lim_r \varphi_{pqr}, \ldots$$

[1] Compare this with Appendix D.

mentioned at the beginning of the present section, in which for every natural sequence of numbers, the functions $\varphi_p, \varphi_{pq}, \varphi_{pqr}, \ldots$ are ultimately continuous (this form of φ is, as we saw, necessary and sufficient for Baire functions). If $B, B_p, B_{pq}, B_{pqr}, \ldots$ are the Baire images (ultimately continuous) traced out by these functions, then Y can obviously be replaced by

$$Y_0 = B \dotplus \mathfrak{S} B_p \dotplus \mathfrak{S} B_{pq} \dotplus \mathfrak{S} B_{pqr} \dotplus \cdots.$$

Accordingly, we may assume the image space separable, and even complete.

Furthermore: If A and Y are arbitrary and $\varphi(x)$ is a Baire function, then the set C of the points (x, y) for which $y = \varphi(x)$ is a Borel set (cf. VII and VIII) in the extended space $A^* = (A, Y)$. For let us denote the distances $y\eta$ in the space Y, as in linear spaces, by $|y - \eta|$, without thereby assuming Y to be a linear space and, for any function $\varphi(x)$ of the image space Y defined in A, let us consider the distance

$$f(x, y) = |y - \varphi(x)|;$$

then this is a real function in the extended space A^*. If $\varphi(x)$ is continuous, then so is $f(x, y)$; and since, in addition, $\varphi_n \rightarrow \varphi$ implies

$$|y - \varphi_n(x)| \rightarrow |y - \varphi(x)|,$$

we see at once that when φ is a Baire function φ^ξ, f is a real Baire function f^ξ. The set $C = [f = 0]$ is therefore an N^ξ of the extended space A^*.

The rest of the proof now continues as it did in IX. Let A be a Suslin set in the separable complete space X, and let Y be separable and complete; (A, Y) is a Suslin set in (X, Y) and is therefore a separable S; the same for C; and the same for B, as a projection of C. If A is, in particular, a Borel set, then so is (A, Y), so is C, and – provided the projection is one-to-one – so is B as well. In this connection, compare § 46.

§ 44. Sets of Convergence

Let a sequence of continuous and – once again – real functions $f_n = f_n(x)$ be defined in the space A; we seek the *set of convergence* C of this sequence, that is, the set of the points x (points of convergence) at which $\lim f_n(x)$ exists. For this it is necessary and sufficient that for every $\sigma > 0$ there exist a term $f_m(x)$ of the sequence that differs by at most σ from all those that follow, that is, one for which

$$(1) \qquad |f_n(x) - f_m(x)| \leqq \sigma \quad \text{for} \quad n > m.$$

From this it follows that: Let $F_m(\sigma)$ (as in § 42, 4) be the set of the points x at which (1) holds for fixed σ and m, and let

$$C(\sigma) = F_1(\sigma) \dotplus F_2(\sigma) \dotplus F_3(\sigma) \dotplus \cdots$$

be the set of those x at which, with σ fixed, (1) holds for any m whatever; then C is the intersection of all the $C(\sigma)$ or – since the sets $F_m(\sigma)$ and $C(\sigma)$ decrease with decreasing σ –

$$C = C(1)\, C(\tfrac{1}{2})\, C(\tfrac{1}{3}) \cdots.$$

$F_m(\sigma)$ is closed, $C(\sigma)$ is an F_σ, and *the set of convergence C is an $F_{\sigma\delta}$*.

This can also be understood this way: If we assume that

$$\bar{f} = \overline{\lim}\, f_n \quad \text{and} \quad \underline{f} = \underline{\lim}\, f_n$$

exist everywhere (that is, are finite), then these are functions of the second class, and in fact, by § 41, (6), $\bar{f}$ is an h^1 of the class $(*, G_\delta)$, and $\underline{f}$ is a g^1 of the class $(F_\sigma, *)$. Their difference

$$\omega(f) = \bar{f} - \underline{f},$$

which is called the *oscillation* of f_n for $n \to \infty$ is, as a function of the second class,[1] of the class $(G_{\delta\sigma}, F_{\sigma\delta})$; the set of the points of divergence $\omega(f) > 0$ is thus a $G_{\delta\sigma}$; the set of the points of convergence $\omega(f) = 0$ is an $F_{\sigma\delta}$. The set of points at which $\lambda < \lim f_n < \mu$ is also an $F_{\sigma\delta}$, specifically, it is the intersection $[\bar{f} = \underline{f}][\underline{f} > \lambda][\bar{f} < \mu] = F_{\sigma\delta}\, F_\sigma\, F_\sigma$. We can now free ourselves from the hypothesis of finite $\bar{f}$ and $\underline{f}$ by means of the bounding transformation $\varphi_n = \dfrac{f_n}{1 + |f_n|}$; the set of the points at which f_n converges is identical with the set of points at which $-1 < \lim \varphi_n < 1$ (whereas $\varphi_n \to 1$ is equivalent with $f_n \to \infty$ and $\varphi_n \to -1$ with $f_n \to -\infty$).

Moreover, the set $[\bar{f} = \infty] = [\bar{\varphi} = 1] = [\bar{\varphi} \geqq 1]$ is a G_δ, and so is the set $[\underline{f} = -\infty]$, and also the sum of the two; that is, *the set D_∞ of the points at which $f_n(x)$ is not bounded is a G_δ*. If – as, for example, in the theory of Fourier series – we form a sequence of continuous functions of a real variable that diverge in this way at all the rational points (so that $f_n(x)$ is not bounded), then the same behavior occurs automatically also at $\aleph$ irrational points; for, by XI of § 26, D_∞ – as a dense G_δ – is of the cardinality of the continuum.

The set of points at which f_n converges to a pre-assigned value is also an $F_{\sigma\delta}$; for example,

[1] It is itself an h^1 of the class $(G_{\delta\sigma}, G_\delta)$, from which nothing more follows, however, than is given in the text.

$$[f_n \to 0] = [\varphi_n \to 0] = [\underline{\varphi} \geqq 0]\,[\overline{\varphi} \leqq 0].$$

But the set at which f_n diverges[1] to ∞ or $-\infty$ is also an $F_{\sigma\delta}$, since

$$[f_n \to \infty] = [\underline{f} = \infty] = [\underline{\varphi} \geqq 1].$$

We have already proved the first half of the theorem:

I. (Hahn). *The set of convergence of a sequence of real continuous functions is always an $F_{\sigma\delta}$, and for every set $C = F_{\sigma\delta}$ it is possible to give a sequence of real continuous functions for which C is the set of convergence.*

For the proof of the second half, we first take C to be an F_σ,

$$C = F_1 \dot{+} F_2 \dot{+} F_3 \dot{+} \cdots, \quad F_1 \leqq F_2 \leqq F_3 \leqq \cdots$$

(F_n closed); we let $D = A - C$ be the complement. The function h, which is defined in

	F_1,	$F_2 - F_1$,	$F_3 - F_2$,	$\ldots$,	D
to be	1,	$\frac{1}{2}$,	$\frac{1}{3}$,	$\ldots$,	0

is upper semi-continuous; for $[h \geqq y]$ is one of the sets F_n, when it is neither the null set nor the whole space. It is the limit of a decreasing sequence of continuous functions $\psi_1 \geqq \psi_2 \geqq \ldots$; since the functions $\psi_n' = \min\,[\psi_n, 1]$ and $\psi_n'' = \max\left[\psi_n', \dfrac{1}{n}\right]$ also converge as a decreasing sequence to h, we may as well assume that $1/n \leqq \psi_n \leqq 1$. The continuous functions $\varphi_n = 1/\psi_n$ for which $1 \leqq \varphi_n \leqq n$ hold form an increasing sequence and converge in C to $1/h$ – that is, to integer limiting values – while they diverge to $+\infty$ in D. Thus this would already constitute a solution of the problem for the case $C = F_\sigma$; to proceed further, we transform it in the following way. We have $0 \leqq \varphi_{n+1} - \varphi_n \leqq n$; if we interpose between φ_n and φ_{n+1} further functions, with fractional index,

$$\varphi_{n+t} = \varphi_n + t(\varphi_{n+1} - \varphi_n) \quad \left(t = \frac{1}{2n}, \frac{2}{2n}, \ldots, \frac{2n-1}{2n}\right)$$

and change the notation by numbering the original and the interposed fractions consecutively with natural numbers, then we obtain a sequence of continuous functions $1 = \varphi_1 \leqq \varphi_2 \leqq \cdots$, $\varphi_{n+1} - \varphi_n \leqq 1/2$. In C, $\lim \varphi_n$ is a natural number; in D, $\lim \varphi_n = +\infty$. The functions

$$f_n = a \sin \pi \varphi_n$$

(a a positive constant) converge to 0 in C and diverge in D; for $(x \,\varepsilon\, D)$

[1] This is called *proper divergence*; it would be better, however, to call it *improper convergence* (Hahn).

at least one φ_n falls into each of the intervals $[k + 1/4,\ k + 3/4]$ of length $1/2$ ($k = 1, 2, 3, \ldots$), and then $(-1)^k \sin \pi\varphi_n \geqq \sin \pi/4$, so that $f_n \geqq a/\sqrt{2}$ infinitely often and, also infinitely often, $f_n \leqq -a/\sqrt{2}$.

Therefore there exists, for every $C = F_\sigma$, a sequence of continuous, uniformly bounded, functions f_n (of absolute value $\leqq a$) *that converge to 0 in C and diverge in $D = A - C$.* (Sierpiński).

Now let $C = C_1 C_2 \ldots$ be the intersection of a sequence of sets $C_m = F_\sigma$; let D_m be the complement of C_m and $D = D_1 \dot{+} D_2 \dot{+} \ldots$ that of C. For every $m = 1, 2, \ldots$ we determine a sequence of continuous functions f_{mn} of absolute value $\leqq 1/m$, so that the limiting value $\lim\limits_n f_{mn}$ exists and is 0 in C_m and does not exist in D_m. Let the double sequence of these functions f_{mn} be written as a simple sequence f_p (say $f_1, f_2, f_3, \ldots = f_{11}, f_{12}, f_{21}, \ldots$). Then the limiting value $\lim f_p$ exists and $= 0$ in C, and does not exist in D. For if $x \varepsilon C$, the inequality $|f_{mn}| \geqq \varepsilon > 0$ can hold for only a finite number of m, because $|f_{mn}| \leqq 1/m$, and then each time for only a finite number of n, because $\lim f_{mn} = 0$; for $x \varepsilon D$ and, say, $x \varepsilon D_m$, the functions $f_{m1}, f_{m2}, \ldots$ already form a divergent subsequence of the f_p. I is thus proved.

If, instead of being continuous, the functions f_n are taken from the system of all the functions of the class (M, N), where the M form a σ-ring and their complements N form a δ-ring, then their set of convergence is a $N_{\sigma\delta}$; the proof is as at the beginning of this section. This also applies to non-real functions (§ 43, 4), provided the image space is complete.

Let us return to real continuous functions and consider, instead of a *sequence* of functions $f_n(x)$, a *family* of functions $f(x, y)$ depending on a real positive parameter y (and which are therefore, for fixed y, continuous functions of $x \varepsilon A$) and whose behavior for $y \to 0$ is to be examined. *The set of convergence C of the points x at which $\lim\limits_{y \to 0} f(x, y)$ exists is itself an $F_{\sigma\delta}$.* For in order that this be the case, it is necessary and sufficient that for every $\sigma > 0$ there exist some $\eta > 0$ such that

$$(2) \qquad |f(x, y_1) - f(x, y_2)| \leqq \sigma \quad \text{for } y_1 < y_2 < \eta.$$

For fixed σ and η the set $F(\sigma, \eta)$ of the points x at which (2) holds is closed (as the intersection of the sets in which the inequality (2) holds for a particular pair y_1 and y_2). The set of points x at which (2) holds for fixed σ and any η is $C(\sigma) = \mathfrak{S}_\eta F(\sigma, \eta)$, for which we can write

$$C(\sigma) = F(\sigma, 1) \dot{+} F(\sigma, \tfrac{1}{2}) \dot{+} F(\sigma, \tfrac{1}{3}) \dot{+} \cdots$$

since the $F(\sigma, \eta)$ increase as η decreases; finally, C is again the intersection of the $C(\sigma)$, or

$$C = C(1)\, C(\tfrac{1}{2})\, C(\tfrac{1}{3}) \ldots,$$

from which we see that C is an $F_{\sigma\delta}$.

The upper limit

$$\bar{f}(x) = \overline{\lim_{y \to 0}}\, f(x, y)$$

is defined by means of

$$\bar{f}(x) = \lim_{\eta \to 0} g(x, \eta), \quad g(x, \eta) = \sup_{y \leqq \eta} f(x, y) \quad (\eta > 0).$$

If it is to exist (for fixed x) — that is, if it is to be finite — then, for sufficiently small y, $f(x, y)$ must be bounded from above and $g(x, y)$ from below; $g(x, y)$ decreases with decreasing y. If $\bar{f}(x)$ exists for every x, then $\bar{f}(x)$ is again a function h^1 of the class $(*, G_\delta)$. In order to see this, we can assume $f(x, y)$, with x fixed, to be bounded from above for *all* $y > 0$ by considering in its stead $\min\, [f(x, y), 1/y]$ — a function that coincides for sufficiently small y, say $y \leqq \eta$, with $f(x, y)$ and is otherwise, for $y > \eta$, in any case, $\leqq 1/\eta$. Under this assumption, $g(x, y)$ exists for every y and, as the least upper bound of continuous functions, is lower semi-continuous (§ 42, 1); furthermore

$$\bar{f}(x) = \lim g(x, 1/n),$$

as the limit of decreasing functions of the first class, is then an h^1. The function

$$\underline{f}(x) = \underline{\lim}_{y \to 0}\, f(x, y)$$

to be defined analogously is — if it is everywhere finite — a g^1 of the class $(F_\sigma, *)$.

For example, for

$$f(x, y) = \frac{\varphi(x + y) - \varphi(x)}{y},$$

where $\varphi(x)$ is a continuous function of the real variable x, we have the following: The set of points at which $\varphi(x)$ is differentiable at the right is an $F_{\sigma\delta}$; the upper right-hand derivate (which is assumed everywhere finite) is an h^1; the lower right-hand derivate is a g^1. The same, of course, holds at the left and, in addition, for both sides (if we do not distinguish between left and right).

In the case of a family of functions, these conclusions (as to the classes of $\bar{f}$ and $\underline{f}$ and also as to the convergence set) can *not* be carried over from the continuous functions to those of the class (M, N); after all, they are based essentially on the fact that the intersection of an *arbitrary* collection (and not only a countable collection) of F is an F and that the sum of an arbitrary number of G is a G. Thus the fact that, when $f(x, y)$ is continuous in x for fixed y (where $f(x, y)$ is bounded from above for fixed x),

$$g(x) = \sup_y f(x, y)$$

is lower semi-continuous, has no analogue for the Baire functions of higher class. If $f(x, y)$ is a Baire function of both variables in the extended space (A, Y), and A is a separable S ($S =$ absolute Suslin set), then it results that $g(x)$ is a function of the class (S, S); for the set $[g > c]$ is obviously the projection of the set $[f > c]$ on the space A, and is thus an S; and in the same way, $[g \geqq c] = \mathfrak{D}_n \left[g > c - \frac{1}{n}\right]$. The sets $[g < c]$ and $[g \leqq c]$ are complements $A - S$. (When, in particular, the space A is Euclidean and $f(x, y)$ is of the first class, then $g(x)$ is of the class $(F_\sigma, *)$ and so is of the second class. For here the projection of an F_σ is itself an F_σ.)

It is instructive to consider some other sets of convergence as well. We suppose x real and y positive; let the real function $f(x, y)$ defined in the upper half-plane $y > 0$ be continuous in x for fixed y. We let (x, y) converge from the upper half-plane to a point $(\xi, 0)$ of the x-axis; depending on the way in which we allow (x, y) to approach $(\xi, 0)$,

$$(3) \qquad (x, y) \to (\xi, 0),$$

the set C of the numbers ξ, or of the points $(\xi, 0)$, for which $\lim f(x, y)$ exists can have different character.

Linear approach. In the case of approach parallel to the y-axis, where it is thus a matter of $\lim_{y \to 0} f(\xi, y)$, we know that C is an $F_{\sigma\delta}$. The same is the case when the approach takes place along the fixed line

$$(4) \qquad x - \xi = ty,$$

which forms the angle α with the y-axis ($-\pi/2 < \alpha < \pi/2$, $t = \tan \alpha$); here we are concerned with the limiting value

$$(5) \qquad \lim_{y \to 0} f(\xi + ty, y) = g(\xi, t)$$

of a function which, if y and t are fixed, is continuous in ξ; and the set $C(t)$ of the ξ where this limit exists is a $F_{\sigma\delta}$. This, then, is the result obtained in an approach *along a fixed direction.*

The sum $\overline{C} = \mathfrak{S} C(t)$ is the set of points at which there is *convergence when they are approached in at least one direction.* $\overline{C}$ is a *Suslin set.* For $f(\xi + ty, y)$ is, for y fixed, a continuous function of the variables ξ

and t; the set Γ of the points (ξ, t) at which the limit (5) exists is an $F_{\sigma\delta}$ in the ξt-plane, and $\overline{C}$ is the projection of Γ on the ξ-axis.

The intersection $\underline{C} = \mathfrak{D}C(t)$ is the set of points at which there is convergence when they are *approached in any direction* (where the limit (5) may, however, depend on the direction). $\underline{C}$ is the *complement of a Suslin set* — namely, of the projection of $E - \Gamma$ on the ξ-axis, where Γ is the set just mentioned and E is the ξt-plane.

Under *approach in a fixed sector*

$$| x - \xi | \leqq ty \qquad (t > 0),$$

the set of convergence is an $F_{\sigma\delta}$, in the case of *approach in at least one* (sufficiently small) *sector* it is an $F_{\sigma\delta\sigma}$, and in the case of *approach in every sector* (no matter how wide), an $F_{\sigma\delta}$; the proofs of these statements are left to the reader.

In the case of a *completely arbitrary approach* (3), the set of convergence C is a G_δ, and this without any assumptions about $f(x, y)$, which therefore need no longer be continuous in x. This is so because it is necessary and sufficient for convergence that for every $\sigma > 0$ the point $(\xi, 0)$ have a plane neighborhood U in the upper half $(y > 0)$ of which

$$| f(x_1, y_1) - f(x_2, y_2) | \leqq \sigma$$

holds for every pair of points. The set $G(\sigma)$ of the points $(\xi, 0)$ which, for fixed σ, have such a neighborhood, is open in the ξ-axis, for every point $(\eta, 0)$ lying in U also has such a neighborhood (contained in U), and $C = \mathfrak{D}G(1/n)$ is a G_δ. This reasoning is basically the same as that which showed that the set of points of continuity of an arbitrary function is a G_δ; this should also be compared with the footnote on p. 246.

CHAPTER X

SUPPLEMENT

§ 45. The Baire Condition

1. Modules and congruences. All the sets to be considered will be subsets of a fixed set E, which we call the "space" and elements of which we call "points." The *symmetric difference* of two sets A and B is the set

$$\begin{aligned}[A, B] &= (A \dotplus B) - AB \\ &= (A - AB) + (B - AB) = [B, A]\end{aligned}$$

of those points that belong to one of these sets but not to the other. If $a(x)$ and $b(x)$ are the characteristic functions (p. 22) of A and B, then $| a(x) - b(x) |$ is the characteristic function of $[A, B]$.

For the three sets A, B, and C, we have

$$(1) \qquad [A, C] \leqq [A, B] \dotplus [B, C].$$

For let $x \varepsilon [A, C]$, say, $x \varepsilon A$, $x \bar{\varepsilon} C$; depending on whether $x \bar{\varepsilon} B$ or $x \varepsilon B$, x belongs to $[A, B]$ or to $[B, C]$.

Furthermore, it is obvious that

$$(2) \qquad [E - A, E - B] = [A, B].$$

If to every element (index) n of an arbitrary set[1] N we assign a pair of sets A_n and B_n, then

$$(3) \qquad \begin{cases} [\mathfrak{S}A_n, \mathfrak{S}B_n] \leqq \mathfrak{S}[A_n, B_n] \\ [\mathfrak{D}A_n, \mathfrak{D}B_n] \leqq \mathfrak{S}[A_n, B_n]. \end{cases}$$

To prove the first formula, let x be a point of the set on the left, and say $x \varepsilon \mathfrak{S}A_n$, $x \bar{\varepsilon} \mathfrak{S}B_n$; thus there exists an n for which $x \varepsilon A_n$, and, at the same time, $x \bar{\varepsilon} B_n$, $x \varepsilon [A_n, B_n]$. The second formula in (3) is proved in the same way, or with the use of (2).

In the Suslin construction, (p. 105), let

$$\begin{aligned} A &= \underset{\nu}{\mathfrak{S}} A_\nu, \quad A_\nu = A_{n_1} A_{n_1 n_2} \cdots \\ B &= \underset{\nu}{\mathfrak{S}} B_\nu, \quad B_\nu = B_{n_1} B_{n_1 n_2} \cdots . \end{aligned}$$

Then

$$(4) \qquad [A, B] \leqq \mathfrak{S}[A_{n_1}, B_{n_1}] \dotplus \mathfrak{S}[A_{n_1 n_2}, B_{n_1 n_2}] \dotplus \cdots .$$

[1] This need not, of course, be a subset of E.

This follows from (3) because

$$[A, B] \leqq \mathfrak{S}_{\nu}[A_\nu, B_\nu],$$

$$[A_\nu, B_\nu] \leqq [A_{n_1}, B_{n_1}] \dot{+} [A_{n_1 n_2}, B_{n_1 n_2}] \dot{+} \cdots .$$

A non-empty system $\mathfrak{M}$ of subsets M of the space E is called *a module* when the following conditions are satisfied:

(α) Every subset of a set of $\mathfrak{M}$ itself belong to $\mathfrak{M}$;
(β) The sum of a finite number of sets of $\mathfrak{M}$ itself belongs to $\mathfrak{M}$.

If, instead of (β), we impose the stricter requirement

(β_σ) The sum of a (finite or) countable number of sets $\mathfrak{M}$ itself belongs to $\mathfrak{M}$,

then the system $\mathfrak{M}$ that satisfies (α) and (β_σ) is called a *σ-module.* Every module contains the null set 0.

The finite sets or (if E is a metric space) the sets nowhere dense in E form a module; the at most countable sets or the sets of the first category in E (the E_{I}) form a σ-module.

On the model of Number Theory and Algebra, we shall call two sets A and B *congruent modulo* $\mathfrak{M}$

$$A \equiv B \quad (\mathfrak{M})$$

if they "differ only by sets $M \varepsilon \mathfrak{M}$" or, more precisely, *if their symmetric difference* $[A, B]$ *belongs to* $\mathfrak{M}$. This can be expressed as follows: The two summands

$$M_1 = A - AB = (A \dot{+} B) - B,$$
$$M_2 = B - AB = (A \dot{+} B) - A,$$

of which the symmetric difference is composed are sets M of the module $\mathfrak{M}$, and since

$$B = AB + M_2 = (A - M_1) + M_2$$
$$= (A \dot{+} B) - M_1 = (A + M_2) - M_1,$$

one of the congruent sets is obtained from the other by subtracting one set M and adding another. We can also say that A and B agree "up to sets M" or "to within sets M" or are identical "except for sets M" or "neglecting sets M." $A \equiv 0$ ($\mathfrak{M}$) means that A belongs to $\mathfrak{M}$. In the following we shall drop the explicit mention of the fixed module in congruences, and instead of $A \equiv B(\mathfrak{M})$ we shall simply write $A \equiv B$.

That $A \equiv A$ and that $A \equiv B$ implies $B \equiv A$ – that is, that the congruence relation is reflexive and symmetric – is trivial; because of (1), it is also transitive; that is, $A \equiv B$ and $B \equiv C$ imply $A \equiv C$. It therefore allows of the division of the subsets of E into classes of congruent sets in which two classes are either disjoint or identical. If $E \equiv 0$, then all the sets are $\equiv 0$, and there is only one class; the other extreme would be for $\mathfrak{M}$ to consist only of the null set 0 and every individual set to form a class by itself.

From (2) it follows that $A \equiv B$ implies $E - A \equiv E - B$.

From (3) it follows that $A_n \equiv B_n$ implies

$$\mathfrak{S}A_n \equiv \mathfrak{S}B_n, \quad \mathfrak{D}A_n \equiv \mathfrak{D}B_n$$

for a finite set of indices n and, in the case of a σ-module, for a countable set also.

In the case of a σ-module, (4) yields

$$\text{if } A_{n_1 \cdots n_k} \equiv B_{n_1 \cdots n_k}, \text{ then } \quad A \equiv B;$$

the Suslin process leaves congruences unaltered.

Now let E be a metric space; we call every open set containing the point x a neighborhood U_x of x. Let $\mathfrak{M}$ again be a fixed module, and let A be an arbitrary set of the space. For the local behavior of A to $\mathfrak{M}$ at a point x of the space we make the following distinction:

x will be called a *null point* of A (for $\mathfrak{M}$) if it has a neighborhood U_x for which

$$(5) \qquad AU_x \equiv 0;$$

otherwise — and therefore when we have

$$AU_x \not\equiv 0$$

for every neighborhood U_x — we call x a *positive* point. The set of positive points will be called A_p and that of the null points A_q; therefore $E = A_p + A_q$. *A_q is open; A_p is closed.* For if $x \varepsilon A_q$, so that x has a neighborhood U_x for which (5) holds, then U_x is contained in A_q, because every point of U_x also has such a neighborhood (namely U_x). We thus have

$$A_q = \mathop{\mathfrak{S}}_{x}^{A_q} U_x$$

if a U_x is assigned to each null point x in accordance with (5), and

$$AA_q = \mathop{\mathfrak{S}}_{x}^{A_q} AU_x,$$

in which every summand is $\equiv 0$. When $\mathfrak{M}$ is a σ-module and E — or, at any rate, A — is separable, then it follows that

$$(6) \qquad AA_q \equiv 0,$$

since, by virtue of VI of § 25, the sum with respect to the U_x (or the

AU_x) can be restricted to countably many of these summands. But equation (6) can also hold when E is not separable (compare Theorem I below).

A point $x \varepsilon E - A_\alpha$ is a null point of A, since it has a neighborhood $U_x = E - A_\alpha$ for which $AU_x = 0$; from this it follows that

$$(7) \qquad A_p \leqq A_\alpha$$

If all the finite subsets of A belong to $\mathfrak{M}$, then $A_p \leqq A_\beta$; if all the countable subsets do, then $A_p \leqq A_\gamma$ (compare § 23).

If $A \equiv B$, then $AU_x \equiv BU_x$ also, and every null point of one of the sets is also a null point of the other, so that $A_p = B_p$ and $A_q = B_q$. (The converse does not hold.)

2. The Baire condition for sets. Let $\mathfrak{M}$ now be the σ-module of the sets of first category (in E). The null points and the positive points of A are here called *points of the first and second categories* of A. We show first that formula (6) holds in every case, even for non-separable spaces E.

I. (THEOREM OF BANACH). *The points of the first category of A lying in A form a set of the first category.*

First we consider the special case that A is contained in A_q, so that we are to prove: *If all the points of A are of the first category, then A is of the first category.* We form a maximal system – that is, one that cannot be extended – of *disjoint* open sets U_x for which $AU_x \equiv 0$; the existence of such a system follows as in § 31 by means of well ordering and because of considerations of cardinality. x runs through a suitable subset of A_q; $U = \sum_x U_x$ is open; $V = E - U$ is closed. Then V is nowhere dense, and the open kernel $V_i = 0$; for were $V_i > 0$, then – depending on whether $AV_i = 0$ or a is a point of AV_i – there could be adjoined to the sets U_x either V_i itself or – since A is of the first category at a – some suitable $U_a \leqq V_i$ for which $AU_a \equiv 0$. We now have $V \equiv 0$,

$$A = AU + AV \equiv AU,$$

and it remains to show that $AU \equiv 0$. As a set of the first category,

$$AU_x = A_{x1} + A_{x2} + \cdots = \sum_n A_{xn}$$

is the sum of a countable number of nowhere-dense sets A_{xn}, which (with x fixed) can be taken as disjoint. Then all the sets A_{xn} are pairwise disjoint, and if we can show that every

$$A_n = \sum_x A_{xn}$$

is nowhere dense, then from

$$AU = \sum_{xn} A_{xn} = \sum_n A_n$$

the result $AU \equiv 0$ follows. Now we obviously have

$$A_{xn} = A_n U_x;$$

from this it follows for the closed hulls (p. 137, (13)) that

$$A_{xn\alpha} \geqq A_{n\alpha} U_x$$

and if G denotes the open kernel $A_{n\alpha i}$ of $A_{n\alpha}$: $A_{xn\alpha} \geqq GU_x$, and thus $GU_x = 0$, since A_{xn} is nowhere dense. Consequently, $GU = 0$, $G = GV \leqq V_i = 0$, $G = 0$, and A_n is nowhere dense.

The special case $A \leqq A_q$ of Theorem I is thus proved; in the general case, we observe that for every subset B of A $A_q \leqq B_q$ clearly holds and, in particular, for $B = AA_q$ we have $B \leqq B_q$, and thus $B \equiv 0$.

The boundary of every open set G or of every closed set F is nowhere dense, so that $G_\alpha - G \equiv F - F_i \equiv 0$; every open set is congruent with a closed set, and conversely. ($G \equiv G_\alpha$, $F \equiv F_i$).

We say that a set A is a *β-set* or satisfies the *Baire condition* — in the wider sense (Kuratowski) — if it is congruent to an open set or to a closed set.

The complement of a β-set is a β-set. For $A \equiv G$ yields $E - A \equiv E - G = F$.

The β-sets form a Borel system.[1] For if $A_n \equiv G_n \equiv F_n$ holds for $n = 1, 2, 3, \ldots$, then it follows that

$$\mathfrak{S}A_n \equiv \mathfrak{S}G_n = G, \quad \mathfrak{D}A_n \equiv \mathfrak{D}F_n = F.$$

All the Borel sets of the space are thus β-sets.

Every β-set is obtained from an open set by leaving off one E_{I} and adding another. If only one of these two operations is to be admitted, then we have: The β-sets are of the form

$$(8) \qquad G_\delta + E_{\mathrm{I}} \text{ or } F_\sigma - E_{\mathrm{I}}.$$

For let $A \equiv G$ be a β-set; the symmetric difference $[A, G]$, as a set of the first category, is contained in a set $D = F_\sigma$ of the first category; if we set $C = E - D = G_\delta$, then $C[A, G] = [CA, CG] = 0$, $CA = CG$, and

$$A = CA + DA = CG + DA,$$

[1] And even a Suslin system (Nikodym).

where CG is a G_δ and DA is an E_{I}. Taking complements yields the second form in (8).[1]

A is a β-set if and only if there exists a set $C \equiv E$ ($E - C$ an E_{I}) *such that* CA *is open, or closed, or simultaneously open and closed in* C.

It is evident that this suffices; if, for example, $CA = CG$ and $C \equiv E$, then $A = EA \equiv CA = CG \equiv EG = G$. The necessity follows thus: If $A \equiv H$ and $C = E - [A, H] \equiv E$, then as above, $C[A, H] = [CA, CH] = 0$ and $CA = CH$. If H is replaced by an open or a closed set, then there exists a $C_1 \equiv E$ for which $C_1 A = C_1 G$, a $C_2 \equiv E$ for which $C_2 A = C_2 F$ and a $C = C_1 C_2 \equiv E$ for which $CA = CG = CF$.

Further necessary and sufficient conditions for β-sets are found with the help of the two sets A_q and A_p of the points of the first and second categories of A. Let us set $B = E - A$. For every set A we have, by (6),

$$(6^*) \qquad A = A(A_p + A_q) \equiv A A_p = A_p - B A_p.$$

As a consequence, the congruences

$$(9) \qquad BA_p \equiv 0$$

and

$$(10) \qquad A \equiv A_p$$

mean the same; they are sufficient for a β-set A (A is congruent to a closed set A_p), but they are also necessary, since (7) and (6*) imply, for a closed set F that F_p is contained in F, so that $F \equiv FF_p = F_p$, and if $A \equiv F$ is a β-set, then $A_p = F_p$ and thus $A \equiv A_p$. (9) states that the points not in A at which A is of the second category form only a set of the first category.

From (10) the congruences

$$(11) \qquad A \equiv A_p \equiv B_q, \quad B \equiv B_p \equiv A_q$$

are derived by taking complements as well as interchanging the sets A and B; each one separately is necessary and sufficient for β-sets, for example

$$A_p \equiv B_q;$$

for it follows from this that $BA_p \equiv BB_q \equiv 0$ — congruence (9). For-

[1] For the reader acquainted with the theory of Lebesgue measure, we point out that there exists a far-reaching analogy between the measurable sets and the β-sets and, in particular, between the sets of measure 0 and the sets of the first category (Sierpiński). The measurable sets are the sets of the form

$$G_\delta - N \quad \text{or} \quad F_\sigma + N,$$

where N is a set of measure 0; this should be compared with (8).

mulas (11) state that a β-set A consists, up to sets of the first category, of the points of the second category of A, or of the points of the first category of $B = E - A$. Finally, we also mention the following characterization of the β-sets:

(12) $\quad A_q \dot{+} B_q$ dense, $\quad A_p B_p$ nowhere dense (in the space E);

that is, the points at which at least one of the sets is of the first category form a dense (open) set; those at which both A and B are of the second category, a nowhere-dense (closed) set. In fact, (12) is sufficient; for from the congruence $B \equiv BB_p$ – which is valid in general – it follows that $BA_p \equiv BA_pB_p$ and, in the case (12), that $BA_p \equiv 0$, that is, (9). On the other hand, by (7), $A_pB_p \leqq A_\alpha B_\alpha = A_f$ (the boundary of A); if $A \equiv F$, $B \equiv G = E - F$, then $A_pB_p = F_pG_p \leqq F_f$; the boundary of a closed set, however, is nowhere dense, and (12) is also necessary.

We call a set A *α-closed* if it is congruent with its closed hull ($A \equiv A_\alpha$), *α-open* if it is congruent with its open kernel ($A \equiv A_i$), and an *α-set* if it is both – that is, if $A_f = A_\alpha - A_i \equiv 0$, that is, if the boundary of A is of the first category. These are all special β-sets. The α-open and the α-closed sets are the complements of each other.

The sum of finitely many α-closed sets, and the intersection of countably many, are α-closed; the intersection of finitely many α-open sets, and the sum of countably many, are α-open.

It suffices to prove the first statement. For $A = \mathfrak{S}A_n$, with the number of summands finite, we have $A_\alpha = \mathfrak{S}A_{n\alpha} \equiv \mathfrak{S}A_n = A$. For $A = \mathfrak{D}A_n$, with finitely many or countably many sets, we have $A_\alpha \leqq \mathfrak{D}A_{n\alpha} = A^*$ and $A^* \equiv \mathfrak{D}A_n = A$; from $A \leqq A_\alpha \leqq A^*$ and $A \equiv A^*$, it follows that $A \equiv A_\alpha$.

If, instead of beginning with the σ-module of the sets of the first category, we begin with the module $\mathfrak{M}_0$ of the *nowhere-dense* sets, and denote congruences modulo $\mathfrak{M}_0$ by $A \sim B$ – that is, $[A, B]$ is nowhere dense – where once more we have $E - A \sim E - B$, and where

$$\mathfrak{S}A_n \sim \mathfrak{S}B_n, \quad \mathfrak{D}A_n \sim \mathfrak{D}B_n$$

follows from $A_n \sim B_n$ for *finitely* many n – then analogues of the β-sets and α-sets can be defined: namely, β_0-sets by means of $A \sim G$ or $A \sim F$ (once more we have $G \sim G_\alpha$ and $F \sim F_i$) and α_0-sets by means of $A_f \sim 0$ – that is, as sets with nowhere-dense boundary. However, the β_0-sets here coincide with the α_0-sets. For since D_α is also nowhere dense when D is nowhere dense, $B = A + D$ implies $B_\alpha = A_\alpha \dot{+} D_\alpha \sim A_\alpha$, and $B \sim A$ or $B = (A - D_1) + D_2$ implies $B_\alpha \sim (A - D_1)_\alpha \sim A_\alpha$, so that when $A \sim B$, we also have $A_\alpha \sim B_\alpha$ and, by taking complements twice, $A_i \sim B_i$ as well. Therefore, if $A \sim F \sim G$, then $A_\alpha \sim F_\alpha = F$ and $A_i \sim G_i = G$, $A_\alpha \sim A_i$.

Let *the sets with nowhere-dense boundary* be called *sets N*; they give rise to the more general sets considered earlier, in the following way:

II. *The α-closed sets are the N_δ, the α-open sets are the N_σ, and the β-sets are the sets* Lim N_n (and are thus simultaneously $N_{\sigma\delta}$ and $N_{\delta\sigma}$).

First, every N_δ is an α-closed set, since the N-sets are α-closed and the α-closed sets form a δ-system. On the other hand, let A be α-closed, $A_\alpha - A = E_{\mathrm{I}}$, or

$$A_\alpha = A + D_1 + D_2 + \cdots,$$

where the D_n are nowhere dense and may be assumed disjoint. If we set

$$A_n = A + D_n + D_{n+1} + \cdots,$$

then $A \leqq A_n \leqq A_\alpha$, $A_{n\alpha} = A_\alpha$, and $A_{n\alpha} - A_n = D_1 + \cdots + D_{n-1}$ is nowhere dense, so that $A_n \sim A_{n\alpha}$ is an N-set, whence $A = \mathfrak{D} A_n$ is an N_δ. On taking complements ($E - N$ is an N), the statement about α-open sets follows. Insofar as the β-sets are concerned, we remind the reader of the definition of $\overline{\mathrm{Lim}}$, $\underline{\mathrm{Lim}}$, and Lim (p. 21); now since we obviously have

$$\underline{\mathrm{Lim}}\, A_n \cdot \underline{\mathrm{Lim}}\, B_n = \underline{\mathrm{Lim}}\, A_n B_n \leqq \overline{\mathrm{Lim}}\, A_n B_n \leqq \overline{\mathrm{Lim}}\, A_n \cdot \overline{\mathrm{Lim}}\, B_n,$$

the existence of $\mathrm{Lim}\, A_n B_n = \mathrm{Lim}\, A_n \cdot \mathrm{Lim}\, B_n$ follows from the existence of $\mathrm{Lim}\, A_n$ and $\mathrm{Lim}\, B_n$, and the same for $\mathrm{Lim}\,(A_n \dot{+} B_n) = \mathrm{Lim}\, A_n \dot{+} \mathrm{Lim}\, B_n$. We now represent a β-set, in accordance with (8), in the form $A = G_\delta + E_{\mathrm{I}}$, or

$$A = C + D, \quad C = \mathfrak{D} C_n, \; D = \mathfrak{S} D_n$$

using open sets $C_1 \geqq C_2 \geqq \ldots$ and nowhere-dense sets $D_1 \leqq D_2 \leqq \ldots$, so that $\mathrm{Lim}\, C_n = C$ and $\mathrm{Lim}\, D_n = D$; then $A_n = C_n + D_n \sim C_n$ is an N-set, and $\mathrm{Lim}\, A_n = A$.

3. The Baire condition for functions. Let the function

$$y = \varphi(x)$$

assign uniquely to every point x of the metric space E a point y of the metric space H (compare p. 222); y is called the image of x; we denote the image of a set A contained in E – that is, the set of the images of the points of A – by $\varphi(A)$. The image $H_0 = \varphi(E)$ of the whole space E may be the whole space H or a subset of the space; we call $y = \varphi(x)$ a mapping of E *onto* H_0, or of E *into* H (and therefore, in case $H_0 = H$, a mapping of E onto H). We call the set of all the points x of E for which $\varphi(x) \varepsilon B$ the *inverse image* $\psi(B)$ of a set $B \leqq H$; obviously, $\psi(B) = \psi(H_0 B)$.

The point x is called a point of continuity of $\varphi(x)$ if for every sequence $x_n \to x$ we also have $\varphi(x_n) \to \varphi(x)$. *The set C of the points of continuity is always a G_δ, the set D of the points of discontinuity is an F_σ.* (Proof as in § 42, 3 for real functions.) We also recall the topological characterization of the points of continuity x (p. 223). *For $y = \varphi(x)$ the inverse image of every neighborhood V_y has x as an interior point.* We can restrict ourselves here to the V_y that belong to a *complete system of neighborhoods* (p. 259) or, as we shall say for the sake of brevity, to a *basis* $\mathfrak{B}$ of the space H. *A basis is a system of open sets from which all the open sets can be obtained by taking sums.* If we therefore let V range over all the sets of a basis and $U = \psi(V)$ over their inverse images, then x is a point of continuity if and only if it is an interior point of every set U to which it belongs, and consequently it is a point of discontinuity if there is at least one U for which $x \varepsilon U - U_i = U_b$ (U_b = border of U). We thus obtain for the set D of the points of discontinuity the simple representation

$$D = \mathfrak{S} U_b, \tag{13}$$

where the sum, as said before, is to be taken over the inverse images $U = \psi(V)$ of all the sets V of a basis of H (or, by virtue of $\psi(V) = \psi(H_0 V)$, of H_0). For a continuous mapping ($D = 0$) there follows the familiar characterization: The inverse images of all the open sets are open (§ 35, I).

The mapping $y = \varphi(x)$ yields, if x is restricted to a set $A \leqq E$, a partial function $\varphi(x \mid A)$, or a partial mapping of A into H (onto $\varphi(A) \leqq H$), under which the inverse image of a set $B \leqq H$ is obviously $A\psi(B)$.

We call $\varphi(x)$ an *α-function* if the set D of its points of discontinuity is of the first category ($D \equiv 0$, $C \equiv E$). Every pointwise discontinuous function (§ 42, 3) is an α-function and, if $E - E_I$ is always dense in E and E is a G_{II}-space (p. 165) – for example, a complete space – then every α-function is also pointwise discontinuous.

We say that $\varphi(x)$ is a *β-function*, or satisfies the *Baire condition* (in the wider sense), if there exists a set $C \equiv E$ for which $\varphi(x \mid C)$ is continuous. These functions are thus continuous "up to sets of the first category" in the sense of p. 296. We remind the reader once more that the points of C are here points of continuity of the partial function $\varphi(x \mid C)$ but not necessarily of the total function $\varphi(x)$.

The connection between α-functions and α-sets and between β-functions and β-sets is established by the following theorem.

III. *For an α-function it is necessary — and, in case H is at most separable, also sufficient — that the inverse image of every open* (closed) *set be α-open* (α-closed).

This follows from (13). If the basis $\mathfrak{B}$ of all the open sets is formed, then when $D \equiv 0$, every $U_b \equiv 0$, $U \equiv U_i$, the inverse image of every open set V is α-open, and the inverse image $E - U = \psi(H - V)$ of every closed set $H - V$ is α-closed. Conversely, it follows from $U_b \equiv 0$, when H is at most separable, by choosing an at most countable basis, that $D \equiv 0$. (It suffices, of course, for H_0 to be at most separable.)

IV. *For a β-function it is necessary — and, in case H is at most separable, also sufficient — that the inverse image of every open set* (or of every closed set, or even of every Borel set) *be a β-set.*

Under the partial mapping $\varphi(x \mid C)$, the inverse image of V, as remarked above, is $C\psi(V) = CU$ and, in case $\psi(x \mid C)$ is continuous, it is open in C: $CU = CG$; it follows from this, for $C \equiv E$, that $U \equiv G$ and that U is a β-set provided that $\varphi(x)$ is a β-function. The statements in parentheses follow by formation of complements, sums, and intersections.

Conversely, if every $U = \psi(V)$ is a β-set and H is at most separable, let V range over an at most countable basis; we assign to every U an open set $G \equiv U$ and form the sum of the symmetric differences $D = \mathfrak{S}\,[U, G] \equiv 0$ and the set $C = E - D \equiv E$ as well; then $CU = CG$; that is, for the partial function $\varphi(x \mid C)$ the inverse image CU of every basis set V is open in C, and consequently the inverse image of every open set is open in $C : \varphi(x \mid C)$ is continuous; $\varphi(x)$ is a β-function.

The characteristic function $\varphi(x)$ of a set A is an α-function (β-function) if and only if A is an α-set (β-set).

This follows from III and IV if we let the space $H = \{0, 1\}$ consist only of the two numbers 0 and 1; all four subsets of H are both open and closed, and their inverse images are E, A, $E - A$, and 0.

Incidentally, the statement follows directly for α-functions from the fact that A_f is the set of the points of discontinuity of $\varphi(x)$; in particular, $\varphi(x)$ is continuous if and only if A is both open and closed, and $\varphi(x \mid C)$ is continuous if and only if CA is both open and closed in C. The statement about β-functions then follows from the characteristic property of the β-sets given in § 45, 2.

We now consider a sequence of mappings $y_n = \varphi_n(x)$ of the space E into the space H which converges for every x, so that

$$y = \lim y_n = \lim \varphi_n(x) = \varphi(x)$$

again gives a mapping of E in H; let $\varphi(x)$ be called the limit function of the convergent sequence $\varphi_n(x)$.

V. *The limit function of a convergent sequence of continuous functions is an α-function.*

VI. *The limit function of a convergent sequence of β-functions is a β-function.*

These theorems, due to Kuratowski, are similar to Theorems V of § 42 and VI of § 43 – in their proofs as well, as we shall see in a moment – but they have the advantage of generality, in that they hold true for every space E. They state that a certain set D is of the first category and that its complement C is $\equiv E$; if, *in particular*, E is a G_{II}-set, then the additional result follows that C is dense in E.

Proof of V. Let the $\varphi_n(x)$ be continuous. The set C of the points of continuity of $\varphi(x)$ is then determined as follows (compare § 42, 3): For $\sigma > 0$, let $P_m(\sigma)$ be the set of the points x at which

$$(\alpha) \qquad yy_m \leqq \sigma,$$

and let

$$G(\sigma) = \mathfrak{S}_m P_{mi}(\sigma)$$

be the sum of the open kernels of these sets for $m = 1, 2, \ldots$; then

$$C = \mathfrak{D}_{\sigma>0} G(\sigma),$$

and because of the monotone decrease of $G(\sigma)$ with σ, we can replace this by

$$C = \mathfrak{D}_n G\left(\frac{1}{n}\right).$$

Namely: If a is a point of continuity of $\varphi(x)$ then, by virtue of

$$b_n = \varphi_n(a) \to \varphi(a) = b,$$

we choose an m so large that $bb_m \leqq \sigma/3$ and then, because of the continuity of $\varphi(x)$ and $\varphi_m(x)$ at the point a, a neighborhood U_a in which $by \leqq \sigma/3$ and $b_m y_m \leqq \sigma/3$; then $yy_m \leqq \sigma$ in U_a, so that $a \,\varepsilon\, P_{mi}(\sigma) \leqq G(\sigma)$; since this holds for every σ, it follows that $C \leqq \mathfrak{D} G(\sigma)$.

Conversely, let $a \varepsilon \mathfrak{D} G(\sigma)$, and for a certain σ and the m belonging to it, let $a \,\varepsilon\, P_{mi}(\sigma/3)$, so that there exists a neighborhood U_a in which $yy_m \leqq \sigma/3$ and, in particular, $bb_m \leqq \sigma/3$ as well; because of the continuity of $\varphi_m(x)$ it is possible, in addition, to choose U_a so that $b_m y_m \leqq \sigma/3$. Therefore $by \leqq \sigma$ in U_a; since this holds for every σ, a is a point of continuity of $\varphi(x)$.

Furthermore, let $F_m(\sigma)$ be the set of those x at which

$$(\beta) \qquad y_m y_n \leqq \sigma \quad \text{for} \quad n = m+1, m+2, \ldots;$$

this set is closed (for each individual n the inequality (β) defines a closed set because of the continuity of $\varphi_m(x)$ and $\varphi_n(x)$; for all the $n \geqq m+1$ it defines the intersection of these closed sets). By virtue of the convergence of the sequence $\varphi_n(x)$, (β) is satisfied at every point x for some suitable m; from this it follows that

$$E = \underset{m}{\mathfrak{S}} F_m(\sigma).$$

On the other hand, however, (α) follows from (β), so that we have $F_m(\sigma) \leqq P_m(\sigma), F_{mi}(\sigma) \leqq P_{mi}(\sigma)$, and

$$\underset{m}{\mathfrak{S}} F_{mi}(\sigma) \leqq G(\sigma).$$

Since now $F_i = F$ always holds, we have $\underset{m}{\mathfrak{S}} F_{mi}(\sigma) \equiv E$ and, all the more, $G(\sigma) \equiv E$, so that $G(1/n) \equiv E$ and $C = \mathfrak{D} G(1/n) \equiv E$, and $\varphi(x)$ is an α-function.

Proof of VI. Let $\varphi_n(x)$ be a β-function, and let $\varphi_n(x \mid C_n)$, with $C_n \equiv E$, be continuous, and $C_0 = \mathfrak{D} C_n \equiv E$. The functions $\varphi_n(x \mid C_0)$ are continuous, and their limit function $\varphi(x \mid C_0)$ is thus an α-function in C_0; that is, its points of continuity form a set C for which $C_0 - C$ is of the first category in C_0 and, all the more, in E: $C \equiv C_0 \equiv E$. $\varphi(x \mid C)$ is continuous, and $\varphi(x)$ is a β-function.

The β-functions thus form a Baire system to which the continuous functions and all the Baire functions of the space E belong.

VII. *Every β-function is the limit function of a sequence of α-functions.*

Let $\varphi(x)$ be a β-function, let $\varphi(x \mid C)$ be continuous, and $E - C = D = E_{\mathrm{I}}$; D is the sum of a sequence of nowhere-dense sets. If these sets are replaced by their closed hulls, D increases but remains an E_{I}, C decreases, and the decreased partial function remains continuous; we can of course take $\mathfrak{D} = \mathfrak{S} F_k$ initially to be the sum of closed nowhere-dense sets F_k and take them to be an increasing sequence

$$D = F_1 + (F_2 - F_1) + (F_3 - F_2) + \cdots = \Sigma(F_k - F_{k-1})$$

with disjoint summands $F_k - F_{k-1}$ $(F_0 = 0)$. To every point $x \,\varepsilon\, D$ there thus corresponds a certain natural number $k(x)$ for which $x \,\varepsilon F_{k(x)} - F_{k(x)-1}$; if a sequence of points $x_n \,\varepsilon\, D$ converges to a point $c \,\varepsilon\, C$, then ultimately $x_n \,\bar{\varepsilon}\, F_k$ for every k (since otherwise c as well would belong to the closed set F_k); therefore $k(x_n) > k$, and hence $k(x_n) \to \infty$.

We now define a mapping $\alpha(x)$ of E into H (and even onto $\varphi(C)$) by setting $\alpha(x) = \varphi(x)$ for $x \varepsilon C$, whereas for $x \varepsilon D$ we choose a point $c(x) \varepsilon C$ having a distance $< \delta(x, C) + 1/k(x)$ from x ($\delta(x, C) \geqq 0$ is the lower distance of x from C) and then define $\alpha(x) = \varphi(c(x))$. This function, we claim, is continuous at every point $c \varepsilon C$ and is therefore an α-function. It is to be shown, for $x_n \to c$, that $\alpha(x_n) \to \alpha(c)$, where we may restrict ourselves to the two cases that the x_n belong either all to C or all to D. For $x_n \varepsilon C$, we have $\alpha(x_n) = \varphi(x_n) \to \varphi(x) = \alpha(x)$ because of the continuity of $\varphi(x \mid C)$. For $x_n \varepsilon D$, we have

$$\delta(x_n, C) \to 0, k(x_n) \to \infty,$$

the distance between x_n and $c(x_n)$ converges to 0, and therefore $c(x_n) \to c$, and $\alpha(x_n) = \varphi(c(x_n)) \to \varphi(c) = \alpha(c)$, also because of the continuity of $\varphi(x \mid C)$.

Now let

$$\varphi_k(x) = \varphi(x) \text{ for } x \varepsilon C + F_k$$
$$\varphi_k(x) = \alpha(x) \text{ for } x \varepsilon D - F_k.$$

These functions, too, are continuous at $c \varepsilon C$, since for $x_n \to c$ and $x_n \varepsilon D$ we ultimately have $x_n \varepsilon D - F_k$, $\varphi_k(x_n) = \alpha(x_n) \to \alpha(c) = \varphi(c) = \varphi_k(c)$. On the other hand, we have $\lim_k \varphi_k(x) = \varphi(x)$, and even $\varphi_k(x) = \varphi(x)$ for all k if $x \varepsilon C$ and for $k \geqq k(x)$ if $x \varepsilon D$. $\varphi(x)$ is thus represented as a limit function of the α-functions $\varphi_k(x)$.

In certain cases – for example, when dealing with real functions $\varphi(x)$ (with H the space of the real numbers) – every β-function is even a limit function of functions for which the set of points of discontinuity is actually *nowhere dense* and not merely of the first category, that is, a limit function of *N-functions*, as we call these functions in analogy to the N-sets with nowhere-dense boundary: the characteristic function of an N-set is an N function, and conversely. If $\varphi(x)$ is a β-function and $\varphi(x \mid C)$ continuous where, as in the proof of VII, we assume $D = E - C = \mathfrak{S} F_k$ with increasing nowhere-dense closed sets F_k, then by the Extension Theorem (Theorem III of § 43) the function $\varphi(x \mid C)$ continuous in $C = G_\delta$ can be extended to a function of the first class

$$f(x) = \lim f_k(x)$$

defined in E, that is, to a limit function of a sequence of continuous functions (continuous in E), where $f(x) = \varphi(x)$ in C. If we then set

$$\varphi_k(x) = f_k(x) \quad \text{for} \quad x \varepsilon E - F_k$$
$$\varphi_k(x) = \varphi(x) \quad \text{for} \quad x \varepsilon F_k,$$

then $\varphi(x)$ is continuous at the points of the open set $E - F_k$, and the set of its points of discontinuity (which are contained in F_k) is nowhere dense. We have $\lim_k \varphi_k(x) = \varphi(x)$: in C we have

$$\varphi_k(x) = f_k(x) \to f(x) = \varphi(x),$$

and at every point of D we ultimately have $\varphi_k(x) = \varphi(x)$.

More generally – and we state this without proof – if H or H_0 is at most separable, then every β-function is a limit function of N-functions, just as every β-set is a limit of N-sets (Theorem II).

4. The restricted Baire condition. If M is a subset of E, then we call $\varphi(x)$ a *β_M-function* when $\varphi(x \mid M)$ is continuous up to sets of the first category (in M), or is a β-function in the space M, that is, when a decomposition $M = C + D$ is possible for which $D = M_{\mathrm{I}}$ and for which $\varphi(x \mid C)$ is continuous. Here it is possible to deduce M from the closed hull M_α as well as from the dense-in-itself kernel M_k; that is, we have:

If $F = M_\alpha$, then a β_F-function is also a β_M-function.

For if $F = C + D$, where D is of the first category in F and $\varphi(x \mid C)$ is continuous, then $\varphi(x \mid MC)$ is continuous, and MD is of the first category in F and so, by XIII of § 27, of the first category in M as well.

If $K = M_k$, then a β_K-function is at the same time a β_M-function.

For (compare p. 296 above),

$$M = H + (S - H) + K,$$

where H is the isolated part and S the separated part of M, then MH_β is closed in MH_α and is nowhere dense, since its complement $MH = H$ is dense in MH_α and, a fortiori, MH_β is an M_{I}. By § 23, (15), S is contained in H_α and $S - H$ in H_β. Furthermore, there exists a D, of the first category in K, and a fortiori in M, for which $\varphi(x \mid K - D)$ is continuous. Eliminating $MH_\beta \dotplus D$ from M leaves $H + C$, where $\varphi(x \mid C)$ is continuous and $CH_\beta = 0$; therefore $\varphi(x \mid H + C)$ is also continuous at the points of C and at the (isolated) points of H; $\varphi(x)$ is a β_M-function.

We say that $\varphi(x)$ satisfies the *restricted Baire condition* or is a *β^*-function* if it is a β_M-function for every M contained in E. For this to hold, it suffices that it be a β_P-function for every *perfect* P; since for $M_\alpha = F$ and $F_k = P$ it is possible to go from P to F and from F to M. The β_M-functions, for fixed M, form a Baire system to which the Baire functions of the space E belong, and the same holds for the intersection of all these systems, that is, for the system of the β^*-functions.

The set A is called a β_M-set if MA is a β-set in the space M, that is, if a set MG open in M (G open in E) exists for which $[MA, MG] =$

$M[A, G]$ is of the first category in M. This is equivalent with the characteristic function $\varphi(x)$ of A being a β_M-function; for $\varphi(x \mid M)$ is the characteristic function of MA for the space M. A satisfies the *restricted Baire condition,* or is a β^*-set, if it is a β_M-set for every M; it suffices for this that it be a β_P-set for every perfect P. If PA is, in particular, of the first category in P for every perfect P, then A is always a β_P-set and therefore a β^*-set (although MA is not always of the first category in M; for example, certainly not when M consists of a single point of A). This is the case of the Lusin set L described on p. 297.

§ 46. Half-schlicht Mappings

1. Borel separability. Two sets A and B of the space A are said to be *Borel separable* if they can be enclosed in disjoint Borel sets P and Q:

$$A \leqq P, \quad B \leqq Q, \quad PQ = 0.$$

This is equivalent to the statement that *A and B are disjoint and are Borel sets in their sum.* For from the Borel separability it follows that

$$AB = 0, \quad A = (A+B)P, \quad B = (A+B)Q;$$

conversely, $(A+B)\,PQ = 0$ follows from these equations, and

$$A \leqq P - PQ, \quad B \leqq Q - PQ.$$

In unsymmetric form the Borel separability of A and B can also be expressed thus: There exists a Borel set P which includes A and excludes $B: A \leqq P, BP = 0$. The Borel separability of A and of $E - B$ is equivalent with: There exists a Borel set P for which $A \leqq P \leqq B$.

If for $m = 1, 2, 3, \ldots$ the sets A_m and B are Borel separable, then so are $A = \mathfrak{S} A_m$ and B. For from $A_m \leqq P_m$ and $BP_m = 0$, it follows, with $P = \mathfrak{S} P_m$, that $A \leqq P$ and $BP = 0$.

If, for $m = 1, 2, 3, \ldots$ and $n = 1, 2, 3, \ldots$, the sets A_m and B_n are Borel separable, then so are $A = \mathfrak{S} A_m$ and $B = \mathfrak{S} B_n$, so that conversely: If A and B are not Borel separable, then there exists at least one pair of sets A_m and B_n that are not Borel separable.

If the sets A_m are pairwise Borel separable, then they are "simultaneously" Borel separable; that is, they can be enclosed in pairwise disjoint Borel sets. For, A_m and $\sum_{n \neq m} A_n$ are Borel separable and are contained in disjoint Borel sets P_m and Q_m; then A_m is contained in $P_m \mathfrak{D}_{n \neq m} Q_n$, and these sets are disjoint.

Before continuing further, we should like to show, following Lusin, how, by use of the concept of Borel separability, the two principal theorems, Theorems III and IV of § 34, concerning Suslin sets can be proved without recourse to transfinite ordinal numbers (§ 34, 2). Let

$$A = \underset{ikl\cdots}{\mathfrak{S}} C_i C_{ik} C_{ikl} \cdots$$

be, in the — for the time being — arbitrary space E, a Suslin set formed with the closed sets $C_i \geqq C_{ik} \geqq C_{ikl} \geqq \ldots$; the indices range over the natural numbers. If we hold initial indices fixed, we obtain the sets

$$A_i = \underset{kl\cdots}{\mathfrak{S}}, \quad A_{ik} = \underset{l\ldots}{\mathfrak{S}}, \quad \ldots$$

with $$A = \underset{i}{\mathfrak{S}} A_i, \quad A_i = \underset{k}{\mathfrak{S}} A_{ik}, \quad A_{ik} = \underset{l}{\mathfrak{S}} A_{ikl}, \ldots .$$

Similarly, we let $$B = \underset{pqr\cdots}{\mathfrak{S}} D_p D_{pq} D_{pqr} \cdots$$

with the corresponding assumptions and notation. Let us assume that A and B are not Borel separable; by virtue of $A = \underset{i}{\mathfrak{S}} A_i$ and $B = \underset{p}{\mathfrak{S}} B_p$, there then exists a non-Borel-separable pair of sets A_i and B_p, next, a non-Borel-separable pair A_{ik} and B_{pq}, etc. Because of $A_i \leqq C_i$ and $B_p \leqq D_p$ (C_i and D_p closed), we have $C_i D_p > 0$ and also

$$C_{ik} D_{pq} > 0, \; C_{ikl} D_{pqr} > 0, \ldots .$$

If now E is separable, then we may assume (p. 217) that the diameters of the C and D converge to 0 as the number of indices increases; if in addition, E is complete, then the sequence of the $C_i D_p, C_{ik} D_{pq}, \ldots$ has a point of intersection which obviously belongs to AB. That is, if A and B are not Borel separable, then they are not even disjoint, or:

In a separable complete space, two disjoint Suslin sets are Borel separable, that is, they are Borel sets in their sum (§ 34, III).

Furthermore, let

$$A = \sum C_i C_{ik} C_{ikl} \cdots$$

be representable with disjoint summands, then

$$A = \sum_i A_i, \quad A_i = \sum_k A_{ik}, \quad A_{ik} = \sum_l A_{ikl}, \ldots$$

with disjoint summands. If E is separable and complete, then the disjoint Suslin sets A_i are pairwise Borel separable and therefore also simultaneously Borel separable: there exist disjoint Borel sets P_i containing A_i which can, in addition, be replaced by $C_i P_i$, so that they may be assumed to be contained in C_i. Similarly, there exist disjoint Borel sets

P_{ik} containing A_{ik} and contained in C_{ik} where, in addition, P_{ik} can be replaced by $P_i P_{ik}$, that is, where it may be assumed to be contained in P_i. In this way, we obtain

$$A_i \leqq P_i \leqq C_i, \quad A_{ik} \leqq P_{ik} \leqq C_{ik}, \quad A_{ikl} \leqq P_{ikl} \leqq C_{ikl}, \ldots$$
$$P_i \geqq P_{ik} \geqq P_{ikl} \geqq \ldots$$

But since $A_i A_{ik} A_{ikl} \ldots = C_i C_{ik} C_{ikl} \ldots$, this is also $= P_i P_{ik} P_{ikl} \ldots$,

$$A = \Sigma P_i P_{ik} P_{ikl} \ldots$$

and, since the sets P with equal numbers of indices are pairwise disjoint, this is equivalent with

$$A = \Sigma P_i \cdot \Sigma P_{ik} \cdot \Sigma P_{ikl} \cdots,$$

and A is a Borel set. *In a separable complete space, every Suslin set that can be represented by means of disjoint summands is a Borel set* (§ 34, IV).

2. Obtaining the *B*-sets. The (single-valued) mapping $y = \varphi(x)$ of A onto B was called one-to-one, or schlicht, if it has a single-valued inverse, so that the inverse image $\psi(y)$ of every point $y \varepsilon B$ consists of only one point; it will be called *half-schlicht* and B will be called the half-schlicht image of A if every inverse image $\psi(y)$ is *at most countable.*

We call the Borel and Suslin sets of *a separable complete* space B-sets and S-sets, for short. From Theorem XIII of § 43 we know that:

The Baire image of an S-set is an S-set; the one-to-one Baire image of a B-set is a B-set.

The special case of *continuous* images has already been treated in Theorem II of § 37. We wish to show that even a half-schlicht Baire image of a B-set is also a B-set and that such a mapping can be split into at most countably many simple Baire mappings of B-sets. We begin by stating a theorem on which the proofs of both statements will be based.

I. *Let the mapping $y = \varphi(x)$ of the complete space A be continuous. Let a sequence of bounded sets*[1]

$$U_p > U_{pq} > U_{pqr} > \ldots$$

open in A, with diameters $\to 0$, *and with the images*

$$V_p = \varphi(U_p), \quad V_{pq} = \varphi(U_{pq}), \quad V_{pqr} = \varphi(U_{pqr}), \ldots$$

be assigned to every dyadic sequence $p, q, r, \ldots$ — that is, one formed from

[1] For brevity, let $P > Q$ (or $Q < P$) mean $P_i \geqq Q_\alpha$; the open kernel of P contains the closed hull of Q. For a sequence $P > Q > R \ldots$ we obviously have

$$PQR \ldots = P_\alpha Q_\alpha R_\alpha \ldots = P_i Q_i R_i \ldots$$

the numerals 1 and 2 — *in such a way that the* 2^n *sets* U *with* n *indices are pairwise disjoint while their images* V *have points in common*:

$$(1) \qquad V_1 V_2 > 0, \quad V_{11} V_{12} V_{21} V_{22} > 0, \ldots$$

Then the uncountable set

$$D = \Sigma U_p U_{pq} U_{pqr} \cdots$$

has an image consisting of but one point, so that the mapping is not half-schlicht.

The proof is exceedingly simple. The intersection $U_p U_{pq} U_{pqr} \cdots$ can be replaced by the intersection of the closed hulls and therefore contains only one point; to different dyadic sequences there correspond different points $x = U_p U_{pq} U_{pqr} \ldots$, and D is of the cardinality of the continuum.[1] If $y = \varphi(x)$, then because of the continuity, the diameters of the images $V_p, V_{pq}, V_{pqr}, \ldots$ also converge to 0. If $\xi = U_\pi U_{\pi\chi} U_{\pi\chi\varrho} \ldots$, then $V_p V_\pi > 0$, $V_{pq} V_{\pi\chi} > 0$, $V_{pqr} V_{\pi\chi\varrho} > 0, \ldots$, and since the sum of two sets with non-empty intersection has a diameter which is at most equal to the sum of the two diameters taken separately, the diameters of

$$V_p \dotplus V_\pi, \quad V_{pq} \dotplus V_{\pi\chi}, \quad V_{pqr} \dotplus V_{\pi\chi\varrho}, \ldots$$

also converge to 0, that is, $\eta = \varphi(\xi)$ coincides with y. Therefore $\varphi(D) = y$ has only one point, and $\psi(y) \geqq D$ is uncountable.

The difficulty consists primarily in the realization of the conditions (1). In the case we shall treat first (Theorem II), the non-vanishing of the sets (1) will be proved by their being non-Borel-separable from a certain other set; in the later case (Theorem IV), by using the fact that the sets U with n indices form "coherent" systems.

For the mapping $y = \varphi(x)$ of A onto B, we call the point y of B a *simple image* or a *multiple image* depending on whether its inverse image $\psi(y)$ consists of one point or of more than one point. The set M of the multiple images can obviously be represented in the form

$$(2) \qquad M = \mathfrak{S} \varphi(U) \varphi(U'),$$

where U and U' range over all the pairs of disjoint sets of a basis (p. 320) of A. From this it follows that:

(A) *For a continuous or a Baire mapping of an* S*-set, the set of multiple images is an* S*-set.*

For the sets U and U' open in A and the images of these sets are S-sets, and the basis can be taken to be (at most) countable.

[1] D is, moreover, a dyadic discontinuum (p. 154).

(B) *If* $y = \varphi(x)$ *is a continuous mapping of the B-set* A *into the separable complete space* Y, *if* $B = \varphi(A)$ *is the image of* A, *and if* M *the set of the multiple images, then every S-set* S *contained in* $B - M$ *is Borel separable from* $Y - B$.

The disjoint S-sets S and M are Borel separable (in Y), and there exists a B-set Q which contains S and for which $QM = 0$. Since BQ is a Borel set in B, its inverse image $P = \psi(BQ)$ is a Borel set in A (§ 35, II) and is therefore a B-set. Inasmuch as $QM = 0$, all the points of BQ are simple images, and therefore BQ, as the one-to-one continuous image of P, is itself a B-set (and thus is a Borel set in Y and not only in B). We have $S \leqq BQ \leqq B$; between S and B there lies the B-set BQ; that is, S is Borel separable from $Y - B$.

(C) *For* $k = 1, 2, \ldots, n$, *let* $y_k = \varphi_k(x_k)$ *be continuous mappings of arbitrary B-sets* A_k *into the separable complete space* Y, *let* $\boldsymbol{B_k} = \boldsymbol{\varphi_k(A_k)}$ *be the image of* A_k, *let* M_k *be the set of the multiple images for* φ_k, *and finally let* B *be any set containing the* B_k *and contained in* Y. *If then* $M_1 \ldots M_n$ *is Borel separable from* $Y - B$, *then* $B_1 \ldots B_n$ *is also Borel separable from* $Y - B$.

Let $D = B_1 \ldots B_n$. By hypothesis, it is possible to interpose a B-set between $DM_1 \ldots M_n$ $(= M_1 \ldots M_n)$ and B. If it has already been established for some k of the series $n, n-1, \ldots, 1$ that a B-set Q can be interposed between $DM_1 \ldots M_k$ and B, then this is also true, we claim, for $DM_1 \ldots M_{k-1}$ (which, for $k = 1$, is to mean the set D). In fact, let

$$DM_1 \ldots M_k \leqq Q \leqq B;$$

then $DM_1 \ldots M_{k-1}(Y - Q)$ is an S-set contained in B_k (because D is contained in B_k), is disjoint to M_k (for $DM_1 \ldots M_{k-1} M_k$ is disjoint to $Y - Q$), is therefore contained in $B_k - M_k$, and consequently, by (B), is Borel separable from $Y - B_k$ and, a fortiori, from the smaller set $Y - B$. Therefore for some B-set Q', we have

$$DM_1 \ldots M_{k-1}(Y - Q) \leqq Q' \leqq B$$

as well as

$$DM_1 \ldots M_{k-1} Q \leqq Q \leqq B,$$

and, adding,

$$DM_1 \ldots M_{k-1} \leqq Q \dotplus Q' \leqq B.$$

This establishes the induction from k to $k - 1$, and D is seen to be Borel separable from $Y - B$.

II. *The half-schlicht continuous image of a separable complete space* A *is a B-set.*

We preface the proof by the following remarks: For any $\delta > 0$, those sets of a basis for the space A that have diameters $< \delta$ themselves form a basis; a separable space thus has for every $n = 1, 2, \ldots$, a countable basis $\mathfrak{B}_n$ consisting of sets U of diameters $< 1/n$. Further: If the non-empty set G is open in A, then the sets $U < G$ (as we stated earlier, this means that U_α is contained in G) belonging to a basis of A form a basis for the space G.[1] In the case that A is separable, G thus has a basis $\mathfrak{B}_n(G)$ which is at most countable and consists of sets $U < G$ with diameters $< 1/n$. Accordingly, we let $p, q, r, \ldots$ range over the natural numbers and let U_p stand for the sets of $\mathfrak{B}_1$, U_{pq} for the sets of $\mathfrak{B}_2(U_p)$, U_{pqr} for the sets of $\mathfrak{B}_3(U_{pq})$, and so on.[2] We therefore have

$$U_p > U_{pq} > U_{pqr} > \ldots,$$

and the sets U with n indices have diameters $< 1/n$. Let $V_p, V_{pq}, V_{pqr}, \ldots$ be the images of $U_p, U_{pq}, U_{pqr}, \ldots$ under the mapping $y = \varphi(x)$.

We prove II in this form: If the continuous image $B = \varphi(A)$ of A is not a B-set, then the mapping is not half-schlicht. Let B lie in the separable complete space Y.

The set of the multiple images in B is, by (2),

$$M = \mathop{\mathfrak{S}}_{p\pi} V_p V_\pi,$$

where the sum is extended over all disjoint pairs of sets U_p and U_π of the basis $\mathfrak{B}_1$. Now B is not Borel separable from $Y - B$ (this means just that B is not a Borel set in Y); by (C) (for $n = 1$) M is also not Borel separable from $Y - B$, so that one of the (at most countably many) summands of M is not Borel separable from $Y - B$; numbering the sets suitably, we therefore have

$$V_1 V_2 \quad \text{is not Borel separable from} \quad Y - B.$$

Let the set of the multiple images under the mapping $\varphi(x \mid U_p)$ of U_p onto V_p be M_p $(p = 1, 2)$; then we have

$$M_1 M_2 = \mathop{\mathfrak{S}}_{\substack{q\varkappa \\ r\varrho}} V_{1q} V_{1\varkappa} V_{2r} V_{2\varrho},$$

where the sum extends over the disjoint pairs $U_{1q}, U_{1\varkappa}$ and $U_{2r}, U_{2\varrho}$ of the bases $\mathfrak{B}_2(U_1)$ and $\mathfrak{B}_2(U_2)$. If $V_1 V_2$ is not Borel separable from $Y - B$, (C) yields, for $n = 2$, that $M_1 M_2$ and – for suitable numbering – that one of the summands

---

[1] This follows from the fact that, by the Separation Axiom ((6) on p. 260), every neighborhood U_1 of x contains a neighborhood $U < U_1$.

[2] If one of these bases is finite, we think of one basis set as being written infintely often.

$$V_{11}V_{12}V_{21}V_{22} \quad \text{is not Borel separable from} \quad Y - B$$

Continuing in this way, we realize the hypotheses of I, and in particular the inequalities (1), in that the sets on the left are not Borel separable from $Y - B$. Hence $\varphi(x)$ is not half-schlicht, and II is proved.

III. *The half-schlicht Baire image of a B-set is itself a B-set.*

Let $y = \varphi(x)$ be a half-schlicht mapping of the B-set A onto B. If $\varphi(x)$ is, first, continuous, then we note (§ 37, III) that A is the image of a separable complete space T, under a one-to-one continuous mapping $x = \xi(t)$, e.g., of a set closed in the Baire null space (the trivial case that A and T are only finite can be excluded). Then $y = \varphi(\xi(t)) = \eta(t)$ is a half-schlicht continuous mapping of T onto B, and therefore, by II, B is a B-set.

In the general case that $y = \varphi(x)$ is a Baire mapping of A into Y (which contains B), we proceed as in the proof of Theorem XIII of § 43. In the product space (A, Y), the set C of the points $(x, \varphi(x))$ is a Borel set and therefore a B-set, since Y can be taken as separable and complete; B is the projection of C onto Y and is therefore a continuous — and in our case half-schlicht — image of the B-set C and, by what has already been proved, is itself a B-set.

3. Cleavability. We call a set P contained in A *cleavable* under the mapping $y = \varphi(x)$ of the space A if P is the sum of a sequence of B-sets that are mapped one-to-one by φ, so that

$$P = \mathfrak{S}P_n, \quad P_n \text{ a } B\text{-set}, \quad \varphi(x \mid P_n) \text{ one-to-one.}$$

Then P itself is of course a B-set and $\varphi(x \mid P)$ is half-schlicht. Moreover, the summand P may, if we wish, be taken as disjoint by replacing P_n by $P_n - P_n \underset{m<n}{\mathfrak{S}} P_m$. (The essence of the condition is that the P_n are to be B-sets; without this provision every set P would be cleavable for half-schlicht $\varphi(x)$.)

A sum of a countable number of cleavable sets is cleavable. Every B-set contained in a cleavable set is itself cleavable.

(D) *Under a half-schlicht Baire mapping of a B-set, the set of the multiple images is a B-set.*

This follows from (2) where, by III, the U and their images are B-sets, and the basis can be chosen so as to be (at most) countable.

(E) *Let $y = \varphi(x)$ be a half-schlicht continuous mapping of the B-set A into the space Y; let $\psi(y)$ be the inverse image of y for $y \varepsilon Y$ and* *let $\psi_h(y)$ be the set of the isolated points of $\psi(y)$. Then the set $P=\sum_y \psi_h(y)$ is cleavable.*[1]

Let $U_1, U_2, \ldots$ be the sets of a basis of A, let $V_n=\varphi(U_n)$ be the image of U_n and, under the mapping $\varphi(x \mid U_n)$, let M_n be the set of the multiple images and $Q_n=V_n-M_n$ the set of the simple images. The sets U_n, V_n, M_n, and Q_n are B-sets, and similarly, the inverse images $P_n=U_n\psi(Q_n)$ of Q_n under the mapping $\varphi(x \mid U_n)$ (for Q_n is a Borel set in V_n, and thus P_n is a Borel set in U_n). Then $\varphi(x \mid P_n)$ is one-to-one, and accordingly, the set $\mathfrak{S}P_n$ is cleavable. But this is the set $P=\sum_y \psi_h(y)$. For if $x \varepsilon \psi_h(y)$, then there exists some U_n for which $\psi(y)U_n=x$, so that $y=\varphi(x)$ is the simple image under $\varphi(x \mid U_n)$, and $x \varepsilon P_n$. And vice versa.

In order to continue the separation of a cleavable portion of A begun here, let us take $\psi_\xi(y)$ to mean, for the ordinal numbers $\xi<\Omega$ (compare pp. 190 and 194) the *coherences* of $\psi(y)$; that is, $\psi_0(y)=\psi(y)$, $\psi_{\xi+1}(y)$ is the set of the points of accumulation of $\psi_\xi(y)$ lying in $\psi_\xi(y)$, so that $\psi_\xi(y)-\psi_{\xi+1}(y)$ is the set of isolated points of $\psi_\xi(y)$; for a limit ordinal η we have $\psi_\eta(y)=\mathfrak{D}_{\xi<\eta}\psi_\xi(y)$. Correspondingly, we set

$$A_\xi=\sum_y \psi_\xi(y) \qquad (A_0=A);$$

then for $\xi<\eta$ we have

$$A_\xi-A_\eta=\sum_y [\psi_\xi(y)-\psi_\eta(y)],$$

and the equation

$$\psi(y)-\psi_\eta(y)=\sum_{\xi<\eta}[\psi_\xi(y)-\psi_{\xi+1}(y)]$$

summed over y, gives

$$A-A_\eta=\sum_{\xi<\eta}(A_\xi-A_{\xi+1}).$$

Under the assumptions of (E), we then have:

(F) *The sets $A_\xi-A_{\xi+1}$ are cleavable.*

By (E), this holds for $\xi=0$. If it is already proved for $\xi<\eta$, then by (3) $A-A_\eta$ is cleavable and is thus a B-set, and A_η is also a B-set. Under the half-schlicht continuous mapping $\varphi(x \mid A_\eta)$, $A_\eta\psi(y)=\psi_\eta(y)$ is the inverse image of y and $\psi_\eta(y)-\psi_{\eta+1}(y)$ is the set of its isolated points; application of (E) yields the cleavability of $A_\eta-A_{\eta+1}$.

---

[1] Here, and in what follows, the sum with respect to y is to extend over $y \varepsilon Y$; the summands may, in part, be empty; for example, $\psi(y)=0$ when y does not belong to $B=\varphi(A)$.

By (3), every $A - A_\eta$ is now cleavable, and for the cleavability of the whole set A it is sufficient that there exist an index η for which $A_\eta = 0$, so that $\psi_n(y) = 0$ for every y. This can also be expressed by saying that the sets $\psi(y)$ are "uniformly" separated, that is, that not only are their smallest coherences (dense-in-itself kernels) empty but all of them are already reached for indices $\leqq \eta$.

In the case of an arbitrary mapping $\varphi(x)$ of the arbitrary space A, we shall say that the sets $U_1, \ldots, U_n$ open in A form a *coherent system* if the intersection

$$D_\xi = \varphi(A_\xi U_1) \ldots \varphi(A_\xi U_n)$$

of the images of $A_\xi U_1, \ldots, A_\xi U_n$ is non-empty for all $\xi < \Omega$; in particular, the intersection $D_0 = \varphi(U_1) \ldots \varphi(U_n)$ is then non-empty.

(G) *If under the arbitrary mapping $\varphi(x)$ of the separable space A the n sets U_k $(k = 1, \ldots, n)$ form a coherent system and $\mathfrak{B}(U_k)$ is an at most countable basis of U_k, then this basis contains two disjoint sets U_{k1} and U_{k2} such that the $2n$ sets U_{k1} and U_{k2} form a coherent system.*

Let $y_\xi \,\varepsilon\, D_{\xi+1}$, so that for every k an inverse image point of y_ξ occurs in $A_{\xi+1} U_k$: $\psi(y_\xi) A_{\xi+1} U_k = \psi_{\xi+1}(y_\xi) U_k > 0$; since $\psi_{\xi+1}(y)$ is the coherence of $\psi_\xi(y)$, $\psi_\xi(y_\xi) U_k$ is infinite.[1] There thus exist in $\mathfrak{B}(U_k)$ two disjoint sets $U_{k1}(\xi)$ and $U_{k2}(\xi)$ depending on ξ which have a non-empty intersection with $\psi_\xi(y_\xi)$. But there exist at most countably many such systems of $2n$ sets U_{k1} and U_{k2}; at least one of them must occur an uncountable number of times, and for an uncountable number of ξ we thus have

$$U_{k1}(\xi) = U_{k1}, \quad U_{k2}(\xi) = U_{k2},$$
$$\psi_\xi(y_\xi) U_{k1} > 0, \quad \psi_\xi(y_\xi) U_{k2} > 0,$$
$$\varphi(A_\xi U_{11}) \varphi(A_\xi U_{12}) \ldots \varphi(A_\xi U_{n1}) \varphi(A_\xi U_{n2}) > 0.$$

This last inequality, valid for uncountably many ξ holds, however, for all ξ, since the A_ξ decrease with increasing ξ, so that the $2n$ sets $U_{11}, \ldots, U_{n2}$ form a coherent system.

IV. *Under a half-schlicht continuous mapping of the separable complete space A, there exists a ξ for which $A_\xi = 0$; A is therefore cleavable.*

We prove that if all the A_ξ are non-empty, then the continuous mapping $y = \varphi(x)$ is not half-schlicht. A itself forms a coherent system, so that there exist in $\mathfrak{B}_1$ (in the notation of the proof of II) two disjoint U_1 and

[1] If P_β is the derived set of P and $P_\alpha = PP_\beta$ the coherence of P, and if U is open, then by § 23, (13) we have $(PU)_\beta \geqq P_\beta U \geqq P_\alpha U$; if $P_\alpha U$ is non-empty, then PU cannot be finite.

U_2 forming a coherent system, and then in $\mathfrak{B}_2(U_p)$ two disjoint U_{p1} and U_{p2} such that U_{11}, U_{12}, U_{21}, and U_{22} form a coherent system, and so forth. Theorem I is now applicable; conditions (1) are now realized because the images of the sets of a coherent system have a non-empty intersection.

V. *A B-set is cleavable under every half-schlicht Baire mapping; that is, it is the sum of a countable number of B-sets that are mapped one-to-one.*

This is reduced to IV as III was reduced to II. If $y = \varphi(x)$ is a half-schlicht map of the B-set A and, to begin with, is continuous, then under the half-schlicht continuous mapping $y = \varphi(\xi(t)) = \eta(t)$ (compare the proof of III), $T = \Sigma T_n$ is cleavable into B-sets T_n which have the one-to-one images $B_n = \eta(T_n)$; since T_n and $A_n = \xi(T_n)$ are also one-to-one maps of each other, so also are A_n and $\boldsymbol{B_n} = \boldsymbol{\varphi(A_n)}$; $\boldsymbol{A = \Sigma A_n}$ is cleavable under the mapping $\varphi(x)$.

In the general case of the Baire half-schlicht mapping $y = \varphi(x)$ of A onto B, we consider the points $z = (x, y)$ of the product space (A, B) and the continuous functions $x = \xi(z)$ and $y = \eta(z)$ (projections of z on A and B). The B-set C of the points $(x, \varphi(x))$ is mapped one-to-one and continuously on A by $\xi(z)$, half-schlicht and continuously on B by $\eta(z)$; $C = \Sigma C_n$ is cleavable here into B-sets C_n having one-to-one images $B_n = \eta(C_n)$ and $A_n = \xi(C_n)$; the B-set A_n is mapped one-to-one onto B_n by $\varphi(x)$, and $A = \Sigma A_n$ is cleavable under the mapping $\varphi(x)$.

APPENDIXES

(A). Appendix to p. 165

The space E is called an F_{II}-set if every closed non-empty set F is of the second category in itself. We call it an F_{I}-set if it is not an F_{II}-set, so that there is some closed non-empty set F that is of the first category in itself. Some remarkable results on this subject have been obtained by Hurewicz:

The space E is an F_{I}-set if and only if it contains a perfect *countable* set P; therefore it is an F_{II}-set if and only if every non-empty perfect set P is uncountable.

In a separable space E, the Borel sets (and even the complements of Suslin sets) are all of them F_{I}-sets, with the possible exception of the G_δ. These latter can be F_{II}-sets; we already know that the G_δ of a complete space, and even of a non-separable space — the Young sets — are, in point of fact, F_{II}-sets (p. 165).

The two following theorems also belong to this order of ideas; in the case of a complete space E, the theorems on cardinality —Theorems VIII of § 26 and I of § 32 — follow from them.

Every set G_δ in the arbitrary space E whose dense-in-itself kernel does not vanish contains a non-empty perfect (in E) subset P. Every uncountable Suslin set in the separable space E contains a non-empty perfect (in E) subset.

(B). Appendix to p. 182

For the method of proof in the text it would be necessary for two points of $P(0)$ to have the separation 0 in $P(0)$ itself and not merely in A. The connectedness of $P(0)$ can be proved somewhat as follows. Let us assume that $P(0) = Q + R$ has been partitioned into the sets Q and R compact in themselves; we join a point $q \varepsilon Q$ to a point $r \varepsilon R$ by means of a $(1/n)$-chain in A, this being possible for every natural number n because $\overline{qr} = 0$. For the points x of the chain let us observe whether the lower distance $\delta(x, Q)$ is less than $\delta(x, R)$ or is at least equal to it; for the first point q, the former is the case, for the last point r, the latter, and consequently the chain must contain a point x_n for which $\delta(x_n, Q) < \delta(x_n, R)$ while for the point y_n immediately following, we already have $\delta(y_n, Q) \geqq \delta(y_n, R)$; in this $\overline{qx_n} \leqq 1/n$ and $x_n y_n \leqq 1/n$. Such pairs of points thus occur for each $n = 1, 2, 3, \ldots$. The sequence x_n has a convergent subsequence $x_\nu \to x$, where $x \varepsilon A$; then we also have $y_\nu \to x$ and, because of the continuity of the separations and the distances, $\overline{qx} = 0$, and $\delta(x, Q) = \delta(x, R)$. Therefore x would have to belong to $P(0) = Q + R$, and this yields a contradiction, since, of the two numbers $\delta(x, Q)$ and $\delta(x, R)$, one is 0 and the other is positive.

(C). Appendix to § 39, 2

Let $t = \varphi(x)$ be a continuous mapping of the compact continuum C, irreducible between the two points a and b, onto the real interval T $(0 \leqq t \leqq 1)$. Let us call the inverse images of the numbers t the *layers* of the mapping φ; let $C(x, \varphi)$ be the layer to which the point x belongs, that is, the set of all the y for which $\varphi(y) = \varphi(x)$. Let us say that the mapping is *monotone* if all the layers are *continua* (containing one or more points); for example, Hahn's Theorem, Theorem VIII, proves the existence, for a composite continuum C, of a *monotone* mapping whose layers are the prime parts. It now follows, from an investigation by Kuratowski, that if C admits of any monotone mappings at all and if $C(x)$ denotes the intersection of the $C(x, \varphi)$ for all the monotone mappings φ for which $\varphi(a) = 0$ and $\varphi(b) = 1$, then these $C(x)$ are themselves the layers of a monotone mapping, which thus realizes a splitting of C into the smallest possible layers. These minimal layers $C(x)$ of Kuratowski now are more deserving of the name prime parts than the sets given this name in § 39, 2, which possibly can be split further into minimal layers.

(D). Appendix to p. 304

The question has been discussed by Banach, the following being his principal result. Let the "modified" Baire functions $f^{\eta+1}$ be defined for $0 \leqq \eta < \Omega$ by the inductive rule:

The f^1 are the functions of the class $(M^1, N^1) = (F_\sigma, G_\delta)$.

For $\eta > 0$, the $f^{\eta+1}$ are the limit functions of convergent sequences of functions $f^{\xi+1}$ $(\xi < \eta)$.

Then for an at most separable image space Y the functions $f^{\eta+1}$ are identical with those of the class $(M^{\eta+1}, N^{\eta+1})$.

Thus, by taking as point of departure in the formation of limit functions the f^1 (which need not, in general, be limits of sequences of continuous functions) rather than the continuous functions, Theorem XII has a converse for the modified Baire functions in the case of an at most separable Y. The question remains open as to how, for a limit ordinal η, the functions of the class (M^η, N^η) are formed from convergent sequences of functions of a lower class, or what conditions correspond, in the general case, to the completeness of systems of real functions (§ 41, 1 and § 43, 1).

(E). Appendix to p. 39

The naive theory of sets, due to Cantor, is, as the author remarks, self-contradictory. We may point for instance to the contradiction discovered by Bertrand Russell: let C be the class of all those classes which are not members of themselves, i.e., the class whose members x are such that $x \notin x$, and consider whether C is a member of itself or not. If $C \notin C$ then C satisfies the condition for membership of C, and therefore $C \varepsilon C$; but if $C \varepsilon C$ then C is one of those classes which is not a member of itself and so *not* a member of C, i.e., $C \notin C$. Many attempts have been made to protect set theory from contradiction. Russell's *theory of types* places objects, classes of objects, classes of classes, and so on, in a hierarchy of types and bans the formation of clases of mixed types, thus preventing a class being a member of itself; type theory, however, produces many curious distortions of mathematics—for instance, a different class of natural numbers in each type. A system of Willard van Orman Quine's known as *New Foundations* replaces type theory by 'potential typing' (in which in place of absolute types an *ad hoc* assignment of types for each relation $x \varepsilon y$ suffices), and utilises a distinction, due to von Neumann, between class and element, only classes which satisfy a condition of *elementhood* being eligible as members of classes; this system was shown (by Barkley Rosser in 1942) to be inconsistent, but a later version was protected from this contradiction by restricting (bound as well as free) variables in the membership axioms to elements. A recent system of Bernays maintains a distinction between class and set, sets being those classes which satisfy an elementhood condition, but dispenses with stratification, following Zermelo in using set-construction axioms.

R. L. G.

(F). Appendix to p. 66

The proof that every set can be well-ordered makes tacit appeal to Zermelo's *Axiom of Choice,* that if M is a set, the elements of which are non-empty sets (pairwise disjoint), then there exists a set which contains one member fo each set which is an element of M. There are many equivalent forms of this axiom; for instance, that every set may be well-ordered, that every cardinal is finite or an aleph, or that all cardinals are comparable. Other equivalent forms are that for any infinite cardinals $m, n,$

(i) $m + n = m \cdot n$;

(ii) $m^2 = m$;

(iii) if $m^2 = n^2$, then $m = n$.

Another equivalent of the Axiom of Choice is known as Zorn's lemma: a non-empty partially ordered set in which every chain has a least upper bound, has a maximal element. A maximal element of a partially ordered set is an element m such that if $m \leqq x$ then $m = x$ (i.e., m is as great as any element with which it is comparable); a chain is a subset of a partially ordered set, any two elements of which are comparable. Another form of Zorn's lemma states that every partially ordered set contains a maximal chain, a maximal chain being a maximal element of the set of chains (partially ordered by the inclusion relation).

It is not known whether the Axiom of Choice is independent of the other axioms of set theory, but K. Gödel has proved (for a version of Bernay's set theory) that if set theory without the Axiom of Choice is free from contradiction then the addition of the Axiom of Choice to this theory will not introduce a contradiction. In the opposite direction, E. Specker has shown that the Axiom of Choice is false in Quine's New Foundations.

R. L. G.

REFERENCES

BERNAYS, P. and A. A. FRAENKEL, *Axiomatic Set Theory* (Amsterdam, 1958).

FRAENKEL, A. A., and Y. BAR-HILLEL, *Foundations of Set Theory* (Amsterdam, 1958).

GÖDEL, K., *The consistency of the axiom of choice and of the generalised continuum-hypothesis with the axioms of set theory* (Princeton, 1940, 1951).

QUINE, W. VAN ORMAN, *Mathematical Logic.* (Revised Edition, Harvard, 1951).

BIBLIOGRAPHY

ALEXANDROV, P., *Topologie, I* (Berlin, 1935).

ALEXANDROV, P. S. and KOLMOGOROV, A. N., *Introduction to the Theory of Sets and the Theory of Functions* (Moscow-Leningrad, 1948).

AUMANN, G., *Reelle Funktionen* (Berlin, 1954).

BACHMANN, H., *Transfinite Zahlen* (Berlin, 1955).

BAIRE, R., *Leçons sur les fonctions discontinues* (Paris, 1905).

BANACH, S., *Introduction to the Theory of Real Functions* (Warsaw, 1951; in Polish).

BANACH, S., *Théorie des opérations linéaires* (Warsaw, 1932; repr., New York, 1955).

BOREL, E., *Eléments de la théorie des ensembles* (Paris, 1949).

BOREL, E., *Les paradoxes de l'infini* (Paris, 1946).

BOREL, E., *Leçons sur la théorie des fonctions* (Paris, 1898; 4th ed., 1950). Cited as *Leçons* (1898).

BOREL, E., *Leçons sur les fonctions de variables réelles* (Paris, 1905; 2nd ed., 1928). Cited as *Leçons,* (1905).

BOREL, E., *Méthodes et problèmes de la théorie des fonctions* (Paris, 1922).

BOURBAKI, N., *Eléments de mathématiques Livres I, III* (Paris, 1940-55).

CARATHEODORY, C., *Reelle Funktionen, I* (Leipzig, 1939; repr., New York, 1946).

CARATHEODORY, C., *Vorlesungen über Reelle Funktionen* (Leipzig, 1918; 2nd ed., 1927; repr., New York, 1948).

DENJOY, A., *L'énumération transfinie* (Paris, 1954).

FRAENKEL, A. A., *Abstract Set Theory* (Amsterdam, 1953; in English).

FRAENKEL, A. S., *Einleitung in die Mengenlehre* (3rd ed., Berlin, 1928).

FRECHET, M., *Les espaces abstraits* (Paris, 1928).

GODEL, K., *Consistency of the Continuum Hypothesis* (Princeton, 1940).

GRAVES, L. M., *The Theory of Functions of Real Variables* (New York, 1946; 2nd ed., 1953).

HAHN, H., *Theorie der reellen Funktionen, I* (Berlin, 1921). Cited as *Theorie.*

HAHN, H., *Reelle Funktionen, I* (Leipzig, 1932; repr., New York, 1948).

HAHN, H. and ROSENTHAL, A., *Set Functions* (Albuquerque, 1948).

HAUSDORFF, F., *Grundzüge der Mengenlehre* (Leipzig, 1914; repr., New York, 1949).

HESSENBERG, G., *Grundbegriffe der Mengenlehre* (Göttingen, 1906).

HOBSON, E. W., *The Theory of Functions of a Real Variable* (Cambridge, 1907; I, 3rd ed., 1927; II, 2nd ed., 1926).

HUREWICZ, W. and WALLMAN, H. *Dimension Theory* (Princeton, 1941).

KAMKE, E., *Theory of Sets* (New York, 1950).

KELLEY, J. L., *General Topology* (New York, 1955).

KURATOWSKI, C., *Topologie, I* (Warsaw, 1933; 2nd ed., 1948).

KURATOWSKI, C., *Topologie, II* (Warsaw, 1950).

LANDAU, E., *Foundations of Analysis* (New York, 1957).

LUSIN, N., *Leçons sur les ensembles analytiques* (Paris, 1930).

LUZIN (Lusin), N., *Theory of Functions of a Real Variable* (2nd ed., Moscow, 1948; in Russian).

MENGER, K., *Dimensionstheorie* (Leipzig, 1928).

MOORE, R. L., *Foundations of Point Set Theory* (New York, 1932).

NATANSON, I. P., *Theory of Functions of a Real Variable* (New York, 1953).

NEWMAN, M. H. A., *Topology of Plane Sets of Points* (2nd ed., Cambridge, 1950).

PIERPONT, J., *Lectures on the Theory of Functions of Real Variables, I and II* (Boston, 1905 and 1912).

ROSENTHAL, A., *Neuere Untersuchungen über Funktionen reeller Veraenderlichen* (Math. Enzykl. II C 9).

SCHOENFLIES, A., *Die Entwickelung der Lehre von den Punktmannigfaltigkeiten, I and II* (Leipzig, 1900 and 1908).

SCHOENFLIES, A., *Entwickelung der Mengenlehre und ihrer Anwendungen* (Leipzig, 1913).

SIERPIŃSKI, W., *Hypothèse du continu* (2nd ed., New York, 1956).

SIERPIŃSKI, W., *General Topology* (Toronto, 1934; 2nd ed., 1952).

SIERPIŃSKI, W., *Leçons sur les nombres transfinis* (Paris, 1928).

SIERPIŃSKI, W., *Les ensembles projectifs et analytiques* (Paris, 1950).

TIETZE, H. and VIETORIS, L., *Beziehungen zwischen den verschiedenen Zweigen der Topologie* (Math. Enzykl. III AB 13).

TUKEY, J. W., *Convergence and Uniformity in Topology* (Princeton, 1940).

DE LA VALLÉE POUSSIN, C., *Intégrales de Lebesgue, Fonctions d'ensemble, Classes de Baire* (Paris, 1916; 2nd ed., 1950).

VITALI, G. and SANSONE, G., *Moderna teoria delle funzioni di variabile reale* (3rd ed., Bologna, 1951).

WHYBURN, G. T., *Analytic Topology* (New York, 1942).

YOUNG, W. H. and YOUNG, G. C., *The Theory of Sets of Points* (Cambridge, 1906).

The periodical *"Fundamenta Mathematicae,"* published in Warsaw since 1920, is devoted primarily to Set Theory.

FURTHER REFERENCES

The following references are intended only to give an account of the origins of the more important concepts and theorems of the subject; we refer the reader for further information to the reports by A. Schoenflies and the review by A. Rosenthal. Most of the theorems about point sets, incidentally, are stated only for one-dimensional space, or at most Euclidean space, and have been considerably transformed.

P. 10. Kowalewski, G., *Einführung in die Infinitesimalrechnung* (Leipzig, 1908), p. 14.

§ 1. In general, we have dispensed with references to Cantor; the contents of the first four chapters and the fundamental concepts of the theory of point sets derive almost exclusively from him. Of his numerous papers we refer the reader primarily to the following:

Über unendliche lineare Punktmannigfaltigkeiten I-VI: Math. Ann., Vol. 15 (1879), p. 1; Vol. 17 (1880), p. 355; Vol. 20 (1882), p. 113; Vol. 21 (1883), pp. 51, 545; Vol. 23 (1884), p. 453. *Beiträge zur Begründung der transfiniten Mengenlehre,* I, II: Math. Ann., Vol. 46 (1895), p. 481; Vol. 49 (1897), p. 207.

P. 11. Genocchi, A. and Peano, G., *Differentialrechnung und Grundzüge der Integralrechnung* (Leipzig, 1899), p. 340.

§ 3. P. 18. Carathéodory, C. *Vorlesungen,* p. 23.

P. 21. Upper and lower limit as ensemble limite complet and ensemble limite restreint, in: Borel, E., *Leçons* (1905), p. 18.

P. 22. de la Vallée Poussin, C., *Intégrales,* p. 7.

§ 5. Theorem III. Bernstein, F., in Borel, E., *Leçons* (1898), p. 103.

§ 7. P. 39. Zermelo, E., Math. Ann., Vol. 65 (1908), p. 261. The reader will find more on the subject of the antinomies in Fraenkel, A., *Einleitung in die Mengenlehre* (1928).

Theorem III. König, J., Math. Ann., Vol. 60 (1904), p. 177.

§ 11. Theorem I. Bernstein, F., *Untersuchungen aus der Mengenlehre,* Thesis (Halle, 1901), p. 34.

P. 61. Minkowski, H., Verh. Heidelb. Kongr. (Leipzig, 1905), p. 171.

P. 62. Dedekind, R., *Stetigkeit und irrationale Zahlen* (Braunschweig, 1872).

§ 12. Zermelo, E., Math. Ann., Vol. 59 (1904), p. 514, and Vol. 65 (1908), p. 107.

§ 13. Important contributions to well-ordering theory have been made by Hessenberg, *Grundbegriffe der Mengenlehre* (1906).

§ 14. P. 80. Hessenberg, G., *Grundbegriffe,* § 75.

§ 15. P. 82. For the question as to $\aleph \geqq \aleph_1$ compare Hilbert, D., Math. Ann., Vol. 95 (1925), p. 181.

§ 16. Hausdorff, F., Leipz. Ber., Vol. 58 (1906), p. 108.

§ 18. Borel, E., *Leçons* (1898), p. 46.

§ 19. Suslin,[1] M., C. R. Acad. Sci. Paris, Vol. 164 (1917), p. 88. Lusin, N., ibid., p. 91. Cf. § 32.

§ 20, 1. In Fréchet, Rend. Circ. Mat. Palermo, Vol. 22 (1906), pp. 17 and 30, a metric space is called class (E) (distance = écart); in later papers it is called class (D) (distance).

§ 20, 3. P. 114. Hilbert, D., Götting, Nachr., Vol. 8 (1906), p. 157.

P. 115. Minkowski, H., *Geometrie der Zahlen* (Leipzig and Berlin, 1910; *repr.,* New York, 1956).

§ 20, 4. Baire, R., Acta Math., Vol. 32 (1909), p. 105.

§ 20, 5. Hensel, K. *Theorie der algebraischen Zahlen,* Vol. I (Leipzig and Berlin, 1908). Kürschák, J., J. für Math., Vol. 142 (1913), p. 212.

§ 21, 1. Complete space, essentially according to Fréchet, M., Rend. Circ. Mat. Palermo, Vol. 22 (1906), p. 23.

§ 21, 3. Cantor, G., Math. Ann., Vol. 5 (1872), p. 123; Méray, C., *Nouveau précis d'analyse infinitésimale* (Paris, 1872).

§ 21, 4. Fréchet, M., Rend. Circ. Mat. Palermo, Vol. 22 (1906) p. 6.

§ 22. Open set: Lebesgue, H., Ann. Mat. Pura Appl. (3), Vol. 7 (1902), p. 242; Carathéodory, C., *Vorlesungen,* p. 40. In the first edition the open sets were called domains (*Gebiete*), a term now used to denote connected open sets.

§ 23. Most of the concepts of this section derive from Cantor. Condensation point: Lindelöf, E., Acta Math., Vol. 29 (1905), p. 184. Dense-in-itself kernel: Hahn, H., *Theorie,* p. 76.

§ 25. The theorems of this section derive mostly from Cantor.

P. 144. Separable (in a slightly different sense): Fréchet, M., Rend. Circ. Mat. Palermo, Vol. 22 (1906), p. 23.

THEOREM IV. Bernstein, F., Thesis (Halle, 1901), p. 44.

§ 26, 1. THEOREM II. Borel, E., Ann. Sci. École Norm. Sup., (3) Vol. 12 (1895), p. 51.

THEOREM III. Lindelöf, E., C. R. Acad. Sci. Paris, Vol. 137 (1903), p. 697; Young, W. H., Proc. Lond. Math. Soc., Vol. 35 (1903), p. 384.

THEOREM IV. Sierpiński, W., Bull. Acad. Sci. Cracovie (1918), p. 49.

§ 26, 3. THEOREM VIII. Young, W. H., Leipz. Ber., Vol. 55 (1903), p. 287; *Theory,* p. 64.

§ 27. P. 163. Baire, R., Ann. Mat. Pura Appl. (3), Vol. 3 (1899), p. 67.

§ 28, 1. Distance $\overline{AB}$: Pompéju, D., Ann. Fac. Toulouse (2), Vol. 7 (1905), p. 281.

§ 28, 2. The sets $\overline{F}, \underline{F}$ (in substance) in Painlevé, P.; see Zoretti, L., J. Math. Pures Appl. (6), Vol. 1 (1905), p. 8; Bull. Soc. Math. France, Vol. 37 (1909), p. 116.

§ 29, 1. Connectedness: Lennes, N. J., Amer. J. Math., Vol. 33 (1911) p. 303.

Continuum: Jordan, C., *Cours d'analyse,* Vol. I (2nd ed., Paris, 1893), p. 25.

---

[1] Michael Suslin (1894-1919) himself published only this one paper.

Domain (going back to Weierstrass): Carathéodory, C., *Vorlesungen,* p. 208, p. 222.

THEOREM III. Janiszewski, Z. and Kuratowski, C., Fund. Math., Vol. 1 (1920), p. 211.

§ 29, 2. P. 177. Hahn, H., Jber. Deutsch Math. Verein., Vol. 23 (1914), p. 319; Wiener Ber., Vol. 123 (1914), p. 2,433.

THEOREM X. Hahn, H., Fund. Math., Vol. 2 (1921), p. 189. Kuratowski, C., Fund. Math., Vol. 1 (1920), p. 43.

P. 179. Mazurkiewicz, S., Fund. Math., Vol. 1 (1920), p. 167.

§ 29, 3. P. 181. Cantor, G., Math. Ann., Vol. 21 (1883), p. 576.

THEOREM XV. Brouwer, L. E. J., Amst. Ak. Proc., Vol. 12 (1910), p. 785.

THEOREM XVII. Janiszewski, Z., Thesis (Paris, 1911) = Journ. éc. Polyt. (2), Vol. 16 (1912), p. 100.

§P. 185. Sierpiński, W., Tôhoku Math. J., Vol. 13 (1918), p. 300.

§ 29, 4. THEOREM XIX. Zoretti, L., J. Math. Pures Appl. (6), Vol. 1 (1905), p. 8.

§ 30, 4. THEOREM VII. Zalcwasser, Fund. Math., Vol. 3 (1922), p. 44.

§ 31, 1. P. 199. Hamel, G., Math. Ann., Vol. 60 (1905), p. 459.

P. 200. Zoretti, L., Ann. Sci. École Norm. Sup. (3), Vol. 26 (1909), p. 487.

P. 201. Janiszewski, C. R. Acad. Sci. Paris, Vol. 151 (1910), p. 198.

§ 31, 2. P. 201. Bernstein, F., Leipz. Ber., Vol. 60 (1908), p. 325.

P. 202. Sierpiński, W., Fund. Math., Vol. 1 (1920), p. 7.

§ 32. THEOREM I. For Borel sets: Alexandroff, P., C. R. Acad. Sci. Paris, Vol. 162 (1916), p. 323; Hausdorff, F., Math. Ann., Vol. 77 (1916), p. 430.

For the theory of Suslin sets compare: Suslin, M., C. R. Acad. Sci. Paris, Vol. 164 (1917), p. 88. Lusin, N., *Ensembles analytiques* (1930). Lusin, N. and Sierpinski, W., Bull. Acad. Cracovie (1918), p. 35; J. Math. Pures Appl. (7), Vol. 2 (1923), p. 53. Sierpiński, W., Bull. Acad. Cracovie (1919), pp. 161, 179.

§ 33. THEOREM I. Sierpiński, W., C. R. Acad. Sci. Paris, Vol. 175 (1922), p. 859.

§ 34, 2. Lusin, N. and Sierpiński, W., J. Math. Pures Appl. (7), Vol. 2 (1923), p. 53.

§ 35, 2. THEOREM III. Jordan, C., *Cours d'Analyse,* Vol. I (2nd ed., Paris, 1893), p. 53.

THEOREM V. Brouwer, L. E. J., Amst. Akad. Proc., Vol. 12 (1910), p. 785.

§ 35, 3. P. 227. Lebesgue, H., *Leçons sur l'integration* (Paris, 1904), p. 105.

§ 36, 1. Peano curves: Peano, G., Math. Ann., Vol. 36 (1890), p. 157. Hilbert, D., Math. Ann., Vol. 38 (1891), p. 459. Knopp, K, Archiv. d. Math. u. Ph. (3), Vol. 26 (1918), p. 103. Lebesgue, H., *Leçons sur l'integration* (Paris, 1904), p. 44.

P. 232. Brouwer, L. E. J., Math. Ann., Vol. 70 (1911), p. 161. On the subject of the Brouwer-Urysohn-Menger dimension theory compare Menger, K., *Dimensionstheorie* (1928).

§ 36, 2. THEOREM II. Sierpiński, W., Fund. Math., Vol. 1 (1920), p. 44.

THEOREM III. Hahn, H., Jahresb. D. Math., Vol. 23 (1914), p. 319; Wiener Ber., Vol. 123 (1914), p. 2,433; Mazurkiewicz, S., Compt. R. Varsovie (III), Vol. 6 (1913), p. 305 (in Polish); Fund. Math., Vol. 1 (1920), p. 191.

§ 37. THEOREMS II and III. Sierpiński, W., Bull. Ac. Crac. (1918), p. 29 and (1919), p. 161; Fund. Math., Vol. 5 (1924), p. 155.

THEOREM IV. Suslin, M., Compt. Rend., Vol. 164 (1917), p. 88.

§ 38. THEOREMS I and II. Sierpiński, W., Compt. Rend., Vol. 171 (1920), p. 24.

THEOREM III. Mazurkiewicz, S., Bull. Acad. Cracovie (1916), p. 490. Alexandroff, P., C. R. Acad. Sci. Paris, Vol. 178 (1924), p. 185. Hausdorff, F., Fund. Math., Vol. 6 (1924), p. 146.

THEOREM IV. Lavrentieff, M., C. R. Acad. Sci. Paris, Vol. 178 (1924), p. 187; Fund. Math., Vol. 6 (1924), p. 149.

§ 39, 1. THEOREM II. Vietoris, L., Monatshefte Math. Phys., Vol. 31 (1921), p. 179.

THEOREM III. Lennes, N. J., Amer. J. Math., Vol. 33 (1911), p. 308; Sierpiński, W., Ann. Mat. Pura Appl. (3), Vol. 26 (1916), p. 131.

§ 39, 2. Hahn, H., Wiener Ber., Vol. 130 (1921), p. 217.

THEOREM VII. Moore, R. L., Math. Zeit., Vol. 22 (1925), p. 307.

§ 40. For more precise information refer to: Rosenthal, A. (Enzycl. II C 9) No. 26, Tietze, H. and Vietoris, L. (Enzykl. III, A, B, 13) ; Fréchet, M., *Les espaces abstraits* (1928) ; Kuratowski, C., *Topologie,* Vol. I (1933) ; Sierpiński, W., *General Topology* (1934).

P. 258. Kuratowski, C., Fund. Math., Vol. 3 (1922), p. 182.

P. 260. Separation axioms: Tietze, H., Math. Ann., Vol. 88 (1923), p. 290.

P. 261. Urysohn, P., Math. Ann., Vol. 94 (1925), p. 309. Tychonoff, A., Math. Ann., Vol. 95 (1925), p. 139.

P. 261. Fréchet, M., Rend. Circ. Mat. Palermo, Vol. 22 (1906).

§ 41. This theory is due primarily to Lebesgue, H., J. Math. Pures Appl. (6) Vol. 1 (1905), pp. 139-216. Cf., Young, W. H., Proc. Lond. Math. Soc. (2), Vol. 12 (1912), p. 260. Hausdorff, F., Math. Zeit., Vol 5 (1919), p. 292.

§ 41, 4. THEOREMS XIII and XIV. Hahn, H., Wien. Ber., Vol. 126 (1917), p. 103. Tietze, H., J. f. Math., Vol. 145 (1914), p. 9. Hausdorff, F., Math. Zeit. Vol. 5 (1919), p. 295.

§ 41, 5. Sierpiński, W., Fund. Math., Vol. 2 (1921), pp. 15, 37; Mazurkiewicz, S., ibid., p. 28; Kempisty, S., ibid., pp. 64, 131.

§ 42. The theorems of this section derive mostly from Baire, R., Ann. di mat. (3), Vol. 3 (1899), pp. 1-122; *Leçons sur les fonctions discontinues* (Paris, 1905).

§ 42, 1. P. 282. Baire, R., Bull. Soc. Math. France, Vol. 32 (1904), p. 125; Tietze, H., J. für Math., Vol. 145 (1914), p. 9; Hausdorff, F., Math. Zeit., Vol. 5 (1919), p. 293.

§ 42, 3. P. 286. Young, W. H., Wien. Ber., Vol. 112 (1903), p. 1,307; Lebesgue, H., Bull. Soc. Math. France, Vol. 32 (1904), p. 235.

P. 285. Hankel, H. Math. Ann., Vol. 20 (1887), p. 89.

P. 285. (*C* and *D* not interchangeable) : Volterra, V., Giorn. Mat. Battaglini, Vol. 19 (1881), p. 76.

§ 42, 4. THEOREM VII. Lebesgue, H. in Borel E., *Leçons* (1905), p. 149 and J. Math. Pures Appl. (6), Vol. 1 (1905), p. 182. de la Vallée Poussin, C., *Intégrales,* p. 121.

THEOREM VIII. Baire, R., Ann. di Mat. (3), Vol. 3 (1899), pp. 16, 30.

§ 42, 5. Kuratowski, C., and Sierpiński, W., Fund. Math., Vol. 3 (1922), p. 303.

§ 43. Cf. Baire, R., Ann. Mat. Pura Appl. (3), Vol. 3 (1899), p. 68; Lebesgue, H., J. Math. Pures Appl. (6), Vol. 1 (1905).

§ 43, 2. THEOREM V. Lebesgue, H., J. Math. Pures Appl. (6), Vol. 1 (1905), p. 205. de la Vallée Poussin, C., *Intégrales,* p. 145.

THEOREM VI. Baire, R., Ann. Mat. Pura Appl. (3), Vol. 3 (1899), p. 81.

P. 297. Lusin, N., Fund. Math., Vol. 2 (1921), p. 155.

P. 298. Sierpiński, W., Fund. Math., Vol. 5 (1924), p. 20.

§ 43, 3. Sierpiński, W., C. R. Acad. Sci. Paris, Vol. 170 (1920), p. 919: Fund. Math., Vol. 2 (1921), p. 74; Fund. Math., Vol. 3 (1922), p. 26; Bull. Acad. Cracovie (1919), pp. 161, 179.

§ 44. THEOREM I. Hahn, H., Archiv. Math. Ph., Vol. 28 (1919), p. 34. Sierpiński, W., Fund. Math., Vol. 2 (1921), p. 41.

§ 45, 2. THEOREM I. Banach, Fund. Math., Vol. 16 (1930), p. 395.

P. 316. Kuratowski, C., Fund. Math., Vol. 16 (1930), p. 390.

The Baire condition became clear and simple only as a result of these two papers. Earlier, properties having thoroughly different and sometimes complicated wordings were referred to as the Baire condition (in the restricted sense, compare § 45, 4) and which, before Banach's Theorem was known, were equivalent only in separable spaces; as to their relationships in arbitrary spaces, compare Steinbach, G., *Beiträge zur Mengenlehre,* Thesis (Bonn, 1930), § 8.

P. 316. Nikodym, O., Fund. Math., Vol. 7 (1925), p. 149.

P. 317. Sierpiński, W., *Hypothèse du continu* (1934; 2nd ed., New York, 1956).

§ 45, 3. Kuratowski, C., Fund. Math., Vol. 5 (1924), p. 75. I have shortened the names *fonction* α*-continue* and β*-continue* used there to α*-function* and β*-function* and have named the α-sets and the β-sets after them.

§ 46. Lusin, N., *Ensembles analytiques* (1930).

§ 46, 1. Lusin, N., C. R. Soc. Polon. Math. (1926), p. 104.

§ 46, 2. Hahn, H., *Reelle Funktionen* (1932), § 42, 4 and § 42, 5.

APPENDIX A. Hurewicz, W., Fund. Math., Vol. 12 (1928), p. 78.

APPENDIX C. Kuratowski, C., Fund. Math., Vol. 3 (1922), p. 200, ibid., Vol. 10 (1927), p. 225.

APPENDIX D. Banach, S., Fund. Math., Vol. 17 (1931), p. 283.

INDEX